Analytical
Hypnotherapy

ANALYTICAL HYPNOTHERAPY

Principles and Practice

E.A. BARNETT, M D

Westwood Publishing Co.

Glendale, CA

Another book by Dr. Barnett
Unlock Your Mind and Be Free
is also available from
Westwood Publishing Co.

ISBN 0-930298-30-6
Formerly ISBN 0-9690835-0-5

DEDICATION

To my wife Margaret

whose loving encouragement and inspiring support has been constant and unwavering throughout this demanding enterprise

List of Illustrations and Tables

PART ONE

25	Figure 1	The Stimulus Response Theory of Hypnosis
29	Figure 2	Conscious/Unconscious Dissociation in Hypnosis
59	Figure 3	Amnesia Capacity Estimation and Hypnotic Phenomena
65	Figure 4	Hypnotic Suggestion and Regression
76	Figure 5	The Functions of the Emotions
77	Figure 6	Parent/Child Conflict as Source of Symptoms
80	Figure 7	Development of Ego States and Parent/Child Conflicts
82	Figure 8	Analytical Hypnotherapy in the Resolution of Parent/Child Conflicts
103	Figure 9	Origin of Symptom Complexes
113	Figure 10	Affect Bridge
121	Figure 11	Ideomotor Questioning – Finger Signals
125	Figure 12	Ideomotor Questioning – Pendulum Movements
133	Figure 13	Relative Depth of Ego States

APPENDIX

460	Table 1	Classification of Patients
461	Figure 1	Number of Sessions of Therapy
464	Table 2	Joint (Therapist/Patient) Evaluations of Therapeutic Results
465	Figure 2	Joint Evaluations of Success of Therapy
466	Figure 3	Relationship Between ACE Score and Outcome of Therapy
467	Figure 4	Outcome of Therapy and Patient Age
469	Table 3	Presenting Symptoms associated with Negative Birth Experience
470	Figure 5	Depth of Trance and Negative Birth Experience

Contents

ix Acknowledgements

xi Preface

1 Introduction

Principles PART ONE

7 The History of Hypnoanalysis

17 The Nature of Hypnosis

33 The Rapid Induction of Hypnosis

47 Hypnotic Phenomena and Hypnotisability

71 Theory of Analytical Hypnotherapy

85 Principles of Analytical Hypnotherapy

101 Therapeutic Indications for Analytical Hypnotherapy

107 Uncovering Techniques in Analytical Hypnotherapy

117 The Ideomotor Questioning Techniques in Analytical Hypnotherapy

Practice PART TWO

137 An Analytical Procedure
171 Critical Experience, Overt and Hidden State Complexes and Multiple Personalities
213 Negative Birth Experience
235 Ego Strengthening and Assertiveness Training
249 Direct and Indirect Suggestion in Analytical Hypnotherapy
259 Common Problems in Analytical Hypnotherapy
325 Some Further Illustrative Case Histories
381 Children and Analytical Hypnotherapy
427 Hypnotisability and Therapy, Optimum Dissociation and ACE
441 Analytical Hypnotherapy and Healing
449 Analytical Hypnotherapist and the Interview

457 Appendix: Results of Therapy
473 Bibliography
489 Index of Names
495 Index

Acknowledgements

A book of this kind cannot be written without the concerted help of many people. Dr David Cheek's lucid explanations and fascinating demonstrations of the power of the ideomotor signal to uncover the source of emotional problems in light hypnosis provided an inspiration to my practice as an analytical hypnotherapist and for this book. Dr Cheek opened a door in my mind which cannot be closed and ultimately made this book possible. I cannot adequately express my gratitude for this or for his kindness in writing the Preface to the book.

Even earlier, I was engaged by the writings of Berne and others on Transactional Analysis and their recognition that more than one set of thoughts and feelings coexist and sometimes conflict within each of us. Their writings fostered an understanding of how hypnosis and particularly analytical hypnotherapy works and have provided a foundation for my own principles and practice.

The encouragement of fellow analytical hypnotherapists who shared my concern for the need to articulate a philosophy of analytical hypnotherapy has been constant and very supportive. Chief among these have been Dr Jeva Lougheed, Dr David Craig and Dr Daniel Stewart whose criticisms of the manuscript have been invaluable.

My research assistant, Alan Bull, Ph.D., has been kind enough to record his findings in the Appendix to the book; this work gives but a small inkling of the vast amount of time and energy he has spent on analysing the results and advising me how best to use them. These results would not have been possible without the cooperation of the Department of Family Practice at Queen's University who made the facilities of the computer department available for this research.

Frances Timleck has given expert editorial assistance with the manuscript; she not only forbore my use of grammar school English but indeed encouraged it. Eric Savoy was a most competent editorial assistant for the final revision of the book. Eileen Potts was an enthusiastic and creative graphic designer. Larry Harris painstakingly prepared the illustrations; Ennis Crawley scrupulously compiled the Index. The conscientious typists were Mrs. Yvonne Keller, Brooke Hetherington, Anna Smol and Mary Holden. I am most grateful to all of them for their spirited teamwork.

Preface

In this book, Dr Edgar Barnett has given us a clear and incisive evaluation of various methods of incorporating hypnosis into the practice of the healing arts.

Each practitioner can take what is needed to improve results without having to change personal philosophy or greatly alter a personalized pattern of therapy already developed.

Dr Barnett has had long experience as a family doctor in England and, since 1966, in Canada. There can be no better resource for information about disturbed human behaviour than the family as a whole and the individuals within that family. But a doctor must know where to look and how to ask before setting about to help a troubled member of that family escape into healthy adaptive freedom in our stressful world. Dr Barnett is eminently qualified for these responsibilities.

He knows that successful therapy depends heavily on two major elements – a willingness for change on the part of the patient and a constant belief that a constructive goal will be reached.

Sometimes readiness for constructive change appears spontaneously and inexplicably at all levels of awareness. This fortuitous event allows a therapist to begin implementation of the process without obstruction. More often, however, the verbalized request for help and the consciously expressed willingness for change are misleading. They are the tip of the iceberg; beneath are contradictory forces of assumed guilt, habits of illness, habits of failure, unfavorable dramatized identifications and unrecognized destructive drives. Newer techniques of hypnoanalysis make it possible to recognize these sources of resistance early in the therapeutic process. Doctor Barnett offers these methods to the reader and shows how resistance can sometimes be circumvented or even eliminated without damaging the self-respect of a patient.

Sometimes the factor of optimistic belief, like the willingness for change, may appear spontaneously and continue without interruption. More often, however, this factor of optimistic belief must be furnished and reinforced by the person to whom the patient turns for help.

Doctor Barnett is blessed with an infectious and communicable faith in the potential for good in people. It has been my privilege to witness this gift in action, to find it demonstrated in his teachings and in his writings.

His faith and his method of projecting that faith are deserving of careful study by those reading this book. Without that projected faith any attempt to help troubled people may fail.

It is not enough to learn ways of uncovering negative subconscious attitudes; we must also be strong in our convictions: *We know it will happen; we expect it to happen.*

David B. Cheek, MD
San Francisco, California

Introduction

Numerous books have been written on the subject of hypnotherapy, each of which sheds a little more light on this very fascinating but still poorly understood subject. Most of these works have concentrated on the varied therapeutic effects produced in the susceptible subject following suggestion in hypnosis. The authors of these studies have often noted the unpredictable effects of suggestion and have sought to discover some correlation with hypnotisability. Unfortunately, hypnotisability itself has been difficult to define, for some subjects who appear to be highly hypnotisable with regard to one hypnotic phenomenon, may be poorly hypnotisable with regard to another. So it is with therapeutic suggestions as well: some apparently highly hypnotisable subjects will accept them readily while others will reject them.

Early in his career as a practising physician, the author was introduced to the greater predictability of drug therapy based as it is currently upon prior thorough research on laboratory animals and clinical trials. From these studies, failures in drug therapy could, in most cases be better understood. It was therefore frustrating to remain ignorant of the reasons why direct suggestion in hypnosis would produce an excellent therapeutic effect in some cases and yet a poor effect in an apparently similar case. Of course it is now becoming increasingly clear that failures in drug therapy are due to inimical circumstances existing in the therapeutic milieu, which may at times be difficult to define because of their subjective nature. Likewise, all direct suggestive therapy − whether or not hypnosis is a feature − can attribute a proportion of failures to subjective factors.

For many years I had been interested in the analytical properties of hypnosis; its ability to locate and uncover memories of experiences, which must have played an important role in the development of

1

presenting symptomatology, is remarkable. The hypnoanalytical approach has often yielded clues not only to the origin of symptoms but also to the subjective changes which account for the variable responses to direct suggestion.

It seems that the behavioural approach to therapy results in failure when the subjective reasons for maintaining symptoms far outweigh any of the external pressures the behaviourist brings to bear upon the patient to change. Initially, in common with most hypnotherapists, I had used only direct suggestion in hypnosis and often found this to be surprisingly effective for a while at least. However, when this approach failed, I became convinced that the therapy itself was not at fault, but rather (for some reason known only to the patient at some deeper level of consciousness), the suggestions as given were not acceptable.

In view of this observation, use of direct suggestion raises as many questions as it answers: Why should a cure occur in one case and yet not in another seemingly similar one? Why is a suggestion acceptable in one instance and not in another? Why is there sometimes a relapse after an apparently successful response to suggestion? Why is there sometimes a conversion of symptoms? These are some of the questions that I and others who have confined themselves to a direct hypnotherapeutic approach to the removal of symptoms have asked.

In seeking answers to these and similar questions I have constructed an approach to therapy which I believe effectively integrates old and new concepts regarding the nature of emotional illness and its response to hypnotherapy. I believe that the analytical approach is the most logical and most likely to increase the incidence of satisfactory cures from emotional and other disorders; it not only seeks to mobilise the unconscious resources rendered accessible through hypnosis but it also deals with any impediment to their use. This approach cannot achieve cures in more than a significant proportion of patients attending for therapy, but it does enable the therapist to understand the reason for failure or limited success in those cases where this occurs.

It is hoped that this book will satisfactorily demonstrate, not only to the non-analytical hypnotherapist but to all other therapists, the effectiveness of an approach which has been greatly underestimated. The concepts and insights set forth in this book are addressed, not only to the hypnotherapist seeking deeper understanding and increased therapeutic effectiveness, but also to those who might benefit by the application of these concepts to other therapeutic fields.

The title, *Analytical Hypnotherapy: Principles and Practice* indicates that there is an underlying logic which pervades the discipline to be detailed. The term *analytical hypnotherapy* is preferred since the more widely known term *hypnoanalysis*, has the connotations originally given it by Wolberg (1945) in which uncovering procedures were advocated as an adjunct to more formal psychoanalytical approaches.

Hypnosis and analytical hypnotherapy have this important difference: Direct suggestion in hypnosis is a one-way communication from therapist to patient. The immediate response of the patient is not a necessary part of therapy (although it is rare for any therapist of note to limit himself to direct suggestion without availing himself of such responses as might occur to monitor the progress of his patient). On the other hand, sensitive and detailed two-way communication is an essential part of analytical hypnotherapy.

Much of this book is devoted to detailing those responses which are of particular value in maintaining this two-way communication. In the sections in which case histories are reported in detail, the obvious responses are described. Every hypnotherapist is aware, however, that many of the responses of his patient are detected at an unconscious level, a sensitivity which the therapist can acquire only through experience. Nevertheless, every attempt has been made to clarify all the principles of analytical hypnotherapy as they occur in practice.

Principles

The History of Hypnoanalysis

Mesmer, the great hypnotist, believed that sick people suffered from a disturbance of their magnetic fields, and that he could rectify these disturbances by the use of magnetics and his own special powers. He did not identify these disturbances, but the positive response to his treatment confirmed their presence. Perhaps the analogy between mesmerism and hypnoanalysis ends there; while Mesmer was preoccupied with magnetic fields, the analytical hypnotherapist uses hypnosis to uncover the source of emotional illness by locating memories of experiences which are responsible for faulty and damaging behaviour patterns. Hypnosis also has the power to initiate a successful unconscious search for more acceptable behaviour patterns.

The first recorded attempt to use hypnosis to uncover the causes of mental illness was Joseph Breuer's (1880-82) treatment of Fraulein Anna O. Breuer discovered that the amnesia characteristic of the hysterical patient could be penetrated by the use of hypnosis to uncover another, unconscious, mind which holds knowledge not normally available to the conscious mind. In the case of Anna O., hypnosis was very easily induced and, in this state, she produced a stream of unconscious material with such little effort that Breuer needed only to listen attentively and without interruption.

A short time after the successful conclusion of the treatment of Anna O., Breuer discussed the case in detail with his young friend, Freud, who was at that time more interested in neurology than in hypnosis. Later however, when studying the subject of hysteria with Charcot, Freud acquired an interest in hypnosis which subsequently was deepened by his work with Bernheim and Liebault. When Freud became involved in the treatment of Frau Emmy von N., he recalled the uncovering techniques taught him by Breuer and began to use them in what he called the *cathartic method*. It is this method which bears a close relationship to the modern practice of analytical hypnotherapy. Freud's use of hypnosis was simply that of direct suggestion, a technique which he had learned from Bernheim (1886).

In 1895, Freud and Breuer jointly published their findings in *Studies on Hysteria*, an important work for anyone interested in the history of analytical hypnotherapy. In this pioneering study, they drew conclusions which have since been substantiated by many practitioners in the field. For example, they theorised that the symptoms of hysteria resulted from the repression of emotions associated with a traumatic experience; because these emotions had not been expressed at the time of that experience, they became the direct cause of the observed symptoms. The reason for the failure to express these emotions, they explained, was directly due either to their unacceptablity at that time, or to the patient's psychic state which inhibited proper expression. Unless these emotions were properly released, Breuer and Freud maintained that they would continue to cause symptoms. This release was the essence of the cathartic method. By the use of hypnosis, the subject could recall the events responsible for his repressed emotion and once again fully experience that emotion. The mere recollection of such events would not suffice; there must always be an abreaction in which the original emotion is experienced in all of its original intensity if it is to be completely discharged. They discovered that often this method proved extremely effective in utterly dispelling symptoms which had heretofore defied the efforts of direct suggestion in hypnosis.

Similarly, Delboeuf (1889) saw the need to take the patient back to the original traumatic experience. Binet (1892) also shared the viewpoint that in hypnotic regression, the patient becomes more susceptible to therapeutic suggestion. Janet (1889), in his interesting study on mental automatism, gave an account of the cure of a hysterical girl by a comparable method of regression. Because Breuer and Freud believed that hysterical symptoms were maintained by the repeated recollection of a traumatic event or series of events, they proposed, for the first time, the idea of repression. They maintained that the initial experience of the patient was one fraught with emotional elements which he wished to forget, and this mechanism of forgetting was itself deliberate, if unconscious, to protect the individual from the painful memory. It is upon this theory of repression that the whole structure of psychoanalysis and hypnoanalysis rests: the postulation of an unconscious mind in which these memories are reposited constitutes an essential part of the understanding of the therapeutic process.

Freud discovered that there were many patients who would not respond to his authoritarian techniques of hypnotic induction, and even some of those who did were not able to produce a state of hypnosis sufficiently deep for the process of catharsis to be effective. He gradually evolved a technique of putting his patients into a state of concentration which he might aid by pressure upon the forehead. Eventually, however, he abandoned all pretence of using hypnosis because of the frequent occurrence of resistance of patients apparently unwilling to cooperate in their own cure. The investigation of such resistance led Freud to many of his later studies and conclusions upon which psychoanalysis has been based. As time went on, he relied less upon direct suggestion and more upon the encouragement of the free flow of ideas and the analysis of such ideas and dreams. Although we know that he evinced a renewed interest in hypnosis at the end of his life, he had rejected it earlier when he stated that 'hypnosis does not do away with resistance but only avoids it and therefore yields only incomplete information and transitory therapeutic success' (Freud, 1953). Such an assertion has been a great blow to the practitioners of hypnotherapy, since many of Freud's followers accepted his teachings as dogma. They thus rejected hypnotherapy and criticised as gullible those who used it.

In spite of Freud's negation, the use of hypnosis for uncovering the causes of problems continued. Wingfield (1920) still emphasised the need to take the patient back to an earlier period of his life and cited cases in which the recall of these memories had enabled recovery from symptoms to take place. During World War 1, hypnosis was found to be of value in dealing with combat neuroses. Hatfield (1920) and Brown (1921) described the use of hypnosis to uncover the memory of traumatic war scenes. After an abreaction of the relevant scene, there frequently was a dramatic recovery from symptoms, but Brown noted that recovery did not occur when the abreaction was merely a recapitulation, rather than the essential reexperiencing, of an earlier (but similar) event really responsible for the symptoms.

Between the two world wars, there was little real interest in the use of hypnosis for uncovering the unconscious causes of emotional problems, since the various schools of psychoanalysis appeared to dominate psychotherapy and the writings of the period. It was not until Watkins (1949) wrote of his treatment of the war neuroses and the rapid and effective way in which these were resolved (in those situations where symptoms were directly due to the psychic trauma of combat) that the renewal of interest in the uncovering properties of hypnosis became apparent. In essence, his approach was similar to that of Breuer and Freud. Watkins found that hypnosis allowed the patient to regress back to the original event and abreact the associated emotions which had apparently been repressed. The distinctive feature of his therapy was that the abreaction would allow the symptoms resulting from previously repressed emotions to disappear and normal emotional health to become established again. The effectiveness of the treatment in the special circumstances of war neuroses may be attributable to the fact that the psychic trauma responsible for the symptoms was of recent origin, and that the repression of emotion had taken place in adult life rather than earlier in childhood. It was therefore more readily accessible to hypnotherapy than the emotional problems that usually present in the psychotherapist's office. Treatment of the war neuroses was often accomplished in one or two sessions; such brevity testifies to the relatively simple nature of the problem despite its often devastating symptomatology. The underlying principle of locating the critical experience and relieving the associated repressed emotion was clearly evidenced.

Lindner (1944) in his book, *Rebel Without A Cause*, described in detail the psychoanalysis of a criminal psychopath in which hypnosis was used to deal with resistance that occurred during therapy. This adjunctive use of hypnosis with psychoanalysis he termed *hypnoanalysis*, and in describing his method, he referred to the general reluctance of psychiatrists to apply hypnosis to their other techniques of psychotherapy. Unfortunately, this reluctance is disappearing only slowly. Lindner's method derived its procedural modes entirely from the Freudian principles of psychoanalysis. He insisted that a specific training in hypnosis was necessary for the patient before any therapy could be instituted. Such training would consist of daily sessions of hypnosis for about a week in which such phenomena as total amnesia, rapid regression, and the facility to talk easily while in hypnosis would be examined. Each patient should have been able to enter deep hypnosis on a signal before therapy was begun. Lindner also implied that all patients could be trained to reach this deep level of hypnosis, although many clinicians would find it difficult to substantiate this viewpoint in their own practices.

Wolberg (1945) advocated a similar use of hypnosis, declaring that one of the chief aims of hypnoanalysis is to bring to consciousness previously unconscious impulses which influence behaviour and which compulsively drive the individual to acts of a maladaptive nature. He observed that in utilising hypnosis as a penetrating tool to uproot traumatic conflicts and experiences, its capriciousness and impermanence were as notable for him as they were for Freud. At the same time, Wolberg reminded fellow psychoanalysts that Freud was not really antagonistic to hypnosis, but only to its improper use, and Freud had never completely discarded hypnosis as a potentially useful method.

In Wolberg's form of hypnosis, the patient is seen almost daily in the usual psychoanalytical manner. Free association is employed until any resistance is encountered, and at the time of resistance, hypnosis is immediately induced. The experience concealed from consciousness is discussed and then a posthypnotic amnesia for this experience is suggested and established. In this manner, unconscious resistances are more readily dissipated, and the hypnoanalyst is able to resolve conflicts that have persisted and would otherwise have remained resistant to therapy.

As did Lindner, Wolberg introduced hypnosis into therapy only when he felt it was necessary to expedite the analysis. Often, many hours of psychoanalysis took place before hypnosis was used. However, he cited several cases where the location of an important experience through the use of hypnosis led to the disappearance of compulsive symptoms and concluded that 'without question, traumatic experiences can serve as foci around which the individual develops symptoms.' He went on to say that intensely traumatic experiences can shock the organism and revive the mechanism of repression by which the vulnerable ego seeks to ward off threats to its intactness. For example, the child can cope with anxieties by projecting them in the form of phobias or he can cope with them by using the mechanisms of repression and dissociation. Even after childhood, these defences persist when no longer really necessary, so that the ego reacts to the original traumatic events as if it is still too weak and vulnerable to deal with them. He described traumatic experiences as condensations of a series of damaging events which come symbolically to stand for such events. While these traumatic events can vary in apparent severity, to the child with limited resources they can all be catastrophic.

Gindes (1951) described further the hypnoanalytical approach by stressing how hypnosis enabled the patient to break through the resistances which are often responsible for the great length of time that must be spent in association before dealing with the relevant problems. He described two essential stages in the hypnoanalytical procedure. The first was that of the location of the repressed material; the second was that of its assimilation with all of the moral, physical, mental, and emotional adjustments which might be necessary. He termed this second stage *hypnosynthesis*. He described how patients were regressed to scenes in the memory, often accompanied by an intense abreaction which had to be dealt with in an atmosphere of calm acceptance.

Gindes also described several techniques for obtaining this information, including the movie picture technique by which the regressed patient reviewed his experiences as if they were occurring as part of a film. He was then able to review these experiences in an objective manner. Another technique used was dream analysis, in which the patient in hypnosis was asked to interpret any significant dreams that he presented. This dream analysis was applied equally as well to dreams induced as a consequence of posthypnotic suggestion. Yet another technique was that of word association, in which associations to lists of words were rapidly given both in and out of hypnosis, and were frequently found to lead to a greater understanding of the emotional conflicts that needed to be dealt with. Positive suggestions directed at the resolution of these conflicts were given in the hypnosynthesis stage.

Even though, as we have seen in our discussion of Lindner, Wolberg and Gindes, the use of hypnosis as an analytical tool had been relegated to the role of an adjunct to formal psychoanalysis, Erickson and Kubie (1941) described the successful treatment of a case of acute hysterical depression solely by a return through hypnosis to a critical phase of childhood. Although Erickson could not truly be described as an analytical hypnotherapist, his ability to sense the nature of the unconscious conflicts in his patients was unparalleled. His ingenuity in devising means of inducing the unconscious mind to mobilise its resources in resolving conflicts was remarkable. Much of this was accomplished through the means of indirect suggestion administered through hypnosis. The analytical hypnotherapist must remain indebted to Erickson because he explored avenues of communication which have advanced immeasurably the practice of analytical hypnotherapy. Of this we shall have more to say later.

Although there are few laymen who have made a significant contribution to the development of analytical hypnotherapy, this survey of the history of the therapeutic approach would be incomplete without mention of Elman (1964), who learned the techniques of hypnotic induction from his father, a stage hypnotist. For a time, Elman was himself a stage hypnotist. His understanding of hypnosis and its induction was so profound that he eventually found himself teaching his techniques to therapists in the major professions. He developed a technique of using hypnosis for analysis, which he claimed to be extremely effective, and which resulted in the disappearance (when the underlying conflict was dealt with) of many longstanding symptoms. In essence, his method depended upon his technical ability to achieve a satisfactory level of hypnosis very rapidly. After rapid induction, he regressed the patient back to a time prior to the onset of the symptom and then brought the patient forward in time to the experience responsible for the symptom's development. He then had the patient describe all that was going on at that time, experiencing everything with all the abreaction of which he was capable. At the same time, he would not only encourage the patient to understand why he had the symptoms, but also to appreciate fully the changes that had occurred in his life which made his initial response to the event unnecessary in the present. He also gave the patient posthypnotic suggestions for relaxation and comfort in those situations previously associated with discomfort. Elman must also be credited with being among the first to discover that patients undergoing surgical anaesthesia often retain the power to hear; although there is almost always a post-anaesthetic amnesia for what has been heard, this information is recoverable in hypnosis (Cheek, 1959). Such information sometimes indicates the source of negative emotional feelings which affect the progress of recovery from surgery.

Cheek's and LeCron's (1968) descriptions of the use of ideomotor responses to establish unconscious signalling, which can effectively locate critical experiences even in light levels of hypnosis, have done much to advance analytical hypnotherapy. More recently, Cheek (1974) has indicated that these techniques can be used to uncover memories of experiences as early as that of birth. This was thought to be impossible prior to this study. He also intimated that even these early experiences can have a strong influence on subsequent behaviour and be responsible for unpleasant symptoms.

In order to complete this short survey of the history of hypnoanalysis, mention must be made of the Neuro-Linguistic Programming (NLP) approach to therapy devised by Bandler and Grinder. In this approach there is no attempt to assume the presence of an unconscious mind. Instead, they postulate that problems occur because the sensory resources are not being fully utilised, and that failures of therapy result from an absence of communication between the patient and his therapist. NLP presumes to be able to locate the deficiency in a patient's use of his resources by defining the representational system that he does use. This leads him into awareness of those resources in which he is deficient. He is then enabled to see and deal with his problem more adequately.

Another important contribution to the understanding of human responses by Bandler and Grinder is their somewhat Pavlovian concept of anchors. An anchor is an event which is the first in a series of events; by its close association with these events an anchor will trigger them when it is itself triggered. Posthypnotic suggestions are regarded as anchors and much of the therapy of NLP is based on the judicious use of nonverbal anchors to control and direct therapy. The reinduction of hypnosis on a posthypnotic cue is a good example of an anchor which is very effective in the highly susceptible. One infers that the same kind of communication would be possible with all (including the normally insusceptible) if only the appropriate anchors were used.

Perhaps Bandler's and Grinder's most valuable contribution to analytical hypnotherapy is the concept that each of us possesses the resources for any change that we might wish to institute; this belief is coupled with the idea that any behaviour, no matter how bizarre and self-damaging, has a positive context. By using the unconscious resources, this context can be enlarged until the unwanted behaviour is changed to become one that remains positive for the whole organism, rather than just a part of it. The technique that is used to accomplish this is termed *reframing*, which has many implications for analytical hypnotherapy, particularly in the theory that there are parts of the personality which are unwittingly in conflict with one another.

The Nature of Hypnosis

Much of the controversy associated with hypnosis is concerned with the premise that hypnosis is a recognisable state. In the face of Barber's (1969) constant and well constructed attacks against this premise (i.e. that hypnosis is a state recognisable solely by certain specific phenomena) the premise has become difficult to support. Indeed, all of the phenomena that have been attributed to hypnosis can be produced without any formal induction. Moreover, they can exist spontaneously. As early as 1823, Bertrand affirmed that 'the psychological phenomena observed during the magnetic state are not exceptional phenomena but are normal or at least phenomena which can be observed under various other conditions.' Orne (1959) also noted that much of what passes for hypnosis is a normal response that might properly be expected in that situation. He also pointed out that simulating subjects can successfully mislead experienced hypnotists into believing that they are hypnotised. Subsequently, attempts to define hypnosis by means of the phenomena normally associated with it are fraught with difficulties.

Barber et al (1974) demonstrated that these phenomena can be reproduced without calling upon the concept of a 'hypnotic state' or 'trance.' They declared that the so-called state of hypnosis was produced by the induction technique, and it was this technique with its content of situational factors that determined the behaviour a given subject would manifest. Subjects would carry out hypnotic behaviour when they had positive attitudes, motivations and expectations which led them to a willingness to think and imagine with the themes presented. Barber et al demonstrated the ease with which a properly motivated subject can be persuaded to develop many of the standard hypnotic phenomena without any evidence of the usual state of hypnosis in which the subject appears asleep or unconscious. Skilled hypnotists make use of hypnotic procedures to produce these positive attitudes, motivations, and expectancies.

London (1967) complicated the issue somewhat when he suggested that hypnosis could operationally be defined as a set of phenomena which a consensus of hypnotists concluded to be hypnotic. However, he omitted to indicate how this consensus could be obtained. More helpfully, he did identify the main issues as: to what extent are induced hypnotic behaviours unique to hypnosis and to what extent is the induction process itself necessary to elicit hypnotic behaviours.

Not only is it difficult to define objectively a 'state' of hypnosis, but even subjectively, Barber (1979) pointed out that highly responsive subjects testify that they have no sense of altered consciousness when responding to hypnotic suggestion and, therefore, do not believe themselves to be in *trance*.

Presented with this very great difficulty of defining hypnosis as a recognisable state (even though everyone is aware that hypnosis appears to be something different from ordinary communication), it is helpful to turn to Hilgard (1977) and his neo-dissociation theory of hypnosis. This theory mediates between the extreme positions of the non-state and the state theorists by proposing that there are degrees of dissociative experience. These degrees depend on shifts in voluntary and involuntary control systems from no dissociation whatsoever up to the massive dissociations of very deep hypnosis. Only when these changes are profound can they be described appropriately as alterations in consciousness.

It is well to pause here and note that no one denies the existence of hypnotic phenomena themselves and even antagonists of the hypnotic state theory recognise that these unusual phenomena are generally foreign to normal human behaviour. They contend, however, that such phenomena can be produced without the necessity of postulating any specific mental or physical state apart from the conditions necessary for optimum compliance.

The problem of what happens when we consider hypnotic phenomena to be present still remains. Hilgard (1977) in his concept of a divided consciousness separated by an amnesic barrier gave some clue as to a possible mechanism. He suggested that memories are present in a divided portion of consciousness and are rendered accessible by the breaking down of the amnesic barrier as it occurs in hypnosis (although this dissociation concept of part of consciousness does not invoke the postulate of the deep unconscious held by Freud [1895]). Memories heretofore unavailable, which become conscious, can properly be described as having been previously dissociated. However, if these memories are not directly available but have to be inferred, they can be thought of as being repressed to the unconscious mind.

It can thus be seen how rapidly one can get caught up in the circuitous argument as to what is conscious and what is unconscious; and yet we know that much of what occurs in hypnosis is not normally conscious even though it may become so. Research into the different functions of the cerebral hemispheres may cast some light on this problem. Gazzeniga, Bogen and Sperry (1962) did exciting work on the functional effects of sectioning the cerebral hemispheres in man and discovered that the two halves of the brain are essentially two separate brains. They found that, in right handed people, the left hemisphere is primarily concerned with verbal behaviour and analytic tasks, whereas the right hemisphere is concerned with more global and patterned tasks such as are used in the imagination, in spatial perception, and in music. Kinsbourne (1972) confirmed these findings when he analysed the movements of the head and eyes in response to questioning. Questions involving analytical thinking produced eye movements to the right, indicating activation of the left analytical hemisphere; questions involving imagination produced eye and head movements to the left, indicating activation of the right hemisphere.

Blakeslee (1980) contended that each half of the brain has its own separate train of conscious thought and its own memories. Whereas the right brain deals in sensory images, the left brain thinks in words and numbers. The left brain also handles language and logical thinking, the right brain controls nonverbal activities. The single brain concept tends to ignore the right brain which appears to be the source of intuition, of creative thinking, and of the imagination. The right brain activity matches the common concept of the unconscious mind. It appears to be a parallel yet subordinate consciousness not usually accessible to awareness. Stimulation of the left hemisphere affects both speech and the muscles; stimulation of the right side produces hallucinations and feelings of double consciousness.

Those subjects who tend to activate the right hemisphere when dealing with problems are found to be the more imaginative and also the more hypnotisable. Those who activate the left hemisphere are drawn more towards the sciences and are, as a rule, more logical in their thinking. They are also less hypnotisable.

These findings lend support to Hilgard (1977) and his neodissociation theory of hypnosis. He pointed out that in well lateralised right handed males, a preference for right handed function was associated with hypnotisability, and the hypnotisable right hander tended to use his right hemisphere more frequently than the non-hypnotisable right hander.

Can we then apply some of this information to a deeper understanding of the nature of hypnosis? This author believes that we must accept the position of the nonstate theorists and conclude that the so-called 'state of hypnosis' is merely a variable set of phenomena produced by the suggestible subject in response to requests by the operator. The standard descriptions of the state of hypnosis are, therefore, no more than a description of a set of responses to a set of specific suggestions; this state will inevitably vary from subject to subject simply because of each subject's uniqueness, a uniqueness which naturally produces a different response to suggestion. Furthermore, this response will also vary with the nature of the suggestions initiating it.

We need only to recall the hypnotic coma of Esdaile (1852) and compare it to the vastly different convulsive states produced by Mesmer (which again were totally unlike the quiet, cooperative, relaxed state so often seen in the modern hypnotherapist's office) to realise that no particular state can be called the *hypnotic state*. They are *all* instances of hypnosis or hypnotic states.

Each of these states represents one of a myriad of possible sets of responses to suggestion. There is no typical state of hypnosis and the search for one must prove futile. Any state labelled *hypnosis* is an artefact recognisable by a conglomerate of unconscious responses to suggestion. The labelling of these responses as *hypnotic* carries with it the implication that other responses are *not* hypnotic. Nothing could be further from the truth even though these responses may have an involuntary quality about them which is distinctive. However, if our definition of hypnosis is restricted to a specific set of responses to suggestion, we run the risk of assuming that a given subject is not hypnotisable if the set of responses does not occur when requested. But, if we accept *any* response to suggestion as evidence of hypnosis (whether or not it be the response we have been taught to expect), this is certainly not the case.

For the analytical hynotherapist, the premise of hypnosis as a recognisable state has no real validity since effective therapy can occur in the absence of any of the accepted signs of hypnosis. It is for this reason that a more useful concept of hypnosis must be sought. We believe that it is more useful to conceive of hypnosis as a dynamic *process* (Barnett 1979) rather than as a *state* and hence to forego the compulsion to regard any given state as hypnosis. Any unconscious response to suggestion is part of the hypnotic process and may be used as a part of therapy. If a definition of hypnosis is demanded, then we can say that **Hypnosis is the process of communication with the unconscious mind recognisable by an unconscious response to suggestion.**

We need now to clarify what is meant by *unconscious*. Here we simply refer to all that is not normally conscious and, consequently, find that we are referring to much that appears to be the function of the right brain. It would then appear that hypnosis can be considered to be the process of communication with the right brain and, whenever we invoke the activities of the right brain, we note that we are inducing hypnotic-like responses. It is in the right brain where much unconscious memory resides, as well as those mental activities which are not available to conscious awareness for much of the time, and which are responsible for responses not normally under voluntary control. It is probable that unconscious responses arise in other areas of the brain apart from the right hemisphere and perhaps are then more deeply un(not)conscious.

Every practitioner of hypnosis knows that there are experiences that, normally, are not voluntarily accessible and remain out of awareness until techniques using involuntary responses render them accessible. It must be assumed that these experiences are recorded in the brain somewhere prior to their availability to conscious awareness and control. For the analytical hypnotherapist the unconscious mind is the repository of all experiences and mental activities which are normally not available to the awareness at any specific moment. The unconscious mind is therefore responsible for those responses which are not under voluntary control.

A more specific definition of hypnosis which has been found satisfactory for analytical hypnotherapy (Barnett 1979) can be stated as follows: **Hypnosis is the process of communication with the unconscious mind recognisable by the presence of unconscious response to suggestion, such response being characterised by lack of voluntary initiation.** This means that hypnosis is characterised by the acceptance of an idea or suggestion without conscious interference. Conversely, it also appears to be unnecessary for conscious thought processes to be interfered with for hypnosis to be present, so long as there is no conscious blocking of this communication with the unconscious mind. The therapeutic process of hypnosis formally commences as soon as the undivided attention of the unconscious mind has been gained and often the process may be active long before it is recognised either by therapist or patient. As his experience with hypnosis increases, the therapist learns to recognise earlier this untrammelled attention of the unconscious mind of the patient and the unconscious responses characteristic of hypnosis.

Using the definition of hypnosis just stated, it becomes clear that hypnosis is being regarded as a continuous and ongoing process not limited by formal induction procedures, and that hypnotherapy is merely the harnessing of this process for the purposes of therapy. Formal techniques of induction of hypnosis are, essentially, methods of securing unconscious attention, establishing this unconscious communication, and of recognising when this communication has become operative. Furthermore, all kinds of unconscious mental activity can be included within this simple definition of hypnosis. Such activities as meditation, deep thinking, day dreaming, fantasising and, of course, self hypnosis all find ready inclusion in this definition.

The popular image of the subject in hypnosis with eyes closed, head bowed and body virtually motionless until directed, is simply the product of a series of suggestions which have been accepted by the suggestible subject. It is no more representative of hypnosis than the image of the chess master contemplating his next move, or the pole jumper marshalling all of his unconscious resources for his next jump. By ceasing to attribute to hypnosis any particular state or phenomenon, the process of hypnosis can be more clearly understood.

Induction Techniques

Let us apply this thinking to a consideration of standard hypnosis induction techniques, since, in this view, induction techniques are patterns of suggestions designed to elucidate readily recognisable unconscious responses. These assure the operator that he is obtaining satisfactory unconscious attention. In addition, these techniques enable the operator to estimate the degree of unconscious attention so secured.

Induction techniques are taught for these very obvious reasons but many students continue to believe — as do most patients — that a demonstrable state must be present before suggestions will be effective. Much time is often spent in eliciting hypnotic phenomena in order to confirm the presence of adequate unconscious attention before therapy is commenced. But in practice, eliciting formal hypnotic responses need not be pursued prior to the administering of therapeutic suggestions, although it is generally agreed that the degree to which these suggestions are likely to be heeded is often proportional to the degree that other hypnotic responses are obtained. However, it is not necessary to produce any formal hypnotic responses such as catalepsy, anaesthesia, etc., in the belief that these will in some way increase the likelihood of acceptance of therapeutic suggestions. The various orthodox methods of inducing hypnosis are merely means of securing unconscious attention and are generally adequate for this purpose; they may perhaps facilitate the ease with which further unconscious communication proceeds, although this has yet to be proven.

Theoretical Considerations

Edmonston (1967) believed that the stimulus-response theory of hypnosis offered the most promise for the understanding, prediction, and quantification of behaviour in hypnosis as it does for all human behaviour. This theory affirmed that a response by an organism was directly related to the stimulus preceding the response. We do not know what mediates a specific response to a stimulus but it is often so constant as to become predictable. Whenever an organism responds in a specific manner to a specific stimulus, we see this as evidence of a stimulus-response mechanism which may remain specific so that, whenever the same stimulus is applied, the same response occurs. For example, whenever an organism consistently responds to the presentation of a noxious stimulus by withdrawal from it, we describe this as a withdrawal response. Much biological activity can be understood in terms of such predictable responses to stimuli (see Fig. 1). The well-known knee jerk reflex is a good example of such a stimulus response. The reaction to the sudden stretching of the quadriceps muscles on the front of the thigh when the tendon below the kneecap is struck is a sudden contraction of that muscle with an obvious upward movement of the suspended foot. The normal tonus of that muscle is, in part, dependent on the intactness of this particular response, and much normal functioning depends on the presence of such inborn reflexes.

Pavlov (1927) demonstrated that more complex responses could readily be superimposed upon inborn reflexes through specific training procedures. These new responses are termed *conditioned responses* and tend to differ in each individual because of the differences of exposure in the learning situations. We are, every moment of our lives, unconsciously responding to stimuli and many of these responses are learned ones which have been superimposed upon inherited reflexes and are the means by which we adapt to the environment. Pavlov's experiments with dogs demonstrated that he was able to induce the normal salivation associated with the presentation of food

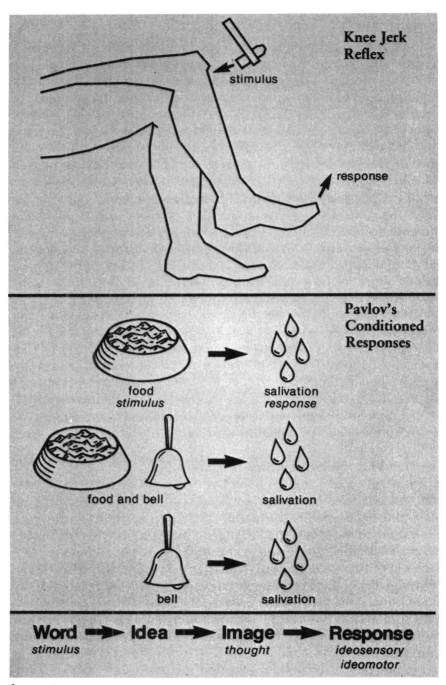

figure 1

merely by sounding a bell. Human beings often respond no less effectively at the sound of the dinner gong.

Human beings, however, differ from dogs in that they are aware of the thoughts that occur when certain ideas are presented to them. The stimulus is rarely as simple as a bell. Human beings have developed a language, each word of which is capable of functioning as a specific stimulus. Groups of words can also produce an idea and the response that a word or a group of words invokes is dependent upon that idea. This idea will vary from one individual to another although the same word or group word stimulus is presented. The modification in each individual is the result of the different associations which each individual has because of his unique lifetime experiences.

It is the contention of this author that hypnosis utilises all of this unconscious mental activity during which ideas are generated in the subject by words or nonverbal stimuli and are unconsciously processed until an appropriate response is produced. This response may be entirely subjective, e.g. imagery and altered sensation (ideosensory) and/or objective, e.g. motor and vasomotor (ideomotor).

Induction methods involve the use of complex reflexes in which the stimuli are usually words or gestures presented to the subject as suggestions. These suggestions initiate ideas which, in turn, effect an expected response. If that response is a motor response, it can readily be monitored by the operator. It is probable that all motor responses are preceded by a sensory one able to be monitored only by the subject. All hypnotic responses therefore involve either an ideosensory or ideomotor response or a combination of both.

The Hand Levitation Induction Technique
A consideration of a popular induction technique such as hand levitation will enable these points so far discussed to be illustrated by examining the probable sequence of events during its performance. In this technique, words are used to suggest to the subject that his hand is about to become light. Prior to the administration of these suggestions, every attempt is made to remove any source of distraction in the environment so that it will remain conducive to his acceptance of the suggestions. Also, attention is given to the subject's internal environment so that there will be no negative thoughts which might prevent him from giving heed to the suggestions. He is then directed to pay close attention to his hand and the sensations that occur there. In so doing, not only is conscious attention increased, but so also is the unconscious attention necessary for effective unconscious communi-

cation, i.e. hypnosis. Suggestions of lightness are then given and, although hypnosis can presume to have begun prior to this, it is only when there is an observable response, or the subject indicates a subjective feeling of lightness, that there is evidence of hypnosis. Sometimes there is no evident ideomotor response even though there is a strong ideosensory response of lightness. Usually an upward movement of the hand or fingers indicates that the suggestions are meeting with the expected response.

Initially there must be an acceptance of the possibility that lightness will occur. There has to be some suspension of the normal disbelief — that is to say, there must be an absence of conscious interference with the unconscious response to the idea of lightness. The idea of lightness occurs because the words used invoke an existing memory of lightness, for, if there is no memory associated with the word lightness, then there can be no corresponding idea of lightness. When this memory is invoked, the sensation of lightness is recalled and reaches some level of awareness. If sufficiently strong, this sensation of lightness is augmented by movement commensurate with the lightness, and the ideomotor response of the levitating hand confirms that the suggestion has met with appropriate unconscious response. The operator is then aware that the process of hypnosis is in progress.

The ease with which this response usually takes place is presumably inversely proportional to the amount of conscious interference involved. Much conscious interference could inhibit the response altogether, either at the level of ideosensory awareness, or at the level of ideomotor expression; conscious awareness would of course inject the recognition that no real change in weight of the hand could have occurred.

As the induction technique proceeds, further suggestions of lightness and movement are given which reinforce the initial responses, and make further responses more likely and effective. Frequently there is the inferred suggestion that, at some point, the subject will enter *trance*. To comply with this suggestion, the subject will experience whatever he considers are the parameters which make *trance* real for him if this is within his power. It may not require much greater effort upon the part of the subject than that he search his unconscious memories for his idea of trance and to respond to that idea in a manner he believes is expected of him. If he succeeds in producing his idea of trance, then he will believe that he was *hypnotised*. If he fails to reproduce this idea (which might include, for example, absence of awareness), then he will not believe that he has experienced hypnosis despite the presence of other profound manifestations of unconscious activity, such as catalepsy or anaesthesia. If amnesia is a part of his idea of trance, and this is manifest posthypnotically, he may deny that he has experienced hypnosis since he is not aware that anything has happened. Or, he may reject the suggestion for amnesia because of a great unconscious need to remember and recall the events of hypnosis in detail and likewise be certain that he did not experience hypnosis. Nevertheless, the hand levitation technique is one that enables the subject to appreciate that something outside his voluntary control occurred as the result of suggestion and he may accept this as a manifestation of hypnosis.

The Eye Fixation Technique

If another popular induction technique is subjected to similar scrutiny, we find that precisely the same principles are invoked and that, once again, both ideosensory and ideomotor responses are involved. In the eye fixation technique, suggestions for progressive relaxation form an integral part of the induction process. Unconscious attention is secured by providing the conscious mind with the increasingly boring task of gazing at a given point. This soon fails to provide sufficient interest to occupy the conscious mind which then readily wanders to other thoughts or perhaps takes a rest. Meanwhile, suggestions for increased fatigue are being readily accepted by the unconscious mind untrammelled by interference from the conscious mind. These suggestions are directed initially at the eye muscles which indicate a response by blinking, fluttering, and eventually closing. Further suggestions for relaxation of other muscles follow until the whole body becomes totally relaxed. Hypnosis is then said to have been deepened although all that we have really observed is increased relaxation due to the acceptance of a series of suggestions for relaxation. There will also be an observable paucity of muscle movement, a generalised relaxation involving the autonomic nervous system with a slowing of the respiratory and cardiac rates, and a flushing of the skin due to relaxation of the musculature of the skin blood vessels. Frequently, the eyes may be seen to take part in this autonomic relaxation with reddening of the conjunctiva and watering of the eyes. These signs have often been attributed to deep hypnosis but, in fact, are nothing more than good responses to suggestions of relaxation and indeed, are more likely to occur in the more suggestible. Had hyperactivity been suggested and accepted (Gibbon 1979), signs of increased activity would be neither more nor less characteristic of the process of hypnosis.

The degree of involvement in the hypnotic process can be estimated by the complexity of the suggestions to which a response is found and indicates the degree of unhampered unconscious activity exhibited by the subject at that time. It does not indicate any specific altered state. If this broad concept of hypnosis and its induction is accepted, then the many deviations from the typical trance so often seen in practice can readily be understood. If the usual concept of deepening of hypnosis is seen simply as a greater involvement in this unconscious internal activity we call hypnosis, then we can more easily understand how it can fluctuate so readily and why it remains so difficult to define (see Fig. 2).

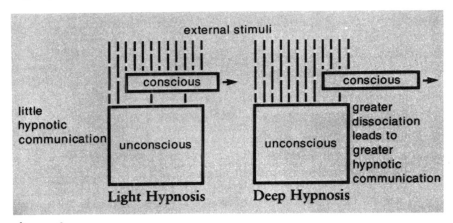

figure 2

As we follow this process of induction, it can be seen how the unconscious activity of the right brain is being encouraged, while the logical and critical activity of the left brain is being discouraged; it can further be understood why this process is likely to be simpler for those who are accustomed to the greater right brain activity of imagination and creativity.

Alerting from Hypnosis

If we agree that hypnosis is to be regarded only as any condition in which there is unconscious response to suggestion, then all that needs to be done to terminate the process is to request the unconscious mind to cease responding to these suggestions. For example, if one of these suggestions has been that the subject should *sleep* (as used to be commonly a part of the induction process), then clearly the subject needs to be directed to stop sleeping when this is no longer required of him. This was how the idea of awakening from hypnosis originally arose, although we now have conclusive proof that the subject responding to the hypnotic suggestion to sleep is never really asleep. He is simply doing his very best to comply with the suggestion to sleep by playing the role to the best of his ability — so well in fact that he may convince everyone, including himself, that he has indeed fallen asleep.

Where the suggestion for sleep has not been given or implied, the idea of awakening is irrelevant. In the therapeutic context, however, it is necessary to discontinue any responses the persistence of which would be in any way unfavourable to the subject (Williams, 1953) and to continue with any responses which would be of therapeutic benefit. Almost any signal may be acceptable to the unconscious mind to indicate that the unconscious attention of hypnosis need no longer be maintained and can thus be reduced to the usual levels. The normal conscious critical and logical pattern of intervention should then become fully operative.

Post Hypnotic Suggestion

Much of the mystery that continues to surround and haunt hypnosis is associated with the phenomenon of post hypnotic suggestion. It has always been a matter of some wonder and amazement that a suggestion given during hypnosis should sometimes appear to have such a compelling effect that it is followed meticulously even some considerable time after its initial administration. Although it is not known by what mechanism a suggestion, fully accepted and approved at an unconscious level, is carried out (faithfully and often without conscious awareness), it is this phenomenon more than any other which confirms the presence of the separate functions of the conscious and the unconscious minds.

For a post hypnotic suggestion to be fully effective, certain conditions must be met: the suggestion must receive full unconscious approval, and it must either be one that also receives conscious approval, or one that has been accepted without conscious awareness. Whenever in the absence of conscious awareness or disapproval such a suggestion is totally accepted unconsciously, it is not subject to inhibition from the conscious mind and is therefore faithfully executed. These are the suggestions which are allowed to remain when hypnosis is terminated. All of therapy is based upon the principle that a decision made at an unconscious level during the period of close attention to the hypnotherapist (defined as hypnosis), will be adhered to during the post hypnotic period. That is, providing that there has always been full, unconscious acceptance of this decision.

Whenever the unconscious mind has accepted a suggestion (whether the response is to be immediate or delayed), it will usually be adhered to with all the determination of which the individual is capable if its commission remains appropriate and is believed to be beneficial. The unconscious mind has resources not available to the conscious mind. For example, the unconscious mind has the ability to monitor the passage of time in a manner that is imperfectly understood but perhaps may be compared with the quartz crystal of the modern timepiece which computes time on the basis of the vibrations of the crystal. So it may be that the unconscious time clock computes the rhythms of the heart beat or some other biological rhythm. In any case, a suggestion given that is to be responded to only after a specific time interval will often be executed at exactly the time suggested. This ability unconsciously to monitor time periods accurately enables many people to awaken from normal sleep at a specific predetermined time.

Post hypnotic suggestions may, for unconscious reasons, meet with only partial acceptance or even with total rejection. The techniques of analytical hypnotherapy are designed to discover the reasons for the rejection of an apparently beneficial suggestion. When the reasons are known, a means might then be found to obviate the need for continuation of the rejection of beneficial suggestions.

Like any other suggestion, a post hypnotic suggestion is unlikely to be accepted and executed should any underlying emotional conflict contrary to its acceptance persist. For this reason, a therapy which can deal with such a conflict and resolve it will enable the patient to gain access to those unconscious resources previously blocked by that conflict. Inappropriate post hypnotic suggestions (e.g. as sometimes given by people in authority to children), if accepted and not cancelled, might also be the source of neurosis since the effects of such suggestions will linger on with the compliance of the unconscious mind. With analytical techniques we are able to locate any original decision that is crippling the individual and thus we can encourage the unconscious mind to discover means of rejecting such a decision as outmoded, harmful and currently irrelevant.

The Rapid Induction of Hypnosis

PART ONE   Chapter 3

In order for the hypnotherapist to evaluate the importance of each perceived response to his suggestions, a clear understanding of the nature of hypnosis is necessary. In the standard induction of hypnosis, the hypnotist is seeking to obtain evidence of appropriate unconscious responses to increasingly complex suggestions until a particular response is obtained which assures him that hypnosis has been secured. Most of the popular induction techniques have been designed on the premise that hypnosis is present only when an unusual and complex response is demonstrable. Because of this assumption the induction of hypnosis is usually regarded as a procedure requiring some time to establish. The operator is enjoined to observe responses to a given sequence of suggestions and to recognise these responses in turn before proceeding to the next in sequence. This process inevitably takes time. Furthermore, if suggestions early in the sequence are not accepted, it is presumed that the more complex suggestions also will not be acceptable and the process is usually halted. The subject is then considered to be a poor subject for hypnosis or even to be unhypnotisable.

Hypnotherapists of considerable experience will, from time to time, meet a subject who exhibits phenomena normally associated with deep hypnosis without such phenomena having been suggested. Such phenomena as total relaxation, amnesia, and hallucinations may have occurred very early in the induction procedure. For such subjects, the induction of hypnosis will have been considered to have been very rapid and have resulted from a high degree of hypnotic susceptibility. Though comparatively rare in clinical experience, there are, in any reasonably sized population, a sufficient number of these high susceptibles who render the task of the stage hypnotist relatively easy once he has used his skills to identify their presence within his audience. However, his ability to induce hypnosis rapidly is not entirely dependent upon this factor alone. London (1967) pointed out that many stage hypnotists are able to induce hypnosis very rapidly by abbreviating the usual induction sequence considerably. He referred to Dave Elman, a former carnival hypnotist, who specialized in training medical personnel in hypnotic techniques and who argued that the complete induction of profound hypnosis in the cooperative subject should never take more than two minutes.

Erickson stated that he rarely gave therapeutic suggestions until hypnosis had developed over a period of twenty minutes (Erickson & Rossi 1974). For the average clinician, however, the long period of time necessary for the induction of hypnosis is a problem which has prevented many from pursuing the use of hypnosis more fully in their practices. This is particularly the case for such practitioners as dentists who usually have a rapid turnover of patients and little time to spend on lengthy induction procedures.

Barber (1977) with the introduction of his Rapid Induction Analgesia method has partly overcome this problem of time-consuming induction. Nevertheless, even in this method (RIA), the rapid induction is based on a previously established cue given in hypnosis and used posthypnotically. The original hypnosis induction takes at least ten minutes. It has been known for a very long time that, once satisfactory hypnosis has been obtained, a posthypnotic cue frequently can be of value in its very rapid reestablishment. This does not solve the problem of the initial lengthy induction of hypnosis. There is, however, a solution which has been discovered not only by the aforementioned stage hypnotists, but by many experienced clinical hypnotherapists. So long as hypnosis is regarded as a trance state — being present only when certain criteria have been met — lengthy induction procedures will continue to be the only means of securing such a state in those subjects capable of it. But when the nature of hypnosis is reconsidered in the manner outlined in the preceding chapter, i.e. as a process of communication with the unconscious mind, a new perspective is obtained.

Hypnosis can now be considered to be present whenever **any** evidence of unconcious communication is obained and **any** unconscious attention secured. By this definition, in effect, the induction of hypnosis is **always** rapid and in fact is probably instantaneous. The only practical problem then, is not induction but the maintenance of the unconscious communication and attention which we call hypnosis. What has, in the past, made the induction of hypnosis appear to be slow and laborious, is the operator's dependence for the recognition of the presence of hypnosis on insensitive criteria which he had elaborated for this purpose. When such criteria are discarded, and hypnosis is regarded as present whenever any evidence of unconscious communication is perceived, then the stage is set for much more rapid recognition of the presence of hypnosis and thus techniques for the rapid induction of hypnosis can be evolved.

Barber and De Moor (1972) postulated that there were as many as nine variables used in the induction of hypnosis which heighten responsiveness to suggestion. They found that these variables merely serve to give rise to positive attitudes, motivations and expectations which in turn produce a willingness to think on and imagine those things suggested. Techniques that produce this attitude of mind in the subject need not be prolonged. For example, in the eye fixation technique, an early suggestion usually given is that the eyes will become heavy and will close. The involuntary nature of the eye closure indicates an unconscious response and further suggestions are added to encourage this and other signs of relaxation. When the nature of hypnosis is accepted as being any unconscious response to suggestion, the experienced hypnotherapist can recognise that he has already made adequate unconscious communication long before the eyes actually close; thus he can immediately utilise this knowledge for more complex suggestions. It is this early recognition of hypnosis which has enabled stage hypnotists to produce the rapid induction that has characterised their performances.

As previously mentioned, Elman (1964) in his writings repeatedly emphasised this rapid entry into hypnosis and taught it as being the most efficient means of inducing hypnosis. He believed that hypnosis occurred when the critical faculty of the conscious mind was bypassed and communication with the unconscious mind (which he called 'selective thinking') was established. The personal experience of this author has confirmed this viewpoint repeatedly and he parts company with Elman only in his view that waking hypnosis differs from other forms of hypnosis in which eye closure forms an essential element of the induction procedure. It is our view that hypnosis can be induced quite readily by the use of any ideomotor response and that eye closure is but a simple and readily acceptable example of this. Any ideomotor or, indeed, any ideosensory response, whether established with or without eye closure, indicates that the conscious critical faculty has been bypassed and that the route to the unconscious is temporarily unobstructed and available for the presentation and possible acceptance of further, more complex suggestions. The hypnotherapist who has recognised this fact perceives many opportunities to establish hypnosis rapidly without resorting to the use of the standard induction techniques. All rapid induction techniques are based upon this understanding; this enables the resources of hypnosis to become more readily available to the hypnotherapist because much of the time usually unnecessarily spent in induction has been eliminated. It certainly behooves the hypnotherapist to be entirely familiar with techniques of rapid induction and, with an understanding of the principles behind such techniques, he will soon evolve equally effective and rapid approaches of his own.

Eye Closure Techniques of Rapid Induction of Hypnosis

Traditionally, hypnosis has been associated with eye closure and almost all induction techniques described involve the shutting of the eyes at some time during the procedure. This not only enables the hypnotist to observe the subject without himself being observed, but also, and more importantly, enables the subject to shut out distracting influences which might be in his field of vision. Hilgard (1977) suggested that hypnotic induction procedures are designed to produce a readiness for dissociative experiences by concealing reality orientation. Earlier, Haley (1958) pointed out that the use of eye closure illustrated what he called the 'double bind' resulting in the dissociation of the control systems (voluntary and involuntary) which provides for further dissociation.

The earlier practitioners equated hypnosis with eye closure and believed that without it there was unlikely to be hypnosis. Elman (1964), in spite of his advanced thinking, held this opinion as well and based the following induction technique on the use of eye closure in which the subject has difficulty in reopening his eyes once the suggestion to close them has been accepted. The response of eye closure is the indication of unconscious communication – the bypassing of the critical faculty – which is established and enlarged by further suggestions. In many cases the procedure takes no longer than a minute and therefore leaves more time for actual therapy and analysis. In the following description of his rapid eye closure technique, which has been successfully taught to many students of hypnosis over the years, the accompanying commentary serves to indicate the interrelationship of therapist to patient during the procedure.

Two Finger Eye Closure Method (Elman)

Verbalisation

Commentary

I would like to show you how you can use relaxation to your advantage so that nothing we do or say here will bother you at all and you can remain comfortable the whole time.

It is not necessary to use the word *hypnosis*. Much of the anxiety frequently associated with the first experience of hypnosis can thereby be avoided. This verbal introduction can be modified to suit the situation (e.g. at the dentist's or hypnotherapist's). No special position is necessary but spectacles must be removed.

Just lean back in the chair and make yourself comfortable.

Now take a long, deep breath and, as you let it out, let go of all of the surface tension and feel relaxed.

Deep breathing is almost always an effective means of relieving tension and producing relaxation.

That's right. See how much better that makes you feel.

This early suggestion is directed at promoting awareness of an unconscious response so that other unconscious responses may be permitted more readily.

When you take another deep breath, you will feel twice as relaxed as you are right now.

A reinforcing suggestion for increased relaxation.

All right, now take another deep breath and open your eyes wide.

'Open your eyes wide' encourages stretching of the eye muscles which renders subsequent relaxation more likely.

Now, let me pull your eyelids shut.

Gently pull the eyelids down with finger and thumb. This is a strong nonverbal suggestion for eye closure.

Relax the muscles under my fingers so that your eyes stay closed.

Now, as I take my fingers away, relax those eye muscles to the point where they just won't work.

Remove the fingers as soon as adequate relaxation is evident.

When *you* are sure that those eye muscles just will not work, test them to make *sure* that they just won't work.

Test them hard, that's right.

Now, let that relaxation spread from your eyes right down to your toes. You will be so relaxed all over that when I lift your hand and let it drop it will be so limp and heavy that it will drop with a plop.

Just let it drop with a plop and you are now more relaxed than you have ever been.

That's right. Now so long as you keep that relaxation in your eye muscles so that they just won't work and spread it all the way down to your toes, nothing we do here will bother or disturb you at all.

'To the point where they just won't work' are the crucial words in this technique since they demand that the subject voluntarily relinquish control of his eye muscles. At first hearing, this may appear to be a challenge but, in fact, it is not. It simply encourages the subject to measure the extent of *his* success in responding to suggestion.

Evidence that the subject is making some attempt to open his eyes should now be observed. It indicates that hypnosis has now begun since this is an obvious unconscious response to suggestion.

Advantage is now being taken of the unconscious communication evidently present to increase relaxation. Observe the increase in relaxation which takes place.

At this point lift up the hand nearest to you at the wrist for about six inches and let it drop. Note the degree of relaxation. It is an excellent indicator of the degree of hypnotic communication already present.

'Nothing will bother or disturb you at all' is a suggestion which often establishes a high level of hypnotic analgesia. In any case, the patient is now ready for specific suggestions, e.g. for anaesthesia or for regression.

Eyes Reopen when Tested   When his eyes reopen, the subject may have misunderstood the directions as a challenge and now feels that he has proved to his satisfaction that he cannot be made to give up his control. It must be made clear to him that he is only being asked to relinquish conscious control temporarily, a relinquishment which you believe that he is well able to make if he so wishes. Encourage him by stressing that you *know* that he has the ability to succeed and can relax his eye muscles to the point where he is certain that they will not work; only when *he* is certain that they will not work will his eyes be unable to open. The knowledge that he has the right to decide on this matter frequently enables success to be achieved and the subject should be congratulated upon this success.

Sometimes the therapist may demonstrate how he can produce eye closure upon himself or he can persuade the subject to imagine that his eyelids are heavy as lead as when awakening from a deep sleep. In some cases, encouraging the subject simply to pretend that the eyes will not work can result in satisfactory eye closure.

The Hand does not Drop into the Lap   If the hand does not drop into the lap in a relaxed manner but slowly descends, or remains suspended, this is further evidence of a resistance to the idea of relaxation. It is advisable then to use the Repeated Induction Technique which repeats the suggestion that there will be greater relaxation after opening and closing the eyes. This is often successful in achieving satisfactory relaxation. Occasionally the hand remains suspended and advantage can be taken of this spontaneous catalepsy to utilise it for the increase of hypnotic involvement. It can be suggested that the hand remain comfortably where it is. In practice these problems occur rarely and are, as a rule, indicative of unconscious resistance which may persist.

With increased experience, and with a cooperative subject, good eye closure (lid catalepsy) can frequently be obtained without the necessity of the hypnotist using his fingers. He simply asks the subject to close his eyes and relax the eye muscles to the point where the subject is sure that they simply will not work. This omission of the use of the fingers obviates the need for removing spectacles.

In this technique there has been unconscious communication from the moment that the suggestions for lid catalepsy have been accepted. This communication is reinforced by the suggestions given for relaxation prior to testing for it (i.e. by letting the hand drop). All rapid induction techniques have these two phases of entry into and reinforcement of hypnosis.

Surprise Cataleptic Technique

The spontaneous catalepsy of the arm that sometimes occurs in the previous induction method is a feature of another rapid induction technique. While both Erickson (1952) and Hartland (1966) were noted teachers of long induction techniques, they were frequently observed to use a rapid induction technique based upon the partly nonverbal induction of limb catalepsy (a technique which has recently been described by Matheson and Grehan [1979]). Nonverbal inductions have the advantage over verbal ones insofar as they are less likely to meet with conscious resistance for the nonverbal message cannot be consciously decoded and understood.

Verbalisation	Commentary
Before we proceed I would like to make two important points.	This statement will always gain the patient's maximum attention. During this period maintain eye contact as far as is possible since this promotes eye fixation.
First of all, it is important what *you* do and not what *I* do. Second, please don't try to make things happen, just let them happen.	This reassures the patient that he will remain in control. This is a direction to the unconscious mind of the patient to assume that control. It also confuses the patient's conscious mind since apparently nothing so far has happened.
I am simply going to pick up your arm like this.	At this point the arm is raised to shoulder level and very gently and slowly let go with contact being maintained long enough to impart the nonverbal suggestion that it should stay where it has been placed. The arm usually becomes cataleptic in response to this nonverbal suggestion.

Verbalisation	Commentary

That's fine. Now just let your eyes close, take a nice deep breath all the way and as you let that breath out, let your body relax all over.

Whether the arm has remained raised or has dropped heavily, there has been an unconscious response which is utilised as a route to greater unconscious communication and greater relaxation.

Just let your eyes remain closed until I ask you to open them again. You will notice that your arm has remained in that position and is floating there without any effort (or has dropped into your lap and is extremely relaxed).

The patient is becoming aware of his unconscious responses and is less conscious of his immediate environment. Hypnosis is proceeding satisfactorily.

As you realize this you become even more deeply relaxed and nothing need bother or disturb you in any way.

These further suggestions increase unconscious involvement and, if the arm is cataleptic, suggestions can now be given that it will become heavy and relax into the lap.

Once again the two phases necessary for the induction of hypnosis are apparent: in the first phase, the nonverbal response of catalepsy or of total relaxation indicates the bypassing of the critical faculty; in the second phase the suggestion of increased relaxation establishes the unconscious communication of the hypnotic process.

Eye Roll – Levitation Induction Technique (Spiegal)

As part of the Hypnotic Induction Profile (HIP, Spiegal, 1973), there is the rapid induction of hypnosis using the eye roll which is then established by means of the suggestion for levitation. Although HIP has proved to be of less value in practice as an indicator of hypnotisability than its originator had hoped, it has nevertheless proved to be very useful for introducing the idea of hypnosis to new patients and for gauging attitudes toward it.

Verbalisation
Please make yourself comfortable and lie back in the chair with your arms resting on the arms of the chair and your feet on the foot-stool.

Commentary
The subject is best seated in a recliner armchair with the operator seated to one side. The nearer arm should be touched with firmness and reassurance.

Now, look towards me. Leave your head in that position and turn your eyes toward your eyebrows – now toward the top of your head. As you continue to look upward, close your eyes slowly. That's right. . . close. . . close. . . good. Keep your eyelids closed and continue to hold your eyes upward. Take a deep breath. . . hold it. . . now breathe out slowly. Let your eyes relax and let your body float. Imagine a feeling of floating, floating, right down through the chair. . . There will be something pleasant and welcome about this sensation of floating.

You should be seated in a position in which the subject can look at you comfortably. Encourage him to roll his eyes upward as far as possible.

For many people, the upward gaze is strongly associated with the relaxation prior to sleep and it is this relaxation and dissociation which is being encouraged by the instruction to let the body float. Hypnosis, in the majority of cases, has already begun. Suggestions for comfort and well-being serve to reinforce it.

As you concentrate on this floating feeling, I am going to concentrate on your left (right) hand and arm and in a while I am going to stroke the middle finger of your left (right) hand. After I do so, you will develop a light movement sensation in that finger which will spread to the other fingers and then to the whole hand, causing it to feel light and buoyant. You will then let it float upward into an upright position. O.K.

Place your hand gently but firmly upon the wrist nearest to you.

After these instructions have been given, commence stroking the hand from the base of the middle fingernail and move gently but firmly upward to the bend of the elbow.

First one finger. . . and then another. . . and as these restless movements develop, your elbow bends and your forearm floats into an upright position.

These instructions are paced to coincide with any observed responses. If none appear after ten seconds, then the suggestions are delivered slowly and deliberately regardless. If there is still no response, wait a further five seconds and gently encircle the wrist with the thumb and middle finger and gently encourage it upward.

Just let it go. Imagine that your hand is like a balloon. Let it float upward. That's it. All the way.	The response to these suggestions is a good indicator of suggestibility and suggestions for further relaxation can now be given.

Once again, we note the two phases of induction: the first phase of bypassing the critical faculty by the sensation of floating and the second phase, that of the actual levitation and subsequent relaxation.

A Rapid Hypnotic Induction Technique for Children

Most children will enter hypnosis very quickly and easily; while an eye closure technique is suitable for most children, some smaller children will object to it. It is always wise to enquire from the child whether it will be O.K. for him to close his eyes.

Verbalisation

Do you like pretend games, Mary? I would like you to pretend something for me, will you? Good. All right, now close your eyes please and while you have them closed, I want you to pretend that they just won't open no matter how hard you try and, so long as you keep pretending, they won't open at all. That's good. Keep pretending until I ask you to stop. Do you have a television at home? O.K., will you switch it on please? What's on?... Can you turn it up a little? Good. What's happening now?

Commentary

The exact wording is not important here and should be adapted to the circumstances. The objective is to invoke the child's imagination, which normally she is using continually in her games of pretence, to gain eye closure. When futile attempts to open the eyes are observed, hypnosis has already begun. It is important to secure the child's agreement to maintain the pretence until you direct her to stop pretending. With an easy extension of her pretence, the child transports herself to her home and regresses to a favourite TV programme. She can be asked to describe in detail all that she sees and hears going on. Hypnosis is established. The body relaxation normally associated with adult hypnosis is often less in evidence with children who remain physically active throughout hypnosis.

The rapidity with which most children enter hypnosis using this technique may initially create doubt as to its effectiveness, but the hypnosis attained is often profound, and such hypnotic phenomena as total anaesthesia and amnesia are often readily demonstrable. All pretence, which forms a large part of the average child's world, involves unconscious (right brain?) imagination. Children, more than do adults, can therefore be said to live at an unconscious level and this presumably accounts for their greater hypnotisability.

The experienced hypnotherapist can use a very similar technique with imaginative adults with minimal modifications. For example, instead of asking the adult, as one would ask the child, to *pretend* his eyes won't open, he would be asked to *imagine* that they won't open; then he can be directed to imagine himself in his favourite place rather than, as with the child, watching television. He is then asked to describe the scene in some detail to establish the hypnotic communication.

By utilising the avenue of access to the unconscious mind which the presenting symptom frequently offers, the analytical hypnotherapist has many opportunities for very rapid induction of hypnosis. Bandler and Grinder (1979) offered a very effective rapid induction technique when, as a part of the technique of reframing, they instructed the client to 'go inside and talk to the part with the symptom.' Since the part creating the symptom is always deeply unconscious, contact with it demands unconscious communication and any response from the part responsible for the sympton indicates that hypnosis is present.

The effective use of the affect bridge (regression over a bridge of common emotion to an earlier situation responsible for that emotion [Watkins 1971]), involves rapid unconscious communication and, when successful, indicates that rapid induction of hypnosis has taken place. Any spontaneous regression to an earlier experience can similarly be utilised by the analytical hypnotherapist to establish hypnosis which can then be rapidly reinduced on a cue associated with the hypnosis.

Hypnotic Phenomena and Hypnotisability

Once the process of hypnosis has been initiated, and communication with the unconscious mind established, the responses to suggestion are described as hypnotic phenomena. These phenomena can be assumed to be limited only by the available resources of the unconscious mind and the degree to which the conscious mind is able to interfere with communication. The complexity of hypnotic phenomena ranges from the simple to the most difficult; and in those subjects in whom the most complex responses are demonstrable, it must be assumed that conscious interference is minimal. However, in those subjects in which few or no hypnotic phenomena are demonstrable, it can be assumed that conscious interference with unconscious communication is high. But it may only be that, in these latter subjects, the unconscious resources are limited and consequently are not available to permit the presentation of the more complex hypnotic responses.

Graham (1977), in his laterality theory, viewed hypnosis in terms of a relative shift of cognitive functioning from the dominant to the nondominant hemisphere of the brain; hypnosis is therefore a construct representing nondominant hemisphere functions. Hilgard (1977), with his neodissociation concept, also appeared to support this viewpoint except that he seemed to regard hypnosis as the function of a dissociated part of consciousness, a part which is normally not active but rather, acts passively until the dissociation of hypnosis occurs. In this author's view, it is the degree of dissociation that determines the complexity of hypnotic phenomena available to the individual at any given time. When the dominant hemisphere is active there is little dissociation; but, as the nondominant hemisphere becomes more active, the responses available to it become evident. Dissociation from the conscious dominant hemisphere has increased.

For example, the simple phenomenon of relaxation and decreased mobility of voluntary muscles is an unconscious (nondominant hemisphere) response. It is readily available to suggestion and requires only minimal dissociation from consciousness (dominant hemisphere) with little awareness of altered consciousness. On the other hand, the more complex phenomena, such as hallucinations, require much greater conscious/unconscious dissociation which is frequently accompanied by a greater subjective sense of altered consciousness. If we adhere to the definition of hypnosis as being the process of unconscious communication, then *any* degree of conscious/unconscious dissociation which permits this communication becomes part of hypnosis.

There is much evidence to suggest that the ability of a given individual to respond to hypnotic suggestion is a character trait which is relatively fixed. Fellows and Armstrong (1977), Hilgard (1970), Davis et al (1978), and Wilson and Barber (1978), all give evidence to suggest that this trait is directly related to the creative and imaginative skills of the individual. A deficiency in these skills may perhaps limit the response to hypnosis. Many writers after Bernheim (1889) have noted the stability of hypnotisability. Others (e.g. Diamond, 1974) assert that hypnotic skills can be learned and hypnotisability improved, although this improvement is likely to be relatively slight. Much apparent improvement in hypnotisability is presumed to be due to the removal of the interference sometimes imposed by the conscious mind during the hypnotic process. If we assume, in the absence of any resistance to the hypnotic process, that the capacity to dissociate is relatively fixed, then the ability to exhibit hypnotic phenomena will also be relatively stable for each subject. However, if this capacity to dissociate is to be properly estimated, we must be certain that all conscious and unconscious resistance is eliminated.

The fact that this dissociation appears to occur more readily in childhood is probably related to the greater use of the imagination in children. We have already discussed how the right brain is more concerned with imagery. The child's greater use of imagery is, presumably, associated with greater activity of the non-dominant hemisphere; therefore he responds more readily to hypnotic suggestion with its demand for unconscious (right hemisphere) responses. Those adults who are more imaginative and creative have been shown (Spanos 1971) to exhibit greater dissociation from conscious external reality in the hypnotic test situation. On the other hand, those adults who habitually use their more logical, verbal and critical conscious mind tend to be less responsive to hypnotic suggestions. This tendency to decreased hypnotic responsiveness increases with age and has been noted by this author (see Appendix) and many others (e.g. Berg and Meline, 1975); (Morgan and Hilgard, 1973). Whether this decrease in hypnotisability is due to organic changes or merely due, with advancing age, to a diminished need for the exercise of the imagination, is a matter for conjecture at this time. Clinically speaking there are many exceptions to this general tendency for the decline in hypnotisability with age.

Although modern techniques of analytical hypnotherapy require minimal evidence of conscious dissociation to be effective, the availability of the capacity to dissociate is of interest to all hypnotherapists since it is upon this that the patient's capacity to respond to suggestion will presumably depend. For example, since the production of lid catalepsy requires very little dissociation in the majority of cases, it is unlikely that a patient who cannot respond to the suggestion for lid catalepsy will be able to produce profound hypnoanaesthesia.

Frankel (1978, 1979) drew attention to the fact that most clinical publications on hypnosis, although rich in detail and interest, have been vitiated by a lack of evidence that the effects produced and reported have indeed been due to hypnosis. He thought this lack derived from the belief of many clinicians that there is no need for formal measurement of the degree of involvement in hypnosis during therapy. Such a viewpoint, he argued, retards the possibility of meaningful communication since the absence of the measurement of hypnosis does not permit it to be distinguished from other therapeutic or relaxation procedures coexisting with it. He further argued from his own experience that measurements of hypnotisability are not incompatible with satisfactory therapy.

Nevertheless, it is evident that the susceptibility scales for hypnosis which have proved satisfactory in the laboratory, are too cumbersome and time-consuming for the use of the busy clinician. Consequently, the clinician tends arbitrarily to estimate hypnotisability by relying on his clinical judgment and applying rather vague descriptions such as medium, deep, etc. to the responses of his patient. Some of these estimates are frequently based upon the apparent amount of relaxation achieved when, in fact, very good relaxation can be obtained by subjects who are unable to respond to any other more complex hypnotic suggestions. Sector (1960), in investigating Erickson's estimation of the hypnotic depth of a group of subjects, discovered that his accuracy was no greater than that achieveable on a purely chance basis.

There have been several attempts to provide the clinician with a simple yet reliable method of estimating hypnotisability in his office. As yet, there has been little experience with which to judge the modern Stanford Hypnotic Clinic Scale (SHCS) or the Creative Imagination Scale (CIS). The Hypnotic Induction Profile (HIP) attempted to solve this problem by providing a method of measuring hypnotisability in the clinician's office which would be part of his routine and take only a short time to perform. Unfortunately, in practice, only the second portion of the Profile — the suggested posthypnotic levitation — has proved of value in giving a clue to hypnotisability. The Eye Roll portion has been found by this author and others (Switras, 1974) and (Sheehan et al, 1979), to bear no correlation to hynotisability as estimated by other hypnotic responses. It has, however, proved to be of value as an excellent means of securing the subject's unconscious attention — a necessary feature of all hypnotic induction procedures.

Mott (1979) pointed out rightly that many clinicians do not believe that hypnotisability is of significance in the clinical use of hypnosis since there is sometimes an apparent dramatic response when only a light trance is demonstrable. In the absence of any testing, however, it is impossible to determine if these cases are using an extensive hypnotic ability which had heretofore gone undetected. A review of the literature indicates that a high correlation exists between hypnotisability and therapeutic responsiveness; therefore, the regular testing of hypnotisability by the clinician would enable him to modify his therapy to take maximum advantage of this ability.

The most striking phenomenon associated with hypnosis is that of posthypnotic amnesia, a phenomenon which has always been considered to be associated with deep hypnosis. Damaser (1964) considered that spontaneous posthypnotic amnesia is always associated with deep trance subjects and is possibly different from that occurring on suggestion. Bramwell (1903) considered such amnesia to occur as a result of the usual suggestion given at that time to sleep. The suggestion to sleep, he held, was also an indirect suggestion for amnesia. Dittborn and Anstequiela (1962) likewise believed that the references to sleep were likely to produce apparent spontaneous posthypnotic amnesia. The Marquis de Puysegar (1784) is originally credited with noting that posthypnotic amnesia is characteristic of deep hypnosis, and both Liebeault (1889) and Bernheim (1888) used the presence of posthypnotic amnesia as an indication of deep hypnosis.

Anderson and Bower (1972) suggested that posthypnotic amnesia involves a disruption in the search component of memory retrieval resulting from the dissociative process of hypnosis. Functionally distinct modes of thought operate in such a way that material present in one is not readily transferrable to the other. There is much evidence (e.g. multiple personalities) to support this explanation.

In any case, posthypnotic amnesia appears to be the one hypnotic phenomenon which might bear a direct relationship to the dissociation process of hypnosis. Lesser degrees of dissociation are accompanied by lesser degrees of posthypnotic amnesia; conversely, greater dissociation can be demonstrated by greater degrees of posthypnotic amnesia. Faced with the problem of discovering whether an individual's response to hypnotherapy has a direct relationship to his ability to respond to suggestion, this author, some years ago, began to search for a readily measurable hypnotic phenomenon which varied directly with the degree of dissociation which appeared to be responsible for hypnotisability. To this end, the author constructed the Amnesia Capacity Estimation method (ACE; Barnett, 1977), which has now been used, with significant success, in more than 1,500 cases. ACE has been devised to estimate an individual's capacity for producing amnesia on suggestion. It operates on the assumption that this capacity is directly dependent upon the individual's ability to dissociate the conscious from the unconscious mind. It is this dissociation following suggestion that renders accessible material which was in varying degrees previously inaccessible to the conscious mind.

It can be postulated that measurement of an individual's amnesic potential by means of ACE provides an index of his capacity for conscious/unconscious dissociation and thereby functions as an indicator of his hypnotisability. Although it may be assumed that the dissociative capacity varies along a continuum, the ACE scale arbitrarily divides that continuum into six stages from 0 (nil dissociation) to stage 5 (total dissociation). Clinical experience has shown ACE to be a reliable and useful tool for estimating hypnotisability and one which has the very real advantage of being easily applicable in any hypnotherapeutic setting. It takes about six minutes to administer and can be adapted to the therapist's usual induction procedure. Grades tend to remain constant for a given subject on repeated testing although the occasional increase in scores does occur and probably reflects a greater familiarity with the process or, what is more likely, a diminution of previous resistances.

All indices of hypnotic susceptibility require the subject's full cooperation for success and ACE is no exception. A persistent, unconscious need to retain the memory of items for which amnesia is suggested sometimes leads the subject to score lower than his maximum capacity. In such cases the subject's maximum dissociative capacity is unlikely to be determinable unless this resistance is overcome. In practice this has proved to be uncommon. Conversely, a subject's desire to please may lead him to simulate amnesia where none truly exists. This simulation can lead to the false assignment of a higher grade of amnesia capacity than is actively present. This is a difficulty that besets all hypnotisability tests, but fortunately, rarely poses a problem.

General Outline of ACE
It is presumed that a subject who does not make any response to hypnotic suggestions has failed to demonstrate any degree of conscious/unconscious dissociation and is therefore to be assigned an ACE grade of zero (0). Alternatively, any positive response reflects the absence of conscious intervention (which would prevent the response) and is presumed to be due to some conscious/unconscious dissociation. This warrants a grading of at least 1 since the subject has demonstrated some capacity for amnesia. For example, when a subject complies with the therapist's suggestion to experience relaxation he is required to forget his current tension in order to respond positively. Similarly, a response to suggested lightness of the hand in the hand levitation induction technique indicates that the subject must have become unaware of the actual weight of the hand – it has been temporarily forgotten. It is assumed that a greater degree of conscious/unconscious dissociation is necessary to produce a visual amnesia for a well known series (e.g. numbers, alphabet, etc) and, when successful, warrants a grading of 2. An even greater degree of dissociation is required to produce selective amnesia for a particular member of a familiar series which, when successful, warrants a grading of 3.

A subject who immediately reenters hypnosis upon the presentation of an appropriate, posthypnotically presented cue, is presumed to have no conscious awareness of that cue; an awareness of the cue would lead to an interference with that response resulting in a slow reentry into hypnosis or no response to the cue at all. Hilgard (1965) found that subjects who did not manifest a posthypnotic amnesia tended not to carry out that suggestion. Sheehan and Orne (1968) held that posthypnotic suggestions are carried out in a different manner when amnesia is not present. However, a subject who responds rapidly to the posthypnotic cue by immediately entering hypnosis is presumed to have an amnesia for that complex instruction and is assigned grade 4.

If a subject has total amnesia for all of the experiences of hypnosis, he clearly has the maximal capacity for amnesia, assumed to be due to total conscious/unconscious dissociation. He is then assigned the maximum grade of 5 unless it is later shown that there has been a return to conscious memory of some of the hypnotic events. Although in addition to the above grades of 0 to 5, intermediate gradings of 2/3, 3/4 and 4/5 permit increased sensitivity in the assessment of ACE performance, the latter scores have yet to be utilised to any great extent in clinical practice.

ACE Verbalisation

Provided that the general principles enunciated above are adhered to, the specific verbalisation for the method of Amnesia Capacity Estimation which follows may be modified somewhat to accommodate the therapist's particular preferences.

Although a rapid induction technique is preferable, any induction technique may be employed. *Any* response to induction gives a score of at least grade 1. Failure to induce any hypnotic response however, results in the temporary assignment of grade 0. Section one is designed to elicit relaxation in lieu of successful induction but would otherwise be omitted. If the verbalisation is successful in obtaining a relaxation response, the subject has reached ACE stage 1 and is assigned an ACE grade of 1; the operator proceeds directly to section two. Section one which follows associates relaxation + hypnosis with eye closure.

In a moment I am going to have you open and close your eyes and you will become twice as relaxed as you are right now. Open your eyes. . . Now close your eyes. . . That's good. The next time I have you open and close your eyes you will be ten times as relaxed as you are now. Open your eyes. . . Close your eyes. . . That's fine. If you have been able to follow my instructions, every muscle in your body will remain relaxed, and when I lift your hand and drop it, it will be so heavy and relaxed that it will drop with a plop. (Test for relaxation by lifting and dropping the subject's hand; a response to the suggestions for relaxation should be easily detected by the rapidity with which the hand drops when released). That's good. Any time I ask you to close your eyes you can relax like this. (This is a posthypnotic suggestion for rapid reinduction).

Stage 1 has now been completed.

Section two is designed to elicit a visual amnesia for a series of numbers. Any familiar series, such as the letters of the alphabet, the days of the week, or the months of the year could be substituted. Those subjects who indicate that they have achieved visual amnesia for the series which persists posthypnotically receive an ACE grade of 2. If the amnesia is not maintained when the eyes are opened, the subject has not been able to reach stage 2 successfully and remains graded at ACE grade 1 and further testing is unnecessary.

Now I would like you to relax your mind just as much as you have relaxed your body. To do that I would like you to picture a blackboard on which numbers from one hundred backwards are clearly visible. Have you got that?. . . Good. In a moment I am going to ask you to call out each number from one hundred backwards and, as you say each number, please wipe it right off the blackboard and right out of your mind before going on to the next number. By the time you get down to ninety-seven your mind will be so relaxed that you will be able to wipe all of the numbers off the blackboard and right out of your mind. All right, now count out loud please. . . (patient counts 100). . . wipe that right off the blackboard and right out of your mind. . . (99). . . off the blackboard and right out of your mind. . . (98). . . right out of your mind. . . (97). . . Now wipe all of the numbers off the blackboard and right out of your mind and when you are sure that they have all gone just say, 'gone'. . . (Patient says *gone*.) Good. Now, in a moment, when I have you open your eyes, those numbers will still be gone and you won't be able to find them at all − they will be completely gone and you will not be able to see them. . . Now open your eyes, please. Are they all gone?. . . Good. Now close your eyes again, please.
Stage 2 has now been completed.

Section three is designed to elicit a posthypnotic selective amnesia for a single member of a familiar series. In the verbalisation that follows, an amnesia for the number 3 in the reverse series of 10 to 1 is suggested. The substitution of any other familiar series, (e.g. days of the week or months of the year) would be equally satisfactory. It is interesting to note, in this context, that Hilgard and Hommel (1961) found evidence to suggest that selective amnesia involves the mechanism of repression and that Spanos and Ham (1973) found that those capable of selective amnesia reported more goal-directed fantasy than did others.

Now, in a moment, after I ask you to open your eyes once again, the numbers will slowly come back one at a time – all except the number '3'. That number will remain blanked out and will not come back at all. It will be as though that number simply does not exist. It is important that you want this to happen. You will find nothing between 4 and 2. . . that number will be completely gone . . . (wait ten seconds or so). . . Now open your eyes please. . . Good. I would now like you to count slowly down from ten please. . . That's fine.

Stage 3 has now been completed.

Any one of four possible responses to section three's suggestions for selective amnesia might have occurred: first, the number '3' was readily recalled. Since no selective amnesia has been demonstrated, the subject must be considered as no more than ACE grade 2 and no further estimation is indicated. Secondly, an abortive attempt to say '3' represents an intermediate degree of amnesia in which there is a verbal inhibition (Spanos and Bodorik, 1977 and Hilgard, 1966). This intermediate degree of amnesia may be designated ACE grade 2/3. [However, the following addendum to Section 3 may successfully encourage these subjects to produce a complete selective amnesia resulting in an ultimate grading of ACE grade 3.

Close your eyes again please. Now you can let that number go completely and when you are sure that it is completely gone, your eyes will open again. . . (eyes open). I would like you to count slowly down from ten please. . . that's fine.]

Thirdly, there was a hesitation at the number 3 without any visible attempt to articulate the number itself. These subjects should be given an ACE grade 3 even though it is clear that selective amnesia may not be complete. Fourthly, the number 3 was completely omitted without any hesitation, i.e. '5,4,2,1.' These subjects have an amnesia capacity of at least ACE grade 3 and may well proceed to score even higher.

The fourth section is used for any subject who has not verbalised the number 3 and has therefore successfully reached the ACE grade 3 capacity for selective amnesia. In this section a cue for reentry into hypnosis is given while the subject is in hypnosis and is to be responded to when the hypnosis is terminated. The cue should be one which the therapist has reason to believe will be acceptable to the subject and one with which both therapist and subject will feel comfortable (such as a touch on the shoulder). It should be administered posthypnotically when the subject appears to be fully alert. A rapid response with immediate reentry into hypnosis indicates an ACE grade of 4; a slow or poor response confirms an ACE grade of 3.

Now close your eyes again please. (wait until the attentiveness of hypnosis is reestablished). When I have you open your eyes again, any time I touch you on the right shoulder like this (any cue can be substituted here), your body will always relax instantly and very deeply. It will be just as deeply relaxed as when you are at home in bed sound asleep at night. . . It will always be the same deep natural relaxation just as when you are sound asleep. It is important that you want this to happen and it will happen. You will find that any time I touch you on the right shoulder like this, you will always be able immediately to relax very, very deeply. When I have you open your eyes, you can forget that I have given you this suggestion but you will be guided by it and will respond to it. . . (wait ten seconds). All right, now open your eyes please. . . That's good, how do you feel? (Give the cue when the subject is clearly alert and note the rapidity of the response. Proceed with section 5 when hypnosis has been completely reestablished.)
Stage 4 has now been completed.

[An addendum to section 4 is designed for use with subjects who initially exhibit a slow response to the posthypnotic reentry cue. If there is a noticeably improved response, the grading may be increased to an intermediate ACE grade of 3/4 and further testing discontinued.
  All right, close your eyes again please, relaxing very deeply. . . That's good. Now, when I have you open your eyes again, the signal that I gave you just now will be ten times as effective. You will find that any time I touch you on the right shoulder, you will always instantly relax so deeply that I will be able to talk directly to your inner mind because your conscious mind will be so relaxed that it will not want to listen to me at all. You don't have to remember that suggestion because you will respond to it so easily. . . (wait ten seconds). . . Now open your eyes please. That's good. How do you feel? (Give reentry cue as before).]

Section five is used with those subjects who have reached stage 4 and is designed to suggest total amnesia for all events occurring during hypnosis. Permanent total posthypnotic amnesia for all events occurring during hypnosis warrants an ACE grading of 5. If this amnesia is only temporary (as revealed by a recollection at a later meeting), then an intermediate grading of 4/5 is assigned.
  Now, your conscious mind does not need to listen to me at all. As

your conscious mind relaxes deeper and deeper, it can forget everything that I say because your inner, unconscious mind is listening to me very carefully and remembering everything that I say... Only your deep inner mind needs to remember... When I have you open your eyes again it will feel as if they have just closed for a moment only... (wait at least ten seconds and then awaken subject with any preferred procedure and return immediately to the preinduction conversation.)

Stage 5 has now been completed.

SUMMARY OF AMNESIA CAPACITY ESTIMATION (ACE) SCALE

Grade	Hypnotic Response	Stage Completed
0	None	—
1	Any hypnotic response (e.g. relaxation) but no series amnesia	1
2	Series amnesia but no selective amnesia (e.g. '3' in series 10 to 1)	2
2/3	Abortive attempt to vocalise the designated number to be selectively dropped from the series	2
3	Selective amnesia with poor response to posthypnotic cue for reentry into hypnosis	3
3/4	Improved but no immediate response to posthypnotic cue	3
4	Immediate response to posthypnotic cue. Some posthypnotic memory for events in hypnosis	4
4/5	Temporary total posthypnotic amnesia	4
5	Permanent total posthypnotic amnesia	5

The ACE scale thus provides the clinical hypnotherapist with a relatively efficient and reliable method of determining his patient's capacity for hypnosis. The therapist's skill, of course, lies in his utilisation of this capacity for maximum therapeutic benefit (see Fig 3).

Amnesia Capacity Estimation and Hypnotic Phenomena

Amnesia Capacity Estimation Method	Memory	Ideosensory Responses				Ideomotor Responses	Vasomotor Responses
		Tactile	Olfactory	Auditory	Visual		
1 	fantasy	partial analgesia	imagery	imagery	imagery	relaxation lid catalepsy	slowing of heart rate
2 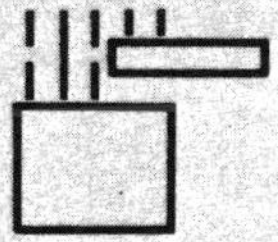	hypermnesia	total analgesia					limb catalepsy	lowering of blood pressure warmth
3 	partial amnesia	partial anaesthesia				immobility	flushing vasodilation
4 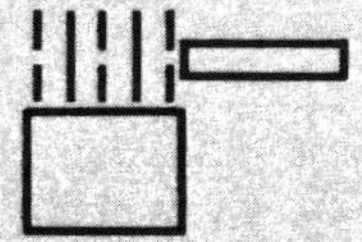	total amnesia	total anaesthesia	olfactory hallucination	auditory hallucination	positive post hypnotic hallucination		vasoconstriction
5 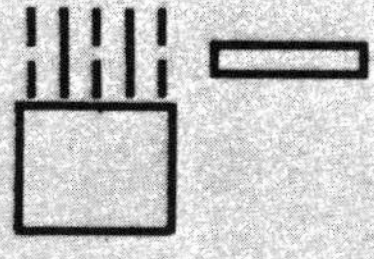	permanent total amnesia			suggested deafness	negative post hypnotic hallucination		

figure 3

Resistance to Hypnosis

In practice, only a small proportion of patients appear to experience total conscious/unconscious dissociation and are to be regarded as highly susceptible subjects. For reasons which still remain inadequately understood, others respond to hypnotic suggestion with varying degrees of dissociation. This failure to respond to suggestion appears, in part, to be due to an active resistance to the ideas proffered by the therapist (even including those integral to any hypnotisability scale). However, even when this active resistance seems to have been overcome and full cooperation of the subject has been obtained, there still appears to remain an innate difficulty in some patients to respond to suggestions, which renders dissociation incomplete. If this were not so, every one would be deeply hypnotisable; and yet, this does not appear to be the case. Let us first consider this passive innate resistance to hypnosis.

Passive Resistance
Spiegel (1974) gave us an excellent description of the highly hypnotisable person which enables us to understand what traits are associated with this ability. By definition, this person scores high on any susceptibility scale, and responds immediately to suggestions for regression, anaesthesia, amnesia, motor responses and hallucinations of all kinds. Perhaps the most striking attribute of the highly hypnotisable person is his trusting disposition which is associated with an almost unreasonable faith and hope in the therapist. This trust is often so complete that there is not a trace of what might be termed a reasonable cynicism. Allied with this deep trust is the ability of these subjects to ignore previous premises and beliefs and replace them readily with new ones. They quickly suspend the usual critical level of judgment based on past experience. As a rule, these people are extremely empathetic, deeply influenced by the moods of others, and very sensitive to the events of the present. They have, in fact, a telescoped time sense such that all events, even those in the past, are viewed as if they exist in the present. Regression is for them relatively easy, and they relive past experiences as if they are still occurring.

Perhaps because of their ready communication with the past, these deeply hypnotisable people have an excellent memory and find it very easy to learn; this learning, however, is likely to be uncritical, with every piece of information absorbed as is. These are the people who are said to have a photographic (eidetic) memory. Coupled with this memory is a great ability to concentrate to such a degree that external events are totally blocked out. In reviewing these traits, it would seem that the highly hypnotisable person is constantly using hypnosis and that some of the problems he experiences result from his failure to use critical judgment.

The increased power of imagery and the reduced critical judgment already mentioned lead us to the hypothesis that, in their daily approach to the problems of living, highly hypnotisable people appear to use their right non-verbal hemisphere rather than the left verbal and logical hemisphere. Children, who are clearly the most highly hypnotisable, presumably become less hypnotisable as they grow older because of the greater customary use of the left hemisphere.

Blakeslee (1980) pointed out that the ability and even the personality of an individual are strongly influenced by his mental habits. One of the most important of these habits is a person's tendency to depend primarily upon either his right or his left brain. Some tasks clearly demand left or right brain approaches, whereas the majority fall into the grey area where either the intuitive or the logical approach can be used with equal success. People tend to favour one approach over the other and some have occupations in which one can function by relying entirely on one hemisphere all the time. The highly intellectual individual is probably using the left verbal hemisphere most of the time while the intuitive artist favours the right brain. Current studies would seem to suggest that this brain laterality is not pronounced in females.

All of this would suggest that hypnotisability, in the passive sense, is something that is gradually unlearned. This depends on the greater or lesser use of the left hemisphere and the extent to which logical functions are demanded by the individual's lifestyle. Thus, unconscious communication (i.e. communication with the right brain) is rendered more difficult for those who are more accustomed to dealing with problems by using the logical left brain. It is possible that even this habitual passive resistance to right brain communication can be reduced by prolonged effort. Erickson (1972) stated that subjects vary in respect to the time required to develop responses to hypnotic suggestions and that low estimates of hypnotic susceptibility are often the result of a disregard of time as an important factor in the development of hypnotic behaviour. He went on to suggest that a time period of four to eight hours of initial training in the induction of hypnosis might be necessary. There are no detailed observations on the improved hypnotisability of subjects exposed to prolonged induction periods of this kind. Earlier, Esdaile (1852) seemed to have been able to produce profound hypnotic phenomena in a high proportion of his subjects using an induction procedure which would often take more than an hour.

Unfortunately, in normal clinical practice, such passive resistance to hypnosis (which might yield to prolonged induction procedures) has to be accepted in the hope that repeated exposure to induction will enable a greater involvement in hypnosis to result. Frequently, this appears to occur so that a subject, who is initially poorly susceptible to suggestion, eventually becomes able to accept much more complex suggestions.

Active Resistance
An active resistance to the induction of hypnosis denotes an *active* rejection of the suggestions for hypnotic responses. An active resistance to suggestion supposes a motivation for that rejection. When these reasons are discovered and examined there is found to be one common denominator, namely, fear. Active resistance to hypnotic suggestion is due to a fear response which results from the suggestion being perceived − at some level of awareness − to be dangerous. Every hypnotherapist soon becomes aware of these active resistances which must be understood if they are to be avoided or dealt with. They can, for the sake of simplicity, be considered as either a conscious resistance (where the reason for it is known) or unconscious, where the individual is unaware of the reason for his resistance. In fact, at a conscious level he appears to be very cooperative.

Conscious Resistance   Anxiety about the process of hypnosis will not only prevent the acceptance of hypnotic suggestion, but may also extinguish hypnotic responses that have already occurred. Much of the art of inducing hypnosis lies in the avoidance of this conscious resistance or of utilising it to obtain unconscious communication. Fear of losing control is perhaps the commonest cause of conscious resistance. A previous unfortunate experience of hypnosis (either personally or as a spectator of demeaning stage hypnosis; as the recipient of uninformed descriptions of hypnosis through such media as television and films; or from poorly informed friends or relatives), is a potent source of this anxiety. The subject believes that through hypnosis he will surrender control to a stranger − the therapist (the rapist?). This feeling is particularly strong at the first meeting where these past unfortunate encounters will unconsciously reinforce this conscious fear.

In spite of much preinduction reassurance that no one in hypnosis really loses control but rather retains it at some level at all times, this fear will persist in most people except for the most trusting (who, as we have already noted, are likely to be the most hypnotisable). Further reassurance that control will not be relinquished may be of help; demonstrating how control can be retained is perhaps the easiest way of dealing with the fear. This can be done by allowing the patient to assume some personal control over the suggestions given so that he monitors them before he allows his unconscious mind to make a response. For example, if levitation is being requested, such a patient might be asked whether it would be all right for his unconscious mind to make the arm light. This approach is the basis of the permissive induction of hypnosis. Once conscious permission is received, all conscious resistance is, by definition, removed. In this way the conscious sentinel rapidly develops sufficient trust in the therapist to allow unconscious communication without interference.

Nonverbal induction techniques also deal with conscious resistance simply by circumventing it. These techniques use suggestions not understood by the conscious verbal mind and therefore they are not open to resistance by it.

It is important for the analytic hypnotherapist to be able to persuade his patient to *allow* things to happen if relevant information concealed in the unconscious memory is to be rendered accessible to therapy. He should encourage his patient to accept any response as satisfactory since even his resistance probably bears some relation to the origin of his symptomatology. Many patients presenting for analytical hypnotherapy possess a poor self image and a constant fear of failure accompanied by a conviction that they cannot succeed. It is essential to reassure such patients that all of their responses are of significance and that profound hypnotic phenomena are not expected of them.

Physical discomfort may prove to be a distraction preventing full cooperation and could be responsible for conscious resistance to suggestion. Every effort should therefore be made to procure as much comfort as possible even though, with a good hypnotic subject, good responses can often be obtained in the presence of evident physical discomfort.

Sometimes there is no obvious reason for apparent conscious resistance to suggestion and at times a direct enquiry will reveal the reason. The resistance may stem from something in the environment such as the induction technique itself or from the therapist's behaviour to which the patient objects. Resistance to hypnosis may arise simply because the patient is in some way angered by the therapist and such anger should be dealt with by open discussion.

Unconscious Resistance   Unconscious resistance tends to manifest itself either as the subject's failure to pay attention to the therapist or an apparent inability to understand what is being asked of him. He may even fall asleep! Alternatively, he may give different responses to those asked for. Such resistance may be primary and appear when the first attempt to induce hypnosis is made. However, it often becomes apparent that a subject who, though initially responsive to suggestion, later develops these signs of resistance and becomes unresponsive to further attempts to elicit hypnotic responses. Suggestions which were previously accepted are ignored.

Unconscious resistance is due to unconscious fear. In this case it is a fear that either unconscious secrets will be revealed to the therapist (as well as to other parts of the psyche), or that changes are likely to be imposed on the patient which he is not ready to accept. At such times, if this resistance is not dealt with, he is very likely to withdraw from therapy. It can be dealt with first by accepting it, and secondly by assuring the patient that he has, at all times, total jurisdiction over what will be dealt with. In order to emphasise the patient's control, all questioning should be prefaced by 'would it be all right if. . . ?' or some such approach which indicates that the patient always retains the right to refuse to comply with any suggestion made.

The continued maintenance of a permissive approach by the analytical hypnotherapist enables the patient to deal with another common unconscious fear — the fear that he will be dominated by the therapist. These fears are often engendered by friends and relatives who learn that the patient is receiving hypnotherapy. Although an authoritative approach may well appear to be more effective in producing the complex dissociative phenomena normally associated with deep hypnosis, unconscious resistance will interfere with the further cooperation which is vital to the success of analytical hypnotherapy. Such an authoritative approach may in fact produce direct antagonism by a hidden ego state. This antagonism will effectively sabotage attempts to attain the objectives of therapy and will ensure that the symptoms remain unaffected.

Here it is important to note that, even in the presence of unconscious resistance, some communication is being made with the unconscious mind. Even the resistance itself is evidence of this communication and can be used by the wise therapist to further the objectives of therapy. It is rare that resistance becomes so complete that there remains no possibility for further unconscious communication. As long as the patient remains in therapy, the skilled — not to mention persevering —

hypnotherapist will continue his search until an acceptable avenue of communication is discovered.

Hypnosis and Age Regression

Perhaps the single most important hypnotic phenomenon of which the analytical hypnotherapist makes use is that of age regression (see Fig. 4). In his primary task of locating unconscious conflicts at their source, he must find means of inducing his patient to recall events that have occurred long ago. The ability that highly suggestible subjects possess of not only recalling long forgotten events in hypnosis, but also reexperiencing them so vividly that they appear to relive them (thus severing contact with the present) is termed age regression. Such an ability has given this phenomenon a separate identification from other phenomena of hypnosis, a separation which this author believes to be undeserved and which introduces an unnecessary complexity into the understanding of these phenomena. It would be better to consider age regression to be at the end of a continuum of conscious/unconscious dissociation where there is no conscious memory operation and only the previous memory is being fully experienced. In fact it is probable that all hypnotic phenomena are produced by an identical process of recall and that, whenever the process of hypnosis is set in motion, unconscious memories must be invoked.

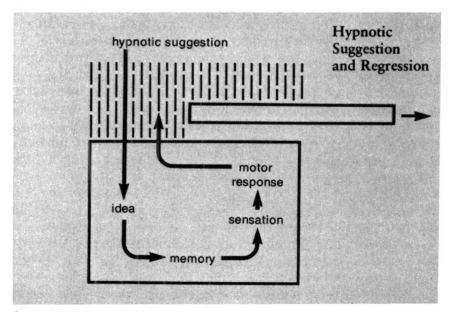

figure 4

Penfield and Lamar (1959), when seeking for brain lesions responsible for epileptic convulsions, noted that stimulation of the right side of the brain with weak electric currents would frequently produce dreamlike states in which the patient experienced visual and auditory hallucinations or had flashback memories. These memories were often present in considerable detail and vividness. Stimulation of the left side of the brain did not produce these memories and resulted only in disturbances of speech and motor activity. This would suggest that the right side of the brain is the storehouse of complex memories and is able to record, in considerable detail, all of the individual's experiences, many of which may never have been consciously perceived. It may be that this ability to record information is maximal in childhood although it is likely that it continues throughout life. When the conscious mind is bypassed in hypnosis, all of this material becomes more readily accessible. The hypnoanalytical techniques to be described owe their success to their ability to reach this recorded material and encourage the unconscious mind to elevate it to conscious awareness.

Unconscious communication in hypnosis is only recognised by the presence of an unconscious response to suggestion; such a response has, of necessity, utilised unconscious memories. For example, in the eye fixation induction technique, if the suggestion for eyelid heaviness is accepted, evidence of acceptance is seen in the blinking of the lids and their eventual closure. However, in order for this to have taken place, the suggestion for heaviness must have been translated somewhere in the mind into feelings of heaviness. Before this can be accomplished, the memory of eyelid heaviness must be invoked if the words are to have any meaning. These memories lie in the right nonverbal hemisphere and, in rendering them accessible, there has to be some regression to the experience creating them. This activity of the right brain is occurring constantly in order to give meaning to words and other stimuli to which the individual is called upon to respond. All of this is performed unconsciously. In hypnosis, we are simply harnessing a process which is continuously in action as a part of everyday living.

Thus the response to suggestion as seen in the blinking of the eyelids and their eventual closure requires that the right brain memories be superimposed upon the left brain's conscious awareness. Similarly, any unconscious response involves unconscious memories which might go back an exceedingly long time in the individual's life and yet these responses often occur almost instantaneously. For the unconscious mind, time is merely a means of indexing memories and nothing more. It is just as easy for the unconscious mind to locate the memory of an event that occurred twenty years ago as it is to locate one that occurred twenty days ago. It is only when we have to use conscious effort to locate these memories that time becomes an important factor in remembering. The skilled analytical hypnotherapist uses techniques which are unfamiliar to the conscious mind in order to locate unconscious memories and unconscious responses. For example, sequential retrogression is a conscious technique for recovering memories, but the analytical hypnotherapist is more likely to be successful when using more direct methods which are unconsciously acceptable and understood. He thus avoids conscious interference resulting from conscious attempts at recall.

Since each individual has the unconscious memories from which all hypnotic phenomena are constructed, it is conceivable that all hypnotic phenomena are potentially available to everyone. It is the degree of conscious/unconscious dissociation present at any given time which determines the complexity of these phenomena. With minimal dissociation perhaps no more than the memory of relaxation will be allowed expression. With greater dissociation the memory of numbness and anaesthesia can be expressed as hypnoanalgesia and hypnoanaesthesia. With total dissociation, the left brain consciousness is in abeyance and the resources of the unconscious mind become fully available. Total anaesthesia, and abundant unconscious imagery in the response to suggestion, are then available. The extent of the amnesia that follows will depend upon how much of this unconscious activity is later communicated to the conscious mind.

Von Neumann (1958) declared that the structure of the brain and its neurons indicated its functional similarity to a highly complex digital computer. Its memory storage capacity is clearly capable of holding much more than the input from the average human being's life experiences and, like a computer, these memories should readily be accessible if the correct search is made for them. It is important for the analytical hypnotherapist to realise that location of memories of past experiences is possible with little or no evidence of conscious/unconscious dissociation, even though such memories may be subject to conscious modification. In these cases an expression such as 'this is so silly' is often heard when unconscious memories come to mind. It is at such times that the maximal available conscious/unconscious dissociation must be encouraged by such exhortations as, 'Just let it happen.'

To sum up then, all hypnotic communication utilises regression in order to be effective. The phenomenon of age regression is being invoked throughout the process of hypnosis as, presumably, it is during normal unconscious activity. An understanding of this fact enables the analytical hypnotherapist justifiably to seek and discover all kinds of techniques designed to recover memories of experiences responsible for symptom complexes. It also enables him to locate unconscious resources within the individual which are most appropriate for dealing with these problems.

Unconscious Resources

Hypnotherapy depends for its effectiveness on the mobilisation and appropriate use of unconscious resources. It may well be that there are many more available than have so far been utilised in therapy. The following resources are those that consistently have proven to be of value therapeutically whether with or without prior analysis.

Relaxation

Relaxation can properly be called an unconscious resource which is extremely valuable therapeutically. It is so often associated with hypnotherapy that it is sometimes confused with hypnosis itself. The ability to produce relaxation is valuable mainly because there are so few mental or physical disorders where tension is not a contributory factor. Tension is often so great as to retard recovery; the use of relaxation can be a potent factor in achieving cure.

Analgesia

Although analgesia as a resource is less accessible than relaxation, it can, when it is available, be a potent factor in recovery. Its use as an adjunct to pain-producing procedures is too well known to require emphasis here. Also, its use in chronic pain syndromes is, when effective, superior to any analgesic drug.

Anaesthesia

A smaller proportion of the population appears to be able to use the resource of hypnoanaesthesia with ease. They are usually regarded as being highly hypnotisable. In the days prior to the development of chemical anaesthesia, it was this resource which made all of Esdaile's well-known series of surgical procedures possible. Presumably, in Esdaile's cases, there was total body anaesthesia; but it is a well-known phenomenon of hypnosis that this hypnoanaesthesia can be available to any part of the body and, often, can be moved readily from one part to another. With this degree of anaesthesia, there is often a total loss of awareness of the anaesthetic part which may feel totally dissociated.

Regression
Although we have said that all hypnosis does, in fact, involve regression, the hypnoanalyst relies on the ability of the unconscious mind to review specific memories and to bring them to a level where they can be subject to reappraisal. An awareness of this process is what is usually considered to constitute regression. At such times, the patient may partially or completely appear to relive a previously forgotten experience; he then becomes able to reevaluate it and divest it of persisting associated emotions which have been responsible for symptoms and which are now seen to be unnecessary.

Imagery
The unconscious mind has the ability to construct new images from old ones and it is this ability that is at the basis of all unconscious creativity and problem solving. It is this resource in particular that is constantly being activated by the hypnotherapist in his efforts to enable the patient to resolve his problems. These images are not restricted to any one of the senses and can involve any or all of the available areas of awareness. All human motivation appears to depend on the construction of projective images followed by the search for means of producing them in reality. The effect of direct suggestion depends largely upon this resource.

Control of Body Function
The unconscious mind appears to be able to exert control over the body in many ways. It probably does this through the medium of the autonomic nervous system aided by the humoral and hormonal mechanisms. For example, the simple suggestion for a part of the body to feel warm is frequently followed by localised vasodilation via the autonomic nervous system. It can also be assumed that psychosomatic disorders rely upon these mechanisms for their origin. Again, in many cases, the effectiveness of direct suggestion can be seen to be due to the activation of this resource.

Healing
Healing is a particular body function and there is increasing acceptance of the notion that the unconscious mind can influence healing to

a considerable degree. This presumably occurs through humoral or autonomic nervous control which is as yet poorly understood. Again, this resource is often available to suggestion in hypnosis if it is unconsciously acceptable.

Post Hypnotic Suggestion
All of these above-mentioned resources are accessible long after the suggestion for their mobilisation has been made. The ability of the unconscious mind to continue to use resources long after the hypnotic encounter, or to reproduce them under predetermined conditions, does not seem to be particularly astounding when its other abilities are considered; nevertheless, a great deal of hypnotherapy depends upon this ability. Suggestions, which are intended to be effective for some time after they have been given in hypnosis, form the mainstay of hypnotherapy and promote the continuance of changes begun during therapy.

This review of the main unconscious resources used in hypnotherapy is in no way intended to be an exhaustive one. However, it does indicate the resources most often used in hypnotherapy and which are probably accessible in some measure to all patients.

Theory of Analytical Hypnotherapy

PART ONE   Chapter 5

In theory, the location and uncovering of the original causes of emotional problems would seem to be the logical first step to diagnosis and treatment in psychotherapy. However, in psychotherapy as in much of orthodox medicine, treatment is usually directed only to the amelioration of symptoms. If the uncovering of emotional problems is logical in theory, why is it not then more widely practised? It is because the analytical approach has often proved to be inordinately time-consuming and has not had the justification of results superior to those therapies directed only at symptom removal. In 1935, Freud had already expressed disappointment with his earlier use of the analytical approach. He had thought that the presentation to the patient of recovered memories of childhood traumas would certainly bring the neurosis and its treatment to a rapid termination. He stated that 'it was a severe disappointment when the expected success was not forthcoming. How could it be that the patient who now knew about his traumatic experience nevertheless still behaved as if he knew no more about it than before?' It was this disappointment which encouraged him to look for other approaches to treating neuroses and to become entrenched in a system of therapy whose duration is commonly measured in years.

Adler (1924), Jung (1928), and Stekel (1940), all had expressed their conviction of the sterility of an approach which concentrated solely upon the uprooting of infantile memories. Rado (1939) also stated that the retracing of early memories was discouraging, since, like the fabled Hydra, as soon as one was dealt with, two others appeared in its place.

Bibring (1937) also joined the forces mounted against uncovering old memories when he questioned the value of abreaction. He believed that although it lessened tension it did not necessarily influence the deep problems which continued to generate it. Often he found that patients would uncover many interesting and crucial experiences but would, nevertheless, continue to cling to their neurotic attitudes.

While Wolberg (1964) accepted the position that an exclusive preoccupation with the past imposed definite limitations in therapy, and that a knowledge of the historical roots of a disorder was in itself insufficient to produce a cure, he maintained that such knowledge was still of tremendous value in therapy because it enabled the neurotic individual to gain self respect when he had mastered old fears. He believed such mastery of anxiety to be a great enhancer of ego strength and that hypnosis not only enabled unconscious material to be brought to a level at which it could more readily be dealt with, but also that, as previously stated by Kubie and Margolin (1944), hypnosis enabled the patient to gain strength directly from the therapist.

If hypnosis did nothing more than raise self-esteem and strengthen ego – as Wolberg, Kubie and Margolin state – it would be performing no small service to patients. But it is the purpose of this book and the intention of this author to demonstrate that hypnosis can, if properly practised, do much more. Hypnosis is unquestionably a powerful tool for the uncovering of memories, but such uncovering is only the first step. Freud was right to observe that knowledge of a traumatic experience is not sufficient in itself to provide a change of behaviour. After identification of the conflicts, the therapist and the patient must work through to a resolution of such conflicts so that the symptoms arising from them can be removed. While it is freely admitted that, frequently, this can be accomplished without the application of the direct techniques of analytical hypnotherapy, this author would argue that the use of these techniques results in a far higher proportion of success than is achieved by nonanalytical therapies.

Every therapist strives to formulate a theoretical construct for his therapy and the analytical hypnotherapist is no exception. The failure of the psychoanalytical approach to produce significant therapeutic results for patients presenting with symptom complexes has cast doubt upon the value of uncovering the historical antecedents of such complexes. We shall demonstrate that it is really the *inadequate* application of the information so gained that is responsible for the poor results. In order to understand how analytical hypnotherapy can be effective, we need to have an understanding of what is happening to those who are suffering from an emotional problem. So that we can better do this, let us examine the function of normal emotions.

The Emotions

Emotions are at their most primitive in the early stages of life and hence can be more easily studied at this time. Immediately after birth, we can observe that the infant already has the capacity to feel discomfort and gives evidence of this sensitivity by crying. This observable response is clearly a protective one, essential for the infant's survival, since it enables him to inform others of his discomfort in the hope that they will find the means of relieving it. His cry summons someone to his aid, usually mother. If she is able to respond satisfactorily to his needs, he will cease to cry. The infant has few other defences at birth except for this obvious expression of hurt or discomfort. In the majority of cases his crying will suffice; if he is cold, his mother will wrap him up; if he is wet, she will change his diaper; if he is hungry, she will feed him. In other words, whenever the infant is uncomfortable, his cry will lead to his obtaining the care necessary for his survival. Mother represents security, comfort, and peace and it is she upon whom the helpless infant must rely to identify and rectify any problem that creates discomfort. Any individual who responds to the infant's cry for help functions as a surrogate mother in that instance.

Sometimes the distress that the infant experiences may be severe or prolonged before the mother can intervene to relieve it. In this case the infant's cries become more insistent, more shrill and more urgent. The infant's movements may become more vigorous and it becomes evident that he is experiencing something more than discomfort and hurt. We are aware, perhaps by empathy, that the infant is experiencing another emotion, namely, fear. Fear is that feeling which supersedes hurt when the source of the discomfort is perceived as life threatening. The infant is helpless and can only cry more loudly and shrilly until mother comes to deal with the source of the distress and the danger. She finally reassures the child that all is well. An older child is able to take a more positive course of action when experiencing fear and move away unaided from the source of his discomfort. He will endeavour to crawl or run to a place where he believes that he will be safe from the danger, but will tend to move towards mother (or a mother figure) where he knows that comfort and security exist. Until he feels he is safe from the danger that threatened him, his emotion of fear will persist.

Still later in life, a third important defence mechanism appears. More certain of his actions and their probable results, the child becomes venturesome and will endeavour to deal with the source of his discomfort and danger by attempting to destroy or repel it with whatever means he has at his disposal. Yelling, hitting out, and other strategies are used to attain this end. When the danger is no longer evident he once again feels comfortable; he has learned how to use the emotion of anger for his own defence.

Thus it is that every human being has the three primary emotions of hurt, fear and anger, each of which has an important role to play in maintaining the individual's survival. Hurt is the awareness of discomfort and pain. In human beings, this is often experienced as sadness – an awareness of persistent hurt. Feelings of rejection, loneliness, and isolation are manifestations of this emotion of hurt. Fear derives its strength from the memory of hurt so that the individual strives to avoid further hurt when danger is imminent. Fear can masquerade as anxiety, terror, or panic, since these words merely serve to describe degrees of intensity of fear. Anger, the third emotion, protects the individual by either scaring away the perceived danger or by annihilating it. It is seen as aggressiveness, hostility or resentment. Each emotion is therefore designed to enable the individual to deal with perceived danger; each is vitally necessary if he is to survive in a world full of hazards. When these emotions fulfil their rightful function there is no emotional disorder. Thus if the child is hurt, he cries and obtains help. Or perhaps he is afraid and runs away from the danger to a haven of security. If this is not advisable or possible, perhaps he can use his third defence, anger, to destroy the source of danger so that all is well. However, should these emotions be denied their rightful expression, they will persist unrelieved. Any emotion is always accompanied by the physiological changes necessary for its functioning; consequently, unexpressed emotion creates an emotional disturbance which can easily have physical effects as well as mental ones. (See Fig. 5).

Mother's Role in Emotional Disorder   Normally, if he is not successful in obtaining help when he is hurt or senses danger, the child can use the emotion of fear to escape it or can become angry and repel or destroy it. The question that the hypnoanalyst asks is this: What happens if the source of the hurt or danger is mother herself? In this context anyone who functions in the role of mother (e.g. father, grandparents, siblings, etc.) in relationship to the child must be considered the mother. If mother, or the mother surrogate, is the source of hurt or danger, the normal emotional responses are confused. They are no longer protective and become valueless. To cry will only attract more hurt and so the emotion of hurt cannot be expressed. If the expected secure place has itself become dangerous, the child cannot employ the emotion of fear since there is no secure place to escape.

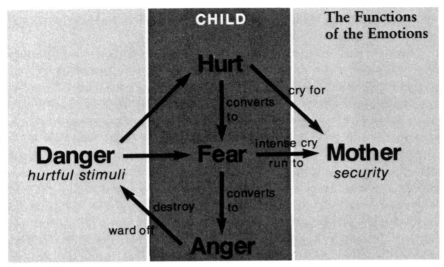

figure 5

Neither can he use the emotion of anger to destroy the source of his hurt since, even if it were possible, he would, at the same time, destroy his source of security. He has no alternative but to block his emotions – to repress them. Emotions, however, do not disappear when repressed but remain to create symptoms for which therapy is sought. For the analytical hypnotherapist it is the repression of normal human emotions which is reponsible for the emotional disturbances presenting for therapy. (See Fig. 6).

Sullivan (1953), in his discussion of the origin of emotional problems concluded that an infant learned to disown parts of itself as a consequence of mother's disapproval. But we are more concerned here with maternal disapproval causing the disowning of normal emotions. The mechanism for the repression or disowning of the emotional part of the self needs to be better understood. Also, we need to understand how it results in emotional distress.

Berne (1961) propounded a theory of human functioning upon which the therapies of transactional analysis are based. In brief, he stated that each of us acts at different times with separate viewpoints because of individual states of mind with their related patterns of behaviour. Each of us has been a child and retains substantial relics of childhood surviving as a complete ego state. We also have a normal brain which is capable of reality testing and this functions as another discrete ego state. Finally, each individual has had parents or others *in loco parentis* and the information derived from our relationships with these important people exists as another ego state. Thus each individual has at least three ego states: the Child, the Adult, and the Parent. In Berne's view, a happy person is one in whom each of these three ego states has important aspects which are *syntonic* with one another. These ego states differ from the Freudian concepts of superego, ego and id (Freud, 1933) in that they are all observable manifestations of the ego representing visible behaviours rather than

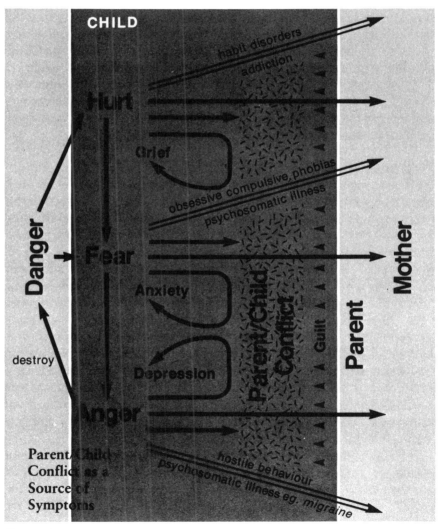

figure 6

hypothetical constructs. Since it is useful for our understanding of emotional disorders, we will here review Berne's theory of ego states.

The Child

The Child ego state results from the experiences the individual undergoes in his early development probably dating from conception onwards. During this period he is recording everything that he feels, hears, and sees, and thereby accumulates a body of information which gives him his awareness as an individual. It is the Child that is the ego state primarily concerned with the emotions and the awareness of them. It is the Child that is the repository of these emotions and which is directly affected by any repression of them. It is therefore the Child part that feels disowned when any emotion is repressed. In order to adapt to its environment, the Child develops an additional ego state whose function is to gather information about his immediate environment for his additional protection. This ego state, initially part of the Child, becomes the Parent ego state.

The Parent

The Parent ego state records all of the information that can be gleaned from those upon whom the child must be dependent. Thus it is that the Parent ego state models itself upon the real parents. It gathers information from them, such as their expectations of the child. This is done through all of the earliest parental communications (e.g. their tone of voice, facial expressions, and all of the verbal and non-verbal rules and regulations with which they surround him). Some of the information that the Parent gathers is positive and approving of the Child; some of it may be negative and disapproving. Like the real parent, the Parent ego state may be nurturing and loving, or it may be critical and punitive, depending on the qualities of the true parent upon whom the Parent ego state is modelled. In hypnoanalytical theory and therapy we are mainly concerned with the *negative* attitudes of the Parent ego state culled as they are from the real parent. These are the source of the motivation for repression of the Child's normal emotions and are responsible for its emotional difficulties.

The data in the Parent is taken straight and without editing from the parents. It includes therefore all of the admonitions, rules and laws that the child hears from his parents and parent surrogates. It includes, as well, all of the signs both of approval and disapproval. These are recorded as *truth* and this is a permanent recording. Through its coercive, sometimes permissive, but more usually restrictive, pressures upon the Child, such data have a powerful effect during his life. The voluminous collection of data is essential to the individual's survival within the group and helps him to avoid those dangers which he has not experienced and of which he can have no personal knowledge. Much of the data in the Parent appears in the 'how-to' category and is acquired by observing how the real parents and parent surrogates deal with things. In this day and age it is of interest to reflect on what influence the parent surrogate, television, might have on the development of the Parent ego state.

Repression   So that the Child becomes and remains acceptable to the true parents, the Parent ego state seeks to modify the Child's behaviour by repressing non-acceptable aspects of it. This is an admirable and proper role for the Parent ego state since it thereby functions to maintain the Child in such a way that the parents, upon whom the Child depends for survival, will not abandon it. It is, in effect, protecting the Child from the wrath of the real parents. Thus a critical and punitive parent will be reflected in a critical and punitive Parent ego state which maintains the Child by repressing its unacceptable behaviour resulting from unacceptable emotions.

Guilt   The parent ego state maintains its repressive influence over the Child by means of the constant reminder that some of its behaviour and emotions are unacceptable to the real parents and that any expression of these might well result in the abandonment of the Child. It is this fear of abandonment which, often very intense, is expressed and felt as guilt. Whenever an individual experiences the feeling of guilt, there is an underlying fear of abandonment. Furthermore, whenever there is guilt, there is a repression by the Parent of part of the Child's normal emotional functioning. This results in a persistent Parent/Child conflict. It is this conflict, always accompanied by feelings of guilt, that may be deeply unconscious and only accessible to skillful analytical hypnotherapy. This conflict is at the centre of all emotional disorders seen by the analytical hypnotherapist; such disorders can be cured only after this conflict has terminated.

The Parent/Child Conflict   Branden (1972) held that repression began as a flight from inner experience – from feelings of pain, fear, frustration, helplessness and rage, and, in fleeing from these feelings, a portion of the being is denied or disowned. This self alienation must be eliminated before self esteem can be constructed. It is this self alienation which is typified by the Parent/Child conflict because the Child is being prevented from expressing his normal emotions, whether they be hurt, anger or fear. He may also be prevented from expressing pleasant feelings if these too are unacceptable. If his very existence is not acceptable, then *all* of his feelings may be repressed. But unexpressed feelings are never obliterated; they always persist in some more acceptable form. For example, repressed anger can be responsible for depression; repressed fear can be the source of anxiety and phobias; repressed sadness is also a cause of depression. Any emotion, when repressed from normal expression, may seek an abnormal expression via the body in the form of a psychosomatic illness. It is interesting to note that Perls (1969) could not accept the term 'repression' since he was very much aware that nothing can be totally repressed. For him, alienation of part of the personality was more of a 'disowning into the unconscious' than it was repression.

Resolution of the Parent/Child conflict removes the need for repression and a previously blocked emotion can once again be properly expressed. When this occurs the symptoms directly resulting from the repression of emotion can be more readily relinquished. How then can this stubborn Parent/Child conflict be terminated? For Berne (1961) the answer was simple: 'deconfusion of the Child by using the decontaminated Adult ego state as a therapeutic ally' was the course for the therapist to take. Consequently, analytical hypnotherapists must take a closer look at the Adult ego state in order to make full use of its potential. (See Fig. 7).

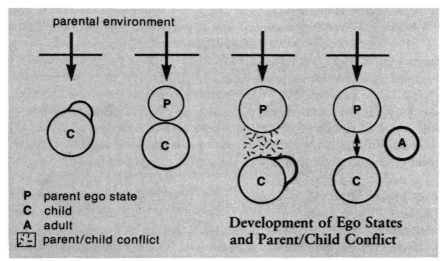

P parent ego state
C child
A adult
[:·:] parent/child conflict

Development of Ego States and Parent/Child Conflict

figure 7

The Adult

This is the third clearly defined ego state which develops early in life from the Child (although probably at a later date than the Parent). At any rate its development in the early years is slower than that of the Parent. The infant begins to learn that he can manipulate his environment. He learns, for example, that he can decide whether or not a particular object will fall simply by initiating actions which are totally under his control. This interaction with his environment gives him a self actualisation which is the beginning of the Adult ego state. Adult data accumulate as a result of the infant's ability to find out for himself about life. This is different from the data so uncritically accepted from his parents by the Parent ego state. It also differs from the instinctive and feeling data which are the essential components of the Child ego state. In fact, the Adult develops a thought concept of life based upon data gathering and data processing.

In early life, the Adult has little information with which to challenge the commands of the Parent ego state or to aid the emotions of the Child ego state. In most people, however, the Adult ego state matures by concerning itself with transforming incoming stimuli into pieces of information which are stored and processed in relationship to other relevant previous experiences. Thus the Adult serves as a means whereby the child can begin to recognise life as it really is, instead of being restricted to evaluating it through the parents' eyes as the Parent does, or through the eyes of the Child's make-believe world. The Adult is, in effect, a data processing computer which can and does reach decisions after computing information from all available sources including the Parent and the Child. It can reexamine data in the Parent to see whether it remains applicable or whether it no longer matches with the facts. It can also examine the data in the Child to determine whether the feelings there are appropriate or irrelevant.

It is on the presence of an intact and mature Adult that all successful psychotherapy depends. This is particularly true for analytical hypnotherapy which cannot succeed without the aid of an effective and cooperative Adult ego state. It is upon the Adult that the analytical hypnotherapist calls to examine the Parent/Child conflict and find new solutions to it. The persistence of symptoms prior to therapy is probably due to the fact that the true nature of the Parent/Child conflict remains concealed from the wisdom of the Adult. It is the hypnotherapist's task to uncover that conflict and expose it to the understanding of the Adult. This kind of uncovering demands considerable skill and takes the therapist to the limit of his ability to facilitate the cure of emotional problems.

The hypnotherapist, then, plays an important role, for without his or her assistance, the deeply buried Parent/Child conflicts would remain beyond the reach of the Adult. The Adult's immense resources, culled from the business of observing life realistically, would be unavailable. The greater portion of this book is devoted to detailing the skills necessary for locating these conflicts, thus ensuring that they are fully exposed to the resources of the Adult ego state for their resolution.

The theory of analytical hypnotherapy may be succinctly summarized as follows: mental illness and emotional disorders are assumed to be due to the ongoing and outmoded conflict between the 'I want' (The Child) part of the personality and the 'I ought' (The Parent) part. This conflict can be resolved only by the application of the 'I will or I can' (The Adult) arbitrator in that conflict. The conflict is terminated when both the Parent and the Child accept the arbitration. (See Fig. 8).

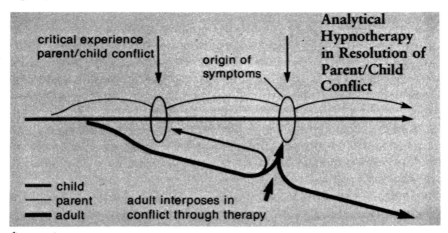

figure 8

Szasz (1961) argued that the very concept of mental illness should be discarded since it promotes a confusion with physical illness and assumes that an external event(s) is responsible for the symptoms. He believes that mental disorders, unlike physical illnesses, are not diseases because they are internally determined. If he is correct in his assumptions, then analytical hypnotherapy, by its emphasis on the use of internal resources for therapy, can properly be regarded as a nonmedical therapy which accomplishes its results without direct external intervention.

It is probable that, as a result of hypnotic suggestion, the Adult ego state points out to the Parent ego state that the repression of the Child and his emotions (initially important for the individual's survival) is no longer necessary. In adult life survival is no longer dependent upon approval of parents; they are no longer in the protective and supportive position vis-a-vis the child that they were in during the onset of the conflict. In fact it may be that the parents themselves are in need of the child's protection, or that they no longer are alive. The Adult may make it clear to the Child that the repressed emotion, although acceptable, is probably no longer necessary and need not be retained since the experience responsible for it has long since been completed.

Central to the whole concept of therapy is the belief that in the presence of an intact Adult there are adequate resources for the resolution of the Parent/Child conflict. Once it is resolved, we can reach the happy position in which Berne (1961) described the Adult, the Child, and the Parent as existing with all important aspects syntonic one with another. At such time, the individual can function as an integrated unit without any of the symptoms which had been a necessary part of his existence prior to therapy.

Principles of Analytical Hypnotherapy

PART ONE   Chapter 6

Berne (1961) regarded therapy as a battle involving four personalities: the Parent, the Child, the Adult (always written with a capital first letter to distinguish them from the usual meaning of these names), and the therapist — with the therapist functioning as an auxiliary Adult. If the patient's Adult can be enlisted alongside the therapist's Adult as a therapeutic ally, then the odds for success are increased. If the therapist can also appeal to the patient's Child, the odds against the Parent are then three to one. This alliance allows an even greater chance of success since, in most of the neuroses, Berne considered the Parent to be the prime target for therapeutic intervention. In hypnosis, the Parent and the Adult are temporarily decommissioned and in regression analysis, the Child is being directly appealed to while maintaining the advantage of retaining the Adult and the Parent. Selavan (1975) agreed with this view, adding that direct communication with the Child in hypnosis allows for the reexamination of critical moments in its life which are still affecting present behaviour. The Adult, present at this communication, can then enable a new decision to be made with a consequent modification of behaviour.

James and Jongeward (1971) claimed that an individual's behaviour is governed by a psychological script which contains the programme for his life drama. The programme is based on the messages the individual, when a child, receives from his parents, and it is therefore largely a function of the Parent ego state. These script messages can be either productive and constructive or non-productive and destructive. To the extent that these script messages are out of tune with the real self (the Child) and its real potential, they can create a pathology which varies from mild to so severe that the individual becomes an absurd caricature of his real self. Some scripts serve the function of giving the individual a realistic idea of what he can accomplish with his talents; others misdirect him to follow unrealistic goals; still others programme the Child for destruction and negate his will to live. James and Jongeward further declared that, when there is an inner conflict between the inner Child and the Parent, the Adult can intervene in the conflict. It can referee, arbitrate, discover compromises and make new decisions for the fuller expression of the inner Child. It can also modify the Parent by accepting or rejecting Parental assumptions on the basis of reality and appropriateness. In order to achieve this integration of the personality, the Adult must gain knowledge about the Child and the Parent ego states.

Branden (1972) advocated the therapeutic value of communicating with the repressed Child and his feelings, observing that one does not destroy an emotion by refusing to feel or acknowledge it (that is merely to disown a part of oneself). If we acknowledge and permit ourselves to reexperience our painful or undesired feelings − without self-pity and without self-condemnation − we facilitate the process of healing integration.

While the analytical approach to therapy would clearly seem to be the most rational one, Freud, as mentioned previously, expressed considerable doubt regarding the therapeutic effectiveness of direct unconscious communication using hypnosis. He felt that hypnosis did not in fact penetrate repression but only masked it, so that cures, though frequently spectacular, were nevertheless temporary. Conn (1977) reiterated this view and every experienced psychotherapist has now come to accept it as a clinical fact: the patient's knowledge of the reason for his behaviour does not spontaneously lead to a cure of it. He went on to assert that it is this fact which has led psychotherapists to forego their previous obsessive and apparently futile search for traumatic infantile memories.

In the face of this kind of opposition to the analytical approach, the analytical hypnotherapist needs to understand why it is that sometimes the approach fails so dismally whereas, at other times, in cases where non-analytical methods have failed, it is extremely successful. This author believes that when analytical hypnotherapy fails, it is frequently due to the fact that its underlying principles have not been fully understood and therefore have not been applied in their entirety.

In spite of Freud's reservation, many analysts have continued to assume that the mere location and identification of the origin of emotional problems would suffice to enable the patient to deal with and become free of such problems. Occasionally, this has indeed proved to be true, and the resulting dramatic cure has been attributed entirely to the patient's insight gained from the presentation of the previously hidden material to consciousness. When such cures do occur following the uncovering of previously concealed important material, they provide a striking demonstration of the potential effectiveness of analytic hypnotherapy. But, unfortunately, these very cases obscure the mechanism whereby insight has been effective. Often, the initial dramatic response is shortlived, and the long term results prove to be disappointing. It would appear from such ineffectual results that greater time spent on a purely behavioural approach might produce more permanent results and one can understand criticisms like Conn's, that the uncovering of the causes of emotional problems is a waste of time. But a number of analysts who share the author's viewpoint believe that the behaviourist approach must always remain incomplete since it attempts to manipulate *only* the external environment. Every analyst believes that the internal environment is of equal importance and must likewise merit the therapist's attention. All hypnotherapists in the course of therapy, whether or not it is analytical, inevitably modify the internal environment; but it is the analytical hypnotherapist who must carry out this process in a structured and systematic manner. The rest of this chapter is devoted to a detailed examination of the principles which underly the most successful analytical approaches to therapy.

Theoretical Considerations

We have considered how the structure of the personality is viewed by the Transactional analyst and how the behaviour responses of the individual are governed by three main groups of learning. Maladaptive behaviour, evidenced by the presenting symptoms, has presumably been learned in an environment where such behaviour was considered by the individual to be the most appropriate that he could devise at that time. Such learning has become so deeply ingrained that the individual does not respond appropriately to changes in the environment and persists with a behaviour pattern which is clearly maladaptive. Such is the nature of Parental script messages. When a patient presents for therapy symptoms of which he consciously wishes to rid himself, we can safely assume that they arise from an unconscious conviction that this was the best response available to him. At the level from which his symptoms originate, the patient's environment is being perceived as it has been, rather than as it truly is. Consequently, the response creating the symptoms unconsciously *appears* to be appropriate and thus the maladaptive behaviour persists. It is the revelation of the Parent/Child conflict (i.e. the unconscious reality), which gives the therapist an understanding of the rationale for the symptoms.

To illustrate this further, let us take the case of a patient with snake phobia so intense that even the drawing of a snake sends her into a panic. She is unable to move into any environment which, by any stretch of the imagination, could possibly be inhabited by snakes. She is frequently subject to attacks of panic because there are so many things that remind her of them. Clearly, she is not responding directly to the environment (which is relatively harmless and certainly does not warrant such an intense fear response), but rather, she is responding to a set of frightening memories that are evoked by the thought of a snake. Such memories are more real to her unconscious mind than the actual environment. For her, this phobic response is therefore entirely appropriate.

In order to help this patient, the analytical hypnotherapist persuades the patient to review in detail, through the medium of regression, those experiences which were responsible for the symptom-producing behaviour. Having identified these experiences, and all of their associated emotional responses, he then activates the Adult within the patient to examine the current inappropriateness of such responses and encourages him to discover improved ways of behaving in the present. It has consistently been the author's experience that, where uncovering has been possible, an inappropriate emotional response has been always discovered to be due to an unresolved Parent/Child conflict. In such a conflict, the expression of the individual's natural response has been repressed because of unconscious guilt due to fear of parental disapproval.

By returning to the critical experiences and reviewing them in the light of his present (Adult) wisdom and understanding, the patient is persuaded to reassess these experiences and then find the resources with which to formulate more effective behavioural responses to the stimuli previously responsible for symptoms. Location of the critical experiences is therefore crucial to therapy, even though it is only a part of the analytical hypnotherapist's task. In order to achieve the cure of symptoms, not only must the therapist enable his patient to recognise the inappropriateness of his responses at the level from which they originate, but also, he must encourage him to discover more effective responses which will ultimately enable him to function more effectively. It is the failure to achieve this latter objective that has been responsible for the recurrence of symptoms in the face of apparently successful therapy.

Analytical hypnotherapy can be broken down into several stages, each of which depends upon an important and logical principle; failure to observe each principle is likely to jeopardise the successful outcome of therapy. These stages and the principles underlying them are as follows.

First Principle
Identification of the Critical Experience(s)   It is this first stage which has always been regarded as the essential one in analytical hypnotherapy. Unfortunately it has also been erroneously held to be the *only* important one by too many therapists. Much time and effort have been expended in devising increasingly effective methods of uncovering critical experiences; all too frequently, the successful location and identification of these experiences have been equated with successful therapy. In truth, therapy has only commenced when this stage has been reached. Furthermore, many analysts have been so readily satisfied by the mere location of these critical experiences that they have remained totally unaware of the pressing need to identify clearly all of the associated emotions that have been repressed which need to be understood and accepted. The failure to complete properly this portion of the first stage of therapy has frequently resulted in the continued concealment of vitally important facets of the critical experience. This concealment remains responsible for the persistence of symptoms. Therefore, no matter what uncovering technique is used, if therapy is to be successful, it is imperative for it to be a technique that enables every detail of the critical experience to be identified and reviewed. It should be noted here that a critical experience is one that, for the individual, has been responsible for a crisis in which a critical decision has been made; upon this decision future behaviour will depend.

Let us now return to the case of our middle-aged female patient suffering from snake phobia to illustrate further the importance of the correct handling of this first stage.

It is not enough to uncover the fact that, at the age of nine years, she had been approached by a young man in a deserted spot who had exposed his erect penis and had asked her to masturbate him. Not only do we need to know that she was extremely frightened by this experience and was always unconsciously reminded of it by anything snakelike in appearance, but we also need to know about the excessive feelings of guilt evoked by the experience. These guilt feelings were the result of the pleasurable sexual fantasies that she began to weave around the incident. It was her natural curiosity (which she considered sinful) as to what it might have been like had she complied with the young man's request that was responsible for these intense guilt feelings. As a devout Roman Catholic, she found herself unable to own to this curiosity and was therefore unable to relieve herself of this guilt in the confessional.

In this first phase of analytical hypnotherapy, the uncovering techniques are used to locate the Parent/Child conflict(s) responsible for the symptoms. In this case of snake phobia the conflict is clearly one between the Child's pleasurable sexual feelings and the Parent's recognition of their inadmissability. It is the guilt that this conflict engenders which is the source of the fear in the snake phobia. It is interesting to note at this point that, although guilt is always an element of all Parent/Child conflicts, it is never more intense than in the phobias.

Second Principle
Understanding the Repressed Emotion and the Associated Feeling of Guilt Unacceptable emotions experienced at the time of the critical event are repressed by the Parent ego state since their expression would meet with profound parental disapproval and the possibility of abandonment, if not physically then at least emotionally. It is the fear of this rejection and the possible parental abandonment which gives to guilt its intense power to control. It is therefore imperative for therapy to be directed at the elimination of such guilt. In order to accomplish this there has to be full acceptance of these repressed emotions as normal and proper. So long as feelings of guilt persist, emotions are rejected and repressed as being improper. It is only when, with the assistance of the Adult's full understanding, the Parent can be assured that the Child is no longer in danger from the expression of its true feelings, that guilt can be withdrawn and the repression that it represents removed.

It is in this stage that the Adult first applies its understanding and wisdom to the Parent/Child conflict. While appreciating that the Parent's strictures were correct and wise at the time they were applied, the Adult is able to convince the Parent that the Child's feelings are indeed normal, proper, and in the present context, totally acceptable. To return to our snake phobia example. Our patient needed to be persuaded that her sexual curiosity at nine years of age was not abnormal. She was able to understand, in the context of her faith, that these feelings are God-given and did not really emanate from the devil, as she had previously supposed. Her own experience as a parent enabled her to accomplish this fairly readily and she was able to pardon herself for her supposed crime and accept the normal healthy sexual feelings of a nine year old girl.

Third Principle
Recognition of the Current Irrelevance of the Previously Repressed Emotion An emotion which has been located, identified and accepted, needs, before it can be relinquished, to be recognised as currently irrelevant to the present environment. The present situation must be seen to be different from that responsible for the original emotion. Furthermore, the past protective nature of the emotion must be seen no longer to be necessary since the individual now has for his defence access to his normal emotions.

Thus our snake phobia patient had to recognise that her fear had not been entirely of snakes nor even of the penis which snakes symbolise. It had been, essentially, a fear of her own sexual interests and of the disaster that she had believed would surely befall her should she acknowledge them. Since her intense fear had not really been of snakes, she could then accept that she need no longer retain that conscious manifestation of her real fear, nor her anxiety about her sexual interests. She knew that she need only keep a normal fear of snakes which she could rely on herself to draw upon if ever it became necessary. In this phase, the wisdom of the Adult is used both by the Child who has hung on to the fears for protection, and by the Parent who has been maintaining the fear of abandonment inherent in the feeling of guilt.

Fourth Principle
Relinquishing the Repressed and Repressing Emotions for Good Although at this stage of therapy there really appears to be no reason for the retention of symptoms, much still remains to be done before the emotions causing them can be relinquished. For years, the Parent/Child conflict has been a way of life for the patient, and thus a means has to be discovered to end the conflict so that these ego states can live in harmony. Once again the Adult is called upon to deliver its wisdom in the task of terminating this conflict. It is at this time that the Parent ego state is further aided to understand that its role of controller of the Child can now be modified since the Adult has information adequate for the task. This may be difficult to accomplish because the

Parent, in the Child's best interests, had been programmed to maintain the controlling feeling of guilt. It will require much encouragement to relinquish this role.

Fifth Principle
Recognition of Resolution of the Parent/Child Conflict A critical experience, and the Parent/Child conflict resulting from it, cannot be regarded as having been satisfactorily dealt with until it is certain that the conflict is indeed at an end and all of the associated, outdated, uncomfortable and unnecessary tensions responsible for the symptoms have been relinquished. So long as the conflict remains, so will the tensions resulting from it. Should tension still remain, it is probable that the Parent has not relinquished its role as controller of the Child by the purveyance of guilt. If this should be the case, a further review of the critical experience is necessary to determine the reason for the persistence of uncomfortable feelings. Once again, the wisdom and understanding of the Adult is enlisted and applied to a further examination of the conflict in order to discover what is still unreconcilable in the feelings of the Child or the opinions of the Parent. When ultimately successful, there is always a feeling of profound relief which marks the completion of this stage of therapy. In the case of our snake phobia patient, she experienced a comfort previously unknown to her and it was this absence of her old tensions that confirmed that she had at last resolved her problem and could remain free from her phobia.

Sixth Principle
Rehabilitation It is one thing to resolve a problem but it is still another to keep it resolved. Rehabilitation indicates that this is the final but certainly not the least important stage of therapy. It is the phase necessary to ensure that the patient makes the essential post therapy readjustments in order to remain free from the symptoms. The world of the patient without his symptoms is vastly different from that with them. Many secondary gains have gone unrecognised during the persistence of the symptoms; they must either be abandoned or new ways found of obtaining similar gains. Once the patient is symptom-free, there will remain a constant temptation, not consciously recognised, to return to the security and familiarity of old patterns of functioning rather than dealing with new problems in more appropriate and beneficial ways. The judicious use of posthypnotic suggestions to give appropriate ego strengthening and to provide training in

assertiveness is an essential part of this rehabilitation phase. It ensure.
that the patient will return to his world equipped to deal with it and
remain symptom free.

Our snake phobia patient had to find other legitimate reasons for
not going on trips into the countryside when for one reason or
another, totally unconnected with her previous snake phobia, she did
not wish to go. She had to learn that she had a right to consider and
express all of her feelings and opinions without any unnecessary
feelings of guilt.

The following excerpt from a tape recording of a session of therapy
is given to illustrate the use of the principles of analytical hypnotherapy in practice. The patient is a thirty-eight year old man who
has come to therapy because of a lack of self confidence and a compulsion to overeat. The patient entered hypnosis easily.

DR. I would like you to see if there are any other Kevins who do not feel comfortable. If you find any, your head will nod for 'yes'. *Head nods.* How old are you there?

> There is good ideomotor com-munication using the head to signal 'yes' and 'no'. One critical experience has already been dealt with. **First principle** − the iden-tification of the critical experience − has begun to be put into opera-tion.

PT Fourteen

DR Fourteen year old Kevin, something is happening there that's really bothering you. What is it?

PT I was drinking again.

DR Drinking again?

PT It's my cousin. What's bother-ing me is that I think he's having some kind of affair with my mother. My father is out drunk in the field. . .

DR How are you feeling?

> Mere location of the critical ex-perience is not enough. All the cir-cumstances that render it a source of conflict must be identified.

PT Ashamed, scared, bitter. . .

DR How do you feel about your cousin?

PT   Very angry at him.

DR   How are you feeling about your mother?

PT   Angry.

DR   Real angry! Is there anything else to know? If there is, your head will nod for 'yes'; if there isn't, your head will shake for 'no'. *Head shakes.*

At this point, all of the relevant information regarding the critical experience and the Parent/Child conflict it has engendered is now presumably accessible to the Adult.

Thirty-eight year old Kevin, fourteen year Kevin has told us about something that is really bothering him. I want you to help him. I want you — he's feeling so hurt and guilty and angry and ashamed and scared — I want you to give him all the help that you can. You've got thirty-eight years of wisdom and understanding to comfort him. When you have done that nod your head for 'yes'. *Nods.* Fourteen year old Kevin, now that you have heard that, do you still have to go on feeling bad up here in 1980?

The **Second Principle** — understanding the repressed emotion (of the Child) and the associated feeling of guilt (repressive force of the Parent) — applies the resources of the Adult to the Parent/Child conflict.

PT   No.

Third Principle — recognition that the repressed emotions are no longer relevant — has been applied.

DR   Okay, thirty-eight year old Kevin, fourteen year old Kevin has said that, now that he has listened to you, he doesn't need to go on keeping those bad feelings any longer. . . He's been keeping all of them for twenty-four years. I want you to find a way for him to let go of these unnecessary, out of date, uncom-

Again the Adult is being called upon to apply its resources as the **Fourth Principle** is being invoked: relinquishing the repressed and repressing emotions. There is no need to enquire into the means

fortable feelings that he has been keeping for so long. When you have found a way to do that your head will nod for 'yes'. *Head nods.* There you are, fourteen year old Kevin, you can let go of those uncomfortable feelings now. You don't need them any more. Finished with, done with, past, over, gone. Let them go. When they've all gone, you can feel they've all gone and when you're sure they're all gone, nod your head for 'yes'. *Head nods.* Good. Now, fourteen year old Kevin, you should be feeling so good now that you've let go of all of those old uncomfortable feelings. You don't need them any more. If you really feel good, please give me a smile. *Smiles.* Feels good eh?

discovered, since it is often too complex to verbalise. After an acceptable means has been discovered, it must be proven to be effective.

Fifth Principle – recognition of the resolution of the Parent/Child conflict – has now been applied and evidence that the conflict resulting from this particular critical experience is at an end is being sought.

At this juncture, the session goes on to deal with other critical experiences relevant to the symptomatology. It is later, when all of these have been satisfactorily dealt with, that the **Sixth Principle** – rehabilitation (which includes suggestions for ego strengthening and assertiveness training), is invoked. This will be dealt with in greater detail in chapter fourteen, but the excerpt from this session was as follows:

PT No, I don't – I didn't like myself.

DR But now, you do like yourself?

PT Yeah.

DR And are you going to go on liking yourself?

PT Yeah.

DR Going to keep yourself trim?

PT Right.

DR And healthy?

PT Right. That's the main thing.

DR For yourself and for the family?

PT For the family especially, yeah.

DR Yes. Are you smiling inside all of the time?

PT I really feel very good, yes.

DR Will you please tell Kevin, up here in 1980, how to do that because he needs to know... When you have told him, let me know...

PT Hmmmm — take the bull by the horns.

DR Okay, now Kevin, here in my chair, will you do that?

PT Yeah.

DR Definitely?

PT Yeah.

DR Right now?

PT Right now.

DR Take the bull by the horns?

PT Yeah.

DR Feels good, eh?

PT It does really.

DR Yes. You're just as good as anybody else, aren't you?

PT Yeah.

DR You like yourself?

PT You bet.

DR You don't need to feel ashamed any more?

PT No.

DR Good. You're going to respect Kevin all the time?

PT Yeah.

DR Can you now say, 'I like Kevin?'

PT Yes.

DR Great. You're going to take care of him, eh?

PT Right.

DR   And keep him safe?

PT   Yes.

DR   Okay. He is the most valuable piece of property that you've got, Kevin, so take good care of him. Right?

PT   Right.

It is of interest to note that the patient's Adult appears to have discovered what he needs to do to remain free of symptoms: 'take the bull by the horns'. The patient's determination to do just this made it unnecessary for him to revert to any of his previous symptomatology. He is now able to implement a way of living that he knew about, but because of his emotional conflicts, had been unable to establish.

SUMMARY OF ANALYTICAL PROCEDURE

Principle	Unconscious Processes	Objectives
Identification of the critical experience	Communication is established with unconscious part (ego state complex) with relevant information. Resistance to that communication (i.e. hostile ego state) must be dealt with. Critical experience is labelled with age of that part with its memory. All emotional components of the critical experience identified whether or not it is consciously available.	Rendering all aspects of the Child/Parent conflict accessible to Adult resources
Understanding the repressed emotion and the associated guilt	Application of unconscious resources of understanding, wisdom, forgiveness, compassion, loving comfort, etc., to the unconscious distressed ego state.	Strong Adult/Parent interaction
Recognition of current irrelevance of repressed emotion	Adult intervention is concentrated upon the Child to relinquish negative feelings with Parental agreement and approval.	Confidence of the Child in future Parent/Adult support in threatening situations must be obtained

Relinquishing the repressed emotions and the repressed guilt	Parental pressures will have to be dealt with by the Adult. The Parent's perceived need to retain a punitive role may create difficulties.	Relief from guilt
Confirmation of resolution of Parent/Child conflict	Comfort at the site of previous Parent/Child conflict is felt and demonstrated by the 'smile test'.	Parent, Child, and Adult are in harmony
Rehabilitation	Secondary gains previously resulting from the symptoms must be abandoned or obtained in new, non-symptom producing ways. Also a means of handling life without previous symptoms must be found and established.	Ego Stengthening – Adult/Child interaction Assertiveness Training – Adult/Parent interaction
Review	Careful follow up to discover and deal with any remnants of Parent/Child conflicts and to discover any active concealed ego state complexes.	Prevention of any relapse into previous symptoms or unwanted behaviour pattern

Therapeutic Indications for Analytical Hypnotherapy

From our previous discussion of the nature of analytical hypnotherapy, it can be seen that the indications for therapy can be presumed to be present in any clinical condition created as a result of a Child/Parent conflict. There must also be presumed the presence of an effective and active Adult ego state. In most cases the presence of a Child/Parent conflict is obvious and the adequacy of the Adult ego state must be assumed until proved otherwise. There are three main groups of symptomatologies which are clearly due to an ongoing Child/Parent conflict. They are: psychosomatic illnesses, emotional disorders and habit disorders and addictions. A brief discussion of these three groups and the repressed emotions which cause them will now follow. (See Fig. 9).

The Psychosomatic Disorders
The list of psychosomatic diseases grows longer every day. In each case, the psychodynamics of the symptomatology is that of a diversion of unacceptable emotions because normal expression is forbidden. The symptoms arise as a result of the expression of these emotions of the psyche or mind via the soma or body.

When fear is suppressed, many of the physiological changes commonly associated with it will persist. Sweating, hyperventilation, cold extremities, tachycardia and hypertension are typical symptoms. One of the more common psychosomatic disorders which has been shown repeatedly to be the result of repressed fear is ulcerative colitis, a devastating condition which sometimes becomes life-threatening and yet seldom is treated from a psychological perspective. Many skin diseases likewise represent a response to an unconscious fear which cannot otherwise be expressed.

Pain in some area of the body where there is no organic lesion to

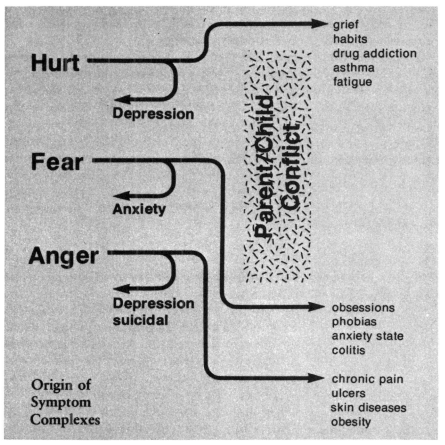

figure 9

account for it is often the result of unexpressed anger. Back pains, neck pains, migraine headaches, persistent pains following injuries and arthritis of different kinds, can all be the consequence of repressed anger. Peptic ulcers have long been known to be associated with repressed anger. They are presumably due to the increased vulnerability of the gastric mucosa following the normal vasomotor changes produced by anger. These changes persist because of the inaccessibility of a normal release of the anger. Again, hypertension is also common in those who are not able to express anger appropriately.

Asthma is perhaps the best example of a psychosomatic disease associated with repressed hurt or sadness. The child who learns that his needs are more likely to be met when he is suffering from asthma soon learns how to develop an attack of asthma as a means of dealing with his feelings of rejection and of obtaining the signs of acceptance that he craves. Certain skin diseases also develop in this way and are exacerbated by feelings of sadness and rejection.

Guilt is an essential constituent of the Child/Parent conflict and is therefore an important factor in all of the problems seen and treated by the analytical hypnotherapist. In some cases its role in the development of symptoms is greater than in others. In such instances the symptoms can be regarded as being self-punitive. Self-excoriating skin disorders, with pruritis as a predominating element where no organic cause can be detected, are good examples of this. Guilt may appear to be non-existent in some of the psychosomatic diseases but this is really an illusion. Analytical procedures will often locate a very deeply concealed guilt which is invariably present and strongly operative in the causation of symptoms.

The Emotional Disorders

The repression of the primary emotions is often more clearly recognisable in the aetiology of emotional disorders.

Phobias, for example, are an obvious result of inappropriately expressed fear, but most of the power of the phobias emanates from the underlying guilt that is always a prime factor. Much of the fear that the phobic patient experiences is, in reality, a fear of the punishment that he unconsciously awaits as a consequence of his transgressions. The phobic sufferer has always had experiences which in themselves have been extremely fearful and that have given him a yardstick by which he can gauge the terror he is certain awaits him. By attributing these fears to certain fearful situations, he endeavours to isolate them and control them. By avoiding the phobic situations he can cope with life in a somewhat limited fashion.

Closely allied to the problem of phobia is that of the obsessive personality. The obsessive personality believes that certain acquired rituals will enable him to avoid those circumstances which he fears will inevitably lead to a terrible fate.

Anxiety is such a common symptom that one might safely say that every patient presenting for hypnotherapy is suffering from it to some extent. Clearly, some of this anxiety is perfectly reasonable, and is relevant to the clinical problem and the therapeutic environment in which the patient finds himself. But much of it results from unexpressed fears repressed by the guilt engendered in the persistent Parent/Child conflict.

When anger is effectively repressed, it can only be experienced as depression, since it is turned in upon the self. It is then accompanied by feelings of dissatisfaction with the self and self-destructive thoughts which are often the prelude to attempts at suicide.

It is probably true to say that all Child/Parent conflicts contain some measure of hurt and rejection and that this hurt will be experienced as sadness or depression. These may sometimes be the presenting symptoms. Unexpressed hurt can often appear as general ill health and fatigue. Interestingly enough, prolonged grief is rarely due to repressed sadness or hurt but is more likely due to repressed anger and feelings of guilt.

Habit Disorders and Diseases of Addiction

All habit disorders which cannot be terminated by an effort of will are serving an unconscious need and are invariably the expression of a Child/Parent conflict. Like all obsessive compulsive behaviour, the habit serves the function of maintaining repression of a normal human emotion. Drug addictions are the cause of much human misery and distress, but the reason for them lies in the effectiveness of certain drugs to suppress emotions which the addict cannot allow normal expression. Often the drug used for this repression appears to be the one that is chosen or permitted by the Parent, and one that the real parent has used to repress his or her feelings (alcoholics often have a family history of alcoholism, or smokers have one or both parents who smoke heavily). Because of the successful repression of unacceptable emotions by drugs, the effective treatment of drug addiction must involve the resolution of the underlying conflict. Any other treatment is either only temporarily successful or only results in the patient discovering and using another device to continue the repression of his unacceptable feelings.

Whether or not it is the raised blood sugar that acts as a tranquillizer, the compulsive overeater has discovered that food makes him feel more comfortable and is a means of dealing with feelings that he will not allow himself to express more appropriately. Many obese patients are aware of the compulsive nature of their eating. It seldom has anything to do with actual hunger, but rather is a ritualistic means of dealing with uncomfortable feelings which they feel bound to suppress. Some have a fear of being thin and feel helpless to deal with situations that they unconsciously believe would overwhelm them. In such cases their motivation is clearly to remain fat and safe. Conversely, the anorectic keeps thin and safe. Many anorectics are also compulsive eaters and express their anger not only in compulsive eating but also in the ritualistic vomiting which must take place immediately afterwards.

There is no need to make a comprehensive list of the many disorders that can benefit from analytical hypnotherapy, since it is not the symptomatology that needs to be treated but the conflict underlying it. When this conflict can be satisfactorily located, analytical hypnotherapy offers the best hope of rapidly resolving it, no matter what symptomatology arises from it. However, it must again be emphasised that the presence of an adequate and cooperative Adult is mandatory if therapy is to be successful. It should be noted here that the prospect of success with many psychotic illnesses is immediately eliminated because the Adult is apparently immobilised and, at least temporarily, is inaccessible to aid the therapist.

Uncovering Techniques in Analytical Hypnotherapy

PART ONE   Chapter 8

It is a fundamental premise in analytical hypnotherapy that the brain is able to record indefinitely every event perceived by the individual throughout his life and that these recordings are stored away essentially unaltered. This assumption is supported, not only by the clinical experience of every hypnotherapist, but in particular by the work of Penfield (1952) in which stimulation of the cerebral cortex evoked intact memories. This evocation indicated that *everything* is stored in detail in the brain and is capable of being played back in the present. Not only are the past events themselves recorded but also the associated feelings occurring at the time. It is this seeing, hearing, and feeling body of data that comprises much of the Child ego state.

Another fundamental premise is that the persistence of the strong emotion associated with the critical experience is responsible for the symptomatology. Thus it is that the prime task of the analytical hypnotherapist is to locate the experience(s) responsible for the symptoms in order that appropriate therapy can be applied to modify them. There have been many techniques, using hypnosis, which have been devised to accomplish this objective. Although the critical experience is always one associated with much distress, for unconscious reasons, the memory of part or all of it has usually been deeply buried in the unconscious mind with barriers erected to prevent its recovery. The techniques to be described here have been designed either to circumvent these barriers or to persuade the unconscious mind to remove them.

Memories would seem to have been filed chronologically; yet the unconscious mind does not appear to do what we are consciously aware of doing when attempting to retrieve a memory of a specific experience. At a conscious level we use the process of association to bring a forgotten memory to consciousness. We start off with one remembered event and gradually, by process of association with other events, rebuild the lost memory to a greater or lesser degree of completeness. For example, if we are trying to remember what occurred on a certain day, we first recall something significant about that day; other events associated with that day will then come to mind until the event that we are seeking is recalled. The unconscious mind, on the other hand, seems to require only one specific detail about an event in order to gain immediate access to all of the other relevant aspects of it.

For the analytical hypnotherapist, this ability is of great importance since the one essential aspect of the critical experience readily available is the emotional disturbance associated with it and which is responsible for the presenting symptoms. All uncovering techniques depend on the association of the concealed experience with either a particular emotion or a specific time. The techniques to be described owe their effectiveness to their ability to locate either an emotion or a specific time. This location in turn unconsciously isolates the associated experience and therefore permits it to be subjected to the examination necessary for therapy.

Every uncovering technique relies upon communication with the unconscious mind and is therefore a manifestation of the hypnotic process. All emotions arise from a deeply unconscious level and, whenever experienced, indicate that unconscious communication has been established. It is part of the hypnotherapist's skill to be able to recognise when an emotion is being experienced, since this immediately puts him in touch with his patient's unconscious mind. Such physiological signs of emotion as flushing of the cheeks, watering of the eyes, increased respiration and nervous body movements, indicate to the therapist that an emotion is being experienced and such signs can then be used to identify the memory of the experience responsible for them.

Induction of Hypnosis for Analytical Hypnotherapy

In order to uncover the critical experience(s) responsible for symptoms, it is necessary first of all to establish the unconscious communication which is the essence of hypnosis. Standard techniques of induction can, of course, be used, but it is well to remember that whenever there is an unconscious response to suggestion, there is already the unconscious attention necessary for the acceptance of further suggestions. The experienced analytical hypnotherapist will often move directly to uncovering as soon as he is aware that the unconscious attention he is seeking is present. Frequently, this may mean that an incisive uncovering technique is put into operation long before any of the generally accepted signs of hypnosis are seen to be present. In any case, such evidence of unconscious response as relaxation, eye closure, catalepsy or good visual imagery etc., is sufficient to indicate that an uncovering technique can be initiated.

Age Regression
Fundamental to all uncovering of forgotten memories is the notion that, in order to reach them, one must regress in time to the experience that has to be recalled. We have discussed, in chapter four, how we believe that all hypnosis is in fact regression at an unconscious level to the memory of a previous experience. However, there are certain popular techniques of uncovering which depend for their effectiveness on encouraging the patient to return to a previous experience with such vividness that it has the appearance of reality. Such techniques are termed *age regression* techniques.

Counting
An example of an age regression technique requires the patient, in hypnosis, to count backwards from his present age to a preselected age, responding meanwhile to the suggestion that at each number he will feel himself to be at the age that the number represents. When he is at the predetermined age, he is encouraged to experience everything that is going on at a specific time at that age. For example, should a birthday be selected, he will then be asked to be at his birthday celebrations and to describe them in detail. When the memory of this experience has been validated and it is clear that the patient is indeed uncovering the specific experience, he is then asked if the present problem exists at that time. If it does, then he is further regressed by counting backwards until a time is located when the current problem has not yet arisen. He is then brought forward in his memory to the time when something happens which initiates the problem and this event is explored in detail and subjected to the therapeutic process.

Pinpointing
Elman (1964) described a variant of the above method in which he would establish age regression to the first grade in school, following the cue of the clicking of his fingers, and once again would further regress or progress the patient in his memory until the time of the onset of the problem was located.

These approaches to the location of the critical experience(s) are direct and often highly effective, but require a level of hypnotic involvement which is not always easy to achieve. A significant proportion of patients are unable to respond to this technique and appear to be using a conscious effort at recall. Unconscious recall, on the other hand, is always apparently effortless, since whatever energy is involved in accomplishing the recall is also unconscious.

The Crystal Ball

Wolberg (1964) described the use of the Crystal Ball with patients who are able to remain in hypnosis with the eyes open. Such patients can be instructed to gaze into the crystal and see significant events in their lives which have contributed to the problem. A glass of water or a mirror reflecting a blank surface can be used equally well and in each case the objective is to encourage the patient to describe the critical experience(s) in detail so that it can be dealt with therapeutically. Although this procedure is clearly limited in its application, Erickson (1954) has advocated a variant of this procedure in which the crystal balls are hallucinated by the patient. In this case, each experience can be given a different hallucinated crystal ball. The need to open the eyes is thus obviated so that hypnosis runs less risk of being disturbed. De Shazer (1978) also reported the successful use of this technique.

Television or Movie Screen Imaging

A very similar technique which has found popularity with various hypnotherapists is the hallucination of the television or movie screen. Important episodes in the development of the symptoms can be reviewed as the subject sees himself on the screen in various situations during his life. This method has also the advantage of allowing the patient to remain dissociated from the memory and he is enabled to describe in a more detached manner than with direct age regression.

The disadvantage which occurs with the more direct method of age regressions is that it involves the subject in an exposure to the memory of what often proves to be an extremely disturbing experience, resulting in an abreaction with which he must deal. If he is able to deal with it satisfactorily, he will usually experience a relief of symptoms; on the other hand, he may not yet be ready to deal with it, and consequently will dispose of this reexperience, which causes intensely uncomfortable emotion, by repressing it once again — often beyond the reach of further therapeutic efforts. This repression will result in the persistence of or even an exacerbation of symptoms which may well prevent him from remaining in therapy.

Ideomotor Questioning

Most of the recent advances in analytical hypnotherapy can be directly attributed to the increased use of the ideomotor questioning techniques. These are to be described in greater detail in the following chapter since they provide the basis upon which the philosophy of analytical hypnotherapy is currently established, but they will be described here briefly. In this technique, unconscious signals of 'yes', 'no' and 'I don't want to answer' are established. As a result, a direct communication with the unconscious mind which is clear and unequivocal (a feature not always present in other uncovering techniques) is established. Much skill is required in the framing of suitable questions which can be answered with a yes or no, but all of the resources of the unconscious mind become readily accessible to this approach. More importantly, the degree of hypnotic involvement necessary for the effective performance of this technique is much less than that required for other hypnoanalytical uncovering techniques, and is consequently more likely to be successful with those subjects who would not be able to respond to other techniques.

To be maximally effective, every analytical hypnotherapist should become familiar with this ideomotor questioning technique. Its use in light hypnosis with minimal conscious/unconscious dissociation makes it possible to accomplish satisfactory hypnoanalysis in almost every case presenting for therapy. At one time, only the subject able to accomplish the significant conscious/unconscious dissociation normally recognised by the phenomena of medium or deep hypnosis could benefit from the available hypnoanalytical techniques, but the ideomotor questioning techniques require very little dissociation to be effective. These techniques are able to locate very deeply buried unconscious memories and resources, rendering them readily accessible to the hypnotherapist and his patient.

The Affect Bridge

Watkins (1971) gave the name *affect bridge* to a technique in which regression is accomplished by means of establishing a direct connection between the present, in which an uncomfortable emotion exists, and the earlier situation in which this same emotion was first experienced. In practice the hypnotherapist draws the patient's attention to the emotion that he is feeling or to the symptom that is present; such emotion is enhanced by increasing the focus of attention, and when sufficiently strong, the therapist is able to lead the patient back to its origin and effectively bridge him from the present to the past causative experience. In this manner the patient is encouraged to deal with the original experience which is really responsible for the current uncomfortable tensions. This technique requires some skill in dealing with the strong abreactions which so often ensue as a direct result of its employment.

The affect bridge is indirectly an important factor in many uncovering techniques and each of those so far described involves the use of emotion to track down the original experience responsible for it. In each case the therapist is seeking associations in the past for present uncomfortable feelings. For example, the technique of visualising episodes of one's life on a screen utilises the uncomfortable feeling existing in the present to locate the memory projected on that screen. Also, in using the ideomotor questioning techniques, an affect bridge is constantly being subtly employed to locate the origin of tensions which may be only partly perceived at a conscious level. The affect bridge technique illustrates very clearly how the hypnotherapist depends entirely upon the associative mechanisms of the mind in his task of uncovering the unconscious origins of problems. (See Fig. 10).

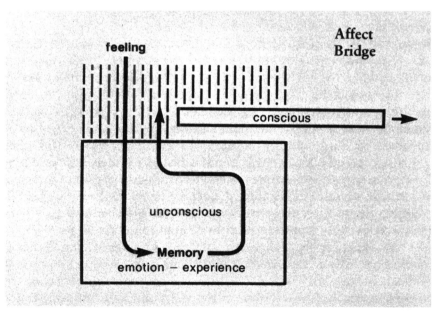

figure 10

Indirect Methods of Uncovering
Less direct methods of uncovering have also been developed by

analysts who have evolved special skills in their interpretation. Every analytical hypnotherapist should acquire these skills because they occasionally offer an alternative avenue of therapy when the direct methods have been rejected by the patient.

Dream Interpretation

Patients will frequently bring to the therapist a recurring dream which they find to be emotionally disturbing and which therefore has some unconscious significance in relationship to their problems. Freud (1938) explored the meaning of dreams and their interpretation as a means of uncovering the factors creating an emotional problem and such interpretation forms a large portion of any psychoanalyst's skill. But the analytical hypnotherapist does not require this skill because he can use the patient's more knowledgeable unconscious mind to provide an interpretation of the dream that it has produced. The patient is asked, in hypnosis, to review his dream in detail and then to spend time seeking an understanding of it. In many cases that understanding cannot be verbalised but it nevertheless leads to a change in the behaviour of the patient and a subsequent modification of symptoms.

Dream Induction

Because of the therapeutic effect that dreaming can initiate, the induction of dreams either during hypnosis or posthypnotically has been advocated and used with great effect. Wolberg (1964) recommended that the subject be first given the suggestion (in medium or deep hypnosis) that he will have a significant dream that night which he will remember and report at the next session. Such dreams can then be subjected to interpretation either in or out of hypnosis and often contribute greatly to an understanding of the underlying problem. Furthermore, patients can be trained to produce a dream in hypnosis which will have relevance to any problem being dealt with. This can prove to be an effective means of harnessing the resources of the unconscious mind in the resolution of emotional problems.

When assisting the patient to interpret his dream, the therapist should bear in mind that all the participants in that dream are likely to be facets of the patient himself and will reveal the complex feelings he has about himself in relation to the current situation. Sometimes, dreams of significance will occur during the therapeutic period, particularly on the night before a session. The opportunity should always be grasped to understand the meaning of such a dream since it usually indicates that some part of the patient's unconscious mind needs to communicate something of importance to the therapist. While dreams can be a useful adjunct to therapy, the analytical hypnotherapist should not rely upon them alone in order to help the patient resolve his problems because he has little control over the direction they will take.

Automatic Writing

Some therapists seem to experience considerable success in training subjects to write automatically (unconsciously). Automatic writing clearly requires significant conscious/unconscious dissociation and the writing hand must be beyond conscious control or awareness. In the use of this technique, unconscious information is communicated to the therapist without conscious knowledge. The usual method of accomplishing automatic writing is to provide the subject with writing materials and a writing board. The suggestion is given that the writing arm and hand are no longer under conscious control or awareness and that questions directed to the unconscious mind will be answered in writing by this hand. Meanwhile the conscious mind is instructed to be busy with other thoughts or to sleep. At times, important information can be gleaned by this method and the astute therapist is enabled to discover what the problem is and what the experience responsible for it is. Unfortunately, the writing may be cryptic and undecipherable except by the patient, who is then asked in hypnosis to examine and interpret it.

A variant of automatic writing requires that everything be done with hallucinated materials. The subject is instructed to imagine himself writing upon a notepad or a blackboard with the appropriate writing materials. He is also warned that he might not immediately understand what has been written but is encouraged to examine the writing until it becomes clear. Although this has the obvious disadvantage of leaving no record of the unconscious communication, it is as effective as other methods of automatic writing and is evidently more economical of time, materials and energy.

The Unconscious Body Image

Freytag (1961) postulated that the hallucinated unconscious body image is the picture that the individual forms of himself in his unconscious mind. Changes in the individual's perception of himself produce changes in the unconscious body image and therefore can be used as a barometer of psychic change and progress. Conversely, the induction of changes in the unconscious body image can therapeutically lead to psychic changes and improvements in the individual's attitudes toward himself.

Freytag suggested to the patient, in hypnosis, that he hallucinate a full length mirror and see his reflection in it. He was then asked to describe what he saw, and it was explained to him that this was merely a reflection of his body as it existed in space. He was then told that everyone has another picture of himself in his unconscious mind which symbolically expresses significant emotional problems and conflicts. This unconscious body image may be perceived as very different from the spatial body image. It may be nude or distorted in some way. On a signal, such as the word NOW, he was told that he would await passively for the spontaneous appearance of this unconscious body image and to describe objectively exactly what he saw.

It had been Freytag's experience that the unconscious body image usually revealed the area in which the emotional pathology was located. Therapy was directed at improving the unconscious body image until it more nearly represented the true mirror image. This was done by examining the attitudes responsible for the distorted body image and subjecting them to more mature present-day understanding.

Hypnoplasty and Hypnodrama

Meares (1957, 1960) has developed a technique during which a patient in hypnosis was encouraged to mould clay or plasticine to express his emotional conflicts, believing that this was an excellent method for dealing with the resistant patient. It was claimed that hypnoplasty enabled dissociated material to be tapped more effectively and that spontaneous regression and abreaction were intensified.

Hypnodrama involves the hypnotised patient being encouraged to play a role in a drama which parallels his own conflict. In such a manner, he is able to reenact his own inner conflicts and discover solutions to them. Both hypnoplasty and hypnodrama appear to demand special skills from the therapist; they may sometimes provide a successful approach to therapy when the more usual approaches have failed to treat concealed problems.

The Ideomotor Questioning Techniques in Analytical Hypnotherapy

The ideomotor questioning techniques are undoubtedly the uncovering techniques of choice. In the hands of the skilled analytical hypnotherapist, these techniques have the advantages of accuracy, versatility, and a simplicity unmatched by any other uncovering method. Furthermore, save for the use of a pendulum in one of these procedures, no additional equipment is required. With the use of these techniques, access to unconscious information (normally associated with age regression in deep hypnosis) is facilitated. This can be accomplished in relatively light hypnosis in which there is little conscious/unconscious dissociation.

Erickson (1961) first observed that certain patients, while explaining their problems, would unwittingly nod or shake their heads in contradiction to their actual verbalisations. He surmised that the head movement was an unconscious ideomotor response indicating unconscious communication. He utilised this observation as a basis for an induction technique particularly with resistant or difficult subjects. As a simple variation, he suggested that the levitation of one hand could signify *yes* and the levitation of the other, *no*. Hypnosis is present whenever this ideomotor activity occurs. Erickson also noted that when patients were asked to review past events, their recall was often accompanied by unconsciously produced ideomotor activity. James (1890) had earlier noted that 'every representation of a movement awakens in some degree the actual movement which is its object,' thereby recognising that ideomotor responses can be associated with unconscious memory. Erickson was more concerned with using ideomotor responses as an induction technique, although he recognised that different responses could be assigned different signals very readily. He also noted that the character of these responses was likely to be slow and deliberate when unconsciously generated.

LeCron (1954, 1968) favoured the use of Chevreul's pendulum to establish ideomotor signals in response to questions. Thus the responses *yes, no, I don't know* and *I don't want to answer* would be assigned to each of the four possible movements of the pendulum. In this manner, by judicious questioning, LeCron found that he could make excellent unconscious communication and thereby uncover relevant information quickly and easily. Later proponents of this method of uncovering have tended to eliminate the signal for *I don't know* since questions must be those for which the unconscious mind has an answer.

Cheek (1968) found that he could achieve identical results by assigning signals to individual fingers which would lift as an ideomotor response to questioning. This ideomotor finger questioning technique is probably the most widely used of the ideomotor techniques at present. In theory, almost any muscle of the body can be adapted to form an ideomotor questioning technique, but the hands and the head are normally used since, in the usual therapeutic encouter, they are the most readily observable parts of the patient's body.

Theoretical Considerations

As has already been stated, it is only through the observation of a response to suggestion that the unconscious communication of hypnosis can be recognised. Such a response may either be sensory or motor and since it is consequent upon an idea (or thought) evoked by the suggestion, it is termed an ideomotor or ideosensory response. Ideosensory responses cannot in themselves be observed although the patient is aware and able to comment upon them. Ideomotor responses, on the other hand, do not require any conscious intervention for them to be accessible to visual monitoring by the therapist.

It is probable that all suggestions elicit an idea, the content of which will depend upon the individual's previous experiences and his understanding of the given suggestion. For example, should the suggestion for lightness be given, the individual's idea of lightness will be unique to him and will be dependent upon his previous experiences associated with the word *lightness*. If the idea of lightness is sufficiently strong, it will evoke memories of lightness which are given substance by a recollection of the sensation of lightness. Again, if this sensation of lightness be sufficiently great, muscular movements associated with the lightness ensue, and an ideomotor response has been induced. This cycle of events can be interrupted by conscious intervention which is one of the factors modifying suggestibility. However, it is probable that once a suggestion is allowed past the conscious critical faculty to the stage where it can become an idea, the ideosensory or ideomotor response can then only be inhibited by unconscious processes which form the other factors modifying suggestibility.

Ideomotor Signals

An ideomotor signal is one that consistently expresses a simple idea when it is exhibited. Such a signal is said to be established if it occurs whenever the idea with which it is associated is present. The most useful ideas for which signals are usually established are simply those of *yes* and *no*. The beauty of the ideomotor signalling techniques is that they do little more than confirm the presence or absence of another idea by the answers *yes* or *no*, but with judicious questioning, they provide direct access to much information that is present in the unconscious mind if it agrees to allow an answer.

In ideomotor signalling, a question is presented which acts as a suggestion. This in turn produces an unconscious idea which, if it matches with a memory, gives a harmonious feeling of *yes*, which in turn produces the ideomotor signal of *yes*. On the other hand, if there is no memory that matches, there is disharmony and a feeling of *no* which results in the ideomotor signal of *no* to indicate a negative answer. In locating a memory which is presumed to be present, only the signal for *yes* is required which indicates that the memory has been located and matches with the description of it in the question. For example, the suggestion may be given the unconscious mind to orient back to the first memory that has anything to do with the onset of the present symptoms, and when it is there, to indicate by the *yes* signal. When the *yes* signal is received, the therapist knows that the memory has been located even though it still remains deeply unconscious. (see Fig. 11).

The ease with which ideomotor signals will allow access to a body of unconscious knowlege, memories and other resources which are not normally accessible to the conscious mind, confirms that the conscious mind is bypassed when using this technique. For example, a conscious answer to a question might well be *yes*, and yet be dramatically opposed by an equally emphatic *no* ideomotor signal. This polarity tends to support Janet's (1889) view that hypnosis is the result of dissociation in which communication is directly with the unconscious mind uninterrupted by the conscious mind. Nevertheless, there need be no other evidence of this dissociation for ideomotor questioning to be effective.

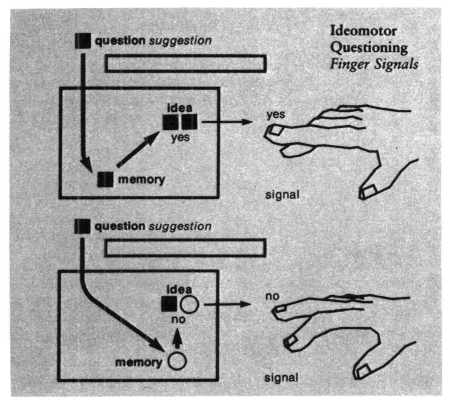

figure 11

The unconscious mind appears to find it much easier to indicate whether a specific idea, thought, or memory is present than to bring it to consciousness. This ready identification of a memory enables much effective therapy to take place. The locating of such a memory is the necessary first step in defining it, dealing with it, and perhaps eventually elevating it to consciousness. The ideomotor questioning technique is therefore the analytical hypnotherapist's most powerful tool in his task of uncovering. In skilled hands, it can justly be likened to the use of the surgeon's scalpel in his probing for the source of physical problems.

The prime indication for the use of the ideomotor questioning techniques in analytical hypnotherapy is to uncover the unconscious reasons for emotional and physical symptoms. The analytical hypnotherapist also uses these techniques to monitor any response to a suggestion that he has given in order to discover whether it has been accepted. Such unconscious responses as those to suggestions for healing, for the relief of pain, amnesia, and the resolution of conflicts can be monitored by the judicious use of ideomotor questioning.

Establishing Ideomotor Signals

Finger Signals   Since ideomotor finger signals are easier to recognise as being unconscious, we will first discuss the establishing of these signals. Every analytical hypnotherapist must learn how to establish, recognise and utilise these signals effectively if he is to gain the maximum benefit from the uncovering powers of hypnosis. There are many methods of establishing the finger signals. The objective is to impart the idea that a given finger will lift effortlessly (unconsciously) whenever the thought *yes* is present and, likewise, another will lift when a thought *no* is present. Similar signals can be developed for *I don't want to answer*, etc. The selection of the fingers can be made either by the patient or the therapist. (See Fig. 11).

The following verbalisation for establishing finger signals allows the patient unconsciously to make a choice of which fingers will respond. In this verbalisation, no formal induction of hypnosis has previously been undertaken, although we now know that as soon as any ideomotor response occurs, the unconscious communication we call hypnosis has already commenced.

Please make yourself comfortable with your hands resting in your lap (or on the arms of the chair — whichever appears to be most comfortable). I would like to show you how you can let your unconscious mind answer questions since your unconscious mind has information regarding your problem that your conscious mind does not have. You have probably noticed how people nod their heads when they agree with you — just as your head is nodding right now — and you have also noticed how they shake their heads when they disagree with you. They are usually unaware that their head is moving at all just as you were unaware that your head was moving until I drew your attention to it. These movements are entirely unconscious and involuntary and I would like to teach your unconscious mind how to answer questions by allowing one finger to float up for *yes* and another finger to float up for *no*. Which hand is your talking hand? *This is a reminder that the patient may already unconsciously use the hand to communicate when gesturing during conversation. If there is no selection of one hand rather than the other, then the dominant hand may be chosen.*

All right now, just close your eyes and listen very carefully to me and let your hands lie comfortably and relaxed. I want you to keep thinking, yes. . . yes. . . yes over and over again and, as you do so, one of the fingers on the talking (or dominant) hand will feel light and will lift — just let it lift. Each time you think *yes* that finger will get lighter and lighter and it will become so light that it will lift. Yes. . . yes. . . yes. . ., that's it. . . each 'yes' makes that finger lift a little higher until it lifts quite high. There. . . Your right index finger (or whichever lifts) is your *yes* finger. Now let it float down again. Good. Now begin to think no. . . no. . . no. . . over and over again and as you do so another finger on the same hand begins to feel light and will lift, just let it lift. . . No. . . no. . . no. . . that's right — just let it lift. . . Now your right middle finger (or whichever lifts) is your *no* finger.

Perhaps there will be some questions which your unconscious mind would prefer not to answer and would wish to indicate this. I would therefore like you to have an *I don't want to answer* finger. Just repeat to yourself over and over, I don't want to answer. . . I don't want to answer. . . and another finger or thumb on the same hand will lift. . . I don't want to answer. . . I don't want to answer. . . That's it. . . your right thumb (or whichever lifts) is your *I don't want to answer* finger.

I will be asking certain questions to which you may have a conscious answer but please let your unconscious mind do its own answering by lifting the yes finger for *yes* or the no finger for *no* and the I don't want to answer finger for *I don't want to answer*. Just let it happen and it will happen.

During this verbalisation, the appropriate fingers have usually been observed to begin to rise within about a minute. More or less persuasion may have to be given to different individuals with the more highly suggestible tending to respond quickly. The unconscious ideomotor response does not commence immediately following a question but only after a variable delay. An immediate response is almost always conscious and the patient should be exhorted to be patient and let it happen rather than forcing it to happen as he evidently is doing. The unconscious ideomotor response is usually a slow and tremulous one and may occur without the subject being aware of any movement; in fact, he may apologise for the absence of response when a good one has already occurred.

Sometimes there is an unduly long delay which tries the patience of both the therapist and the subject and, in spite of much encouragement, no response is seen to occur. In such cases it is appropriate for the therapist to assign signals to selected fingers and this will often meet with unconscious acceptance. The assignment of signals is also a rapid and effective way of establishing them when other hypnotic responses of an ideomotor nature have previously been obtained (as in a prior induction procedure).

It should be noted that each ideomotor response is in itself evidence of unconscious communication and must be regarded as part of the process of hypnosis. In the majority of cases, ideomotor finger responses are readily established, but we will later consider those cases in which signals are not readily established since these pose special problems in uncovering.

Chevreul's Pendulum   When a pendulum is held suspended from the hand, it can rarely be held motionless. Movements of the hand eventually become translated into a swinging movement of the pendulum. It has long been known that these movements can vary with questions or ideas in the mind of the person holding the pendulum. The movements are clearly ideomotor and provide an excellent medium for establishing ideomotor signals. A satisfactory pendulum for this purpose can be constructed from almost any object which can readily be suspended on about eight to ten inches of thread or string. (see Fig. 12).

In much the same manner as when using the fingers alone, a specific movement of the pendulum is designated a signal. There are four readily recognisable different movements of the pendulum which allow for up to four separate signals. They are: backwards and forwards, side to side, circular clockwise and circular anticlockwise. A simple verbalisation for establishing these signals could be as follows:

> I would like you to allow me to teach your unconscious mind how to signal answers to my questions by moving this pendulum in one direction for *yes* and in another direction for *no*. Simply allow your elbow to rest on this arm of the chair (or any accessible firm surface) and hold this pendulum so it hangs comfortably from your fingers. You do not need to make any conscious effort to move it. Now the pendulum can move freely in any direction. It can move in a circular motion either clockwise or anticlockwise, or it can move in a straight line either side to side, or backwards and forwards, in response to your thoughts. I want you first of all to commence to think yes. . . yes. . . yes. . . over and

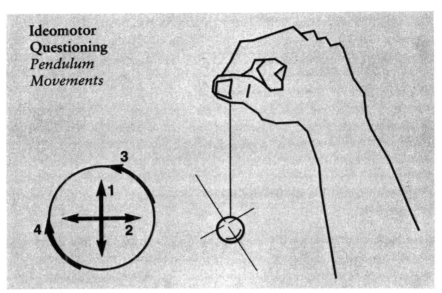

Ideomotor Questioning *Pendulum Movements*

figure 12

over to yourself and as you do so, the pendulum will begin to move in one of the four directions. Just let that happen. Yes. . . yes. . . yes. . . that's good. . . yes. . . yes. . . yes. . . It is now moving in a clockwise direction (or whatever) and as you keep thinking *yes* it moves even more strongly in that direction. That means that the clockwise motion (or whatever) is your unconscious mind's signal for *yes*.

I would now like you to stop thinking *yes* and start thinking *no*.

no. . . no. . . and as you do so, the movement of the pendulum changes and begins to move in a different direction. No. . . no. . . no. . . over and over again. . . that's good. . . no. . . no. . . no. . . There it is now swinging from side to side (or whatever). That is your unconscious mind's signal for *no*.

Perhaps your unconscious mind might not want to answer every question that is asked and would like to have a signal for I don't want to answer. . . I don't want to answer. . . There, the pendulum is now swinging back and forth (or whatever). That is your inner mind's signal for *I don't want to answer*.

At this point, the hypnotherapist is aware that excellent hypnotic communication has been established. The degree of dissociation is often parallel to the strength of the signal and there will probably be other signs of deep inner concentration with some evidence of withdrawal from the environment. This dissociation also denotes that unconscious attention is good and that the process of hypnosis is taking place. The eyes may or may not remain open depending upon the preference of the patient and/or the therapist.

As with the finger signals, the pendulum movements may not become apparent. Again, the assignment of signals to the different movements can be made by either the therapist or the patient. As with any other suggestion, the absence of response is often indicative of an unconscious resistance to the process of hypnosis. Fortunately only a small proportion of patients attending the hypnotherapist will fall into this category.

Head Signals Although unconscious movements of the head are already present as ideomotor signals for *yes* and *no*, and can readily be used when unconscious communication has been established, their common use as a *conscious* means of signalling *yes* and *no* render these movements readily susceptible to conscious influence and control. Although there is a characteristically delayed, slow and persevering feature about unconscious ideomotor responses, it is not always easy to determine whether such a response to a question is truly unconscious. Head signals in particular are readily obtainable since they are natural unconscious responses and have the added advantage of being rapidly established and of allowing easy observation of facial expressions during questioning. While they require a deeper level of hypnotic involvement than finger signals to be satisfactory, their use should always be considered with a patient whose unconscious attention appears to be good. A verbalisation might be as follows:

Please close your eyes, keep them closed and remain as comfortable as you can. That's good. I would like to talk to the back of your inner mind and I would like you to allow it to answer my questions by automatically nodding your head for *yes* or automatically shaking it for *no*. Please resist any temptation to move your head deliberately but when it wants to move on its own, please let it do so.

I would like you to imagine yourself in a place where you are doing something that you really enjoy doing. When you are there, your head will automatically nod for *yes* to let me know that you are there. When your head starts to nod, just let it. It will be your inner mind telling me that you are relaxing in a place where you like to be. And, as you relax in that place where you want to be, doing something that you enjoy, your deep inner mind will simply nod your head for *yes* to let me know. There. . . your head is beginning to nod. . . just let it. That's good. Please continue to enjoy that pleasant place and whatever it is that you are imagining yourself doing. I would like your deep inner mind to answer my questions by either nodding your head for *yes* or shaking it for *no*. If that would be all right with you, your head can once again nod for *yes*. If that is not O.K., then your head will automatically shake for *no*.

In many cases this approach is sufficient to secure adequate unconscious attention for spontaneous head movements to occur in response to questions. These may sometimes be very slight although definite, and are usually slow and persevering. Sometimes further suggestions for increased relaxation may be necessary before they will occur; if they do not occur, then other ideomotor techniques should be used. Other ideomotor techniques should also be resorted to if it seems clear that the head movements are consciously activated. When unconscious head movements do occur, hypnotic communication is always adequate. The use of imagery, initiated either by the therapist or by the patient (as above), encourages conscious relaxation so that these ideomotor movements can more readily be established unhampered by conscious interference.

Furthermore, head signals can be instituted (as can any ideomotor signalling) after unconscious communication has previously been established by some other hypnotic induction procedure. The one disadvantage of using head signals is that the subject has no signal to indicate that he does not want to answer, and so a failure to reply has to be interpreted as being *I don't want to answer*, even when answers have previously been given satisfactorily. With all ideomotor signalling, questions must always be clear and unambiguous and phrased in such a way that only a yes or a no is required to answer them satisfactorily. How, what and why questions cannot be used and will create only confusion. Anyone who has observed or has taken part in the game of 'Twenty Questions' knows that there is much information that can be gained from questions requiring only *yes* and *no* answers.

Ideosensory Questioning Techniques
There are some therapists (notably Bandler and Grinder, 1979) who

advocate the use of unconsciously produced physiological responses which may be ideosensory or ideovasomotor. Such physiological changes as flushing, tachycardia, or a feeling of warmth can be used to signal yes or no. For example, an increase in tension could be accepted for yes and a decrease for no. Hypnoanalytical techniques are applied in precisely the same way as when using the ideomotor signals. Bandler and Grinder believe that such unconsciously preferred signals are likely to be more effective than the constructed ideomotor signals similarly used to make unconscious communication.

Some Problems in the Performance and Interpretation of the Ideomotor Finger Signals

In a significant minority of cases, certain difficulties will be encountered in the performance and interpretation of ideomotor finger signals. Technically, it is easier to deal with signals that are restricted to one hand. Earlier methods which included the assignment of signals to both hands are best avoided by the analytical hypnotherapist for two reasons. First of all, it is easier to attend to one hand and avoid the effort of having to repeatedly glance from one hand to the other. Secondly, the free hand can give other signals should this become necessary. The author's preference is for the right hand, simply because this is usually the nearer and more easily observed. However, one must always be prepared to use either hand.

The strength of ideomotor signals bears a direct relationship to the subject's other hypnotic responses. A subject with clear ideomotor signals is very likely to exhibit other responses of the good hypnotic subject and conversely, the subject with poor ideomotor responses is also very likely to have other poor hypnotic responses. As with every general rule, there are notable exceptions, but the strength of ideomotor signals can give a rough estimate of hypnotisability.

Poor or Absent Finger Signals

Perhaps it is the difficulty of establishing satisfactory ideomotor finger signals in a significant minority of patients which has precluded the wider use of the ideomotor questioning techniques. In most of these cases, absent or poor finger responses, when the technique has been properly administered, is part of a general resistance to the hypnotic process. This resistance may be either conscious or unconscious. If it is conscious, it is most often due to a fear of yielding control, whereas unconscious resistance is usually due to a fear of disclosure. Ideomotor questioning is more likely to be satisfactorily established when such fears have been adequately dealt with in the preinduction period, as recommended in Chapter Four.

Absent Signals A small proportion of subjects, even after every encouragement and reassurance have been given, still do not develop any ideomotor finger signals. Such movements as do occur are obviously voluntary and have none of the characteristic tremor and hesitancy of the involuntary responses. In these cases certain manoeuvres may succeed in initiating an involuntary response. Raising a finger while instructing the patient to think yes and nod his head for yes may succeed in encouraging the finger to remain suspended involuntarily as an ideomotor signal for yes. If successful, the procedure is repeated with another finger while the patient is shaking his head for no and thinking no. Again, this finger should remain suspended in a cataleptic fashion.

Should this approach fail, persistent conscious resistance may be the cause and may be overcome by seeking conscious involvement in the responses. The subject should be asked to sense which finger feels different when he thinks yes and consciously to lift that finger as soon as he experiences the yes feeling. If successful, this procedure is repeated for the other signals of no, and I don't want to answer. During subsequent questioning, the patient should be encouraged to lift consciously whatever finger feels that it wants to lift in response to the questions. Sometimes this begins to occur without conscious effort as the hypnotic process becomes more securely established.

Since some subjects appear to have a poor unconscious kinesthetic sense, another effective way of establishing signals is to ask the subject to visualise a blackboard on which the words yes or no appear prominently. He is then exposed to simple questions and asked to raise the yes finger consciously whenever the yes reappears on his mental blackboard and the no finger whenever the no appears. Once again, good signals will sometimes become unconsciously established. In other cases, simple verbal reporting of the answers appearing on the blackboard will render these ideosensory signals effective.

Poor Signals Signals may be established but remain poor, being small in amplitude with the finger scarcely lifting from the arm of the chair, and also so much delayed that there is a long interval between question and answer. This makes it very arduous for the therapist to observe and detect them. For delayed movements, nothing but patience on the part of the therapist will suffice, coupled with reassurance to the patient that things are progressing satisfactorily.

Improved recognition of the very small movements may be accomplished in a variety of ways. One method which is frequently effective is to allow the signalling hand to hang loosely over the end of the arm of the chair and to observe the movements of the tips of the fingers either from the side or from above. Very slight movements of the finger tips can readily be detected in this manner. Similarly, placing the elbow on the arm of the chair and the forearm in a vertical position so that the hand hangs comfortably in an almost horizontal position, is another means of rendering slight movements more readily detectable. In this context, it is the author's experience that very slight movements of the signalling fingers are as important analytically as larger movements and should be attributed their full significance.

Sometimes, a slight ideomotor response produces contraction of the appropriate extensor muscles of the fingers, and although this may be insufficient to produce visible movement of the fingers, the appropriate extensor tendon can be seen to contract and this contraction provides an adequate visible ideomotor signal. Gentle palpation of the tendons will sometimes provide an adequate tactile signal for monitoring of the ideomotor responses. Any method which enables the therapist to recognise even the slightest unconscious response is of value and should be used. Occasionally these slight responses can be increased by a conscious rehearsing of the respective movement in response to commands for yes and no and the unconscious signals then become sufficiently strong to make communication easy.

Fading Signals
Sometimes, ideomotor finger signals which initially seem to be satisfactory, fade and eventually disappear altogether, and there is no further response to questioning. This is always an indication of unconscious resistance to the uncovering process. Further inquiry indicates that questioning has given rise to unconscious anxiety concerning the material that has been, or is likely to be, revealed. While reassurance may be effective in reestablishing communication, experience has shown that these patients often discontinue therapy because they are aware of an unconscious reluctance to cooperate and consequently become uncomfortable with therapy.

Confusing Finger Signals
A sure sign of resistance at an unconscious level is evident when more

than one finger lifts in response to questions. Occasionally this may merely indicate that the question is ambiguous and cannot be answered with a simple yes or no and rephrasing of the question may meet with a satisfactory response. If it does not, this is clearly an unconscious attempt to conceal the answer without apparently withdrawing cooperation. Whenever this attempt to confuse by the presentation of more than one signal persists, it is probable that the first signal presented is the more meaningful one. It can be assumed that the presence of one signal, immediately followed by the opposite one, is indicative of the presence of two directly opposed unconscious opinions seeking expression. It is in such cases that the separation of these opposing viewpoints on separate hands can be of great value.

The Other Hand Signals

A fascinating observation is the occasional spontaneous emergence of signals on the hand for which they had not initially been established. One should always watch the other hand for the appearance of these spontaneous signals during ideomotor questioning. This is now the main rationale for confining the original signals to one hand in order to leave the other hand available for further information.

Signals may appear in the other hand in the absence of responses in the originally designated hand. They may also appear simultaneously and either confirm or contradict them. In the author's experience, the meaning of the signals is usually the same in both hands; if the right index finger has been designated as yes and the left index finger lifts, it also signifies yes. These other hand signals are usually deeply unconscious and may occur without any conscious awareness whatever. The wise therapist will note them without informing his patient of their presence until he has had an opportunity to assess them. These signals lead to the assumption that a different part of the unconscious mind is seeking communication with the therapist by means of that hand and may wish to do so without informing any other part of the patient's mind of its intentions.

This phenomenon has resulted in the construction of a specific technique designed to accomodate the expression of a different viewpoint coexisting in the unconscious mind. This technique is of value when, as noted in the previous section, conflicting signals are seen. In such cases the other hand is stroked and the suggestion is given that a deeper part of the mind would like to answer questions by using the other hand. These new signals are sometimes more clear and distinct than the original ones, even when the original signals have become faded or confused.

Change of Signal
Generally speaking, signals once established tend to remain stable and unaltered. On occasion, however, confusion arises because signals have become transposed and the original yes signal has become the no signal and vice versa. So, whenever answers begin to make no sense, the signals should be rechecked to see if their original meaning has been altered. Should any considerable interval occur between sessions, or from the last period of questioning, it is always possible that a change in signals has occurred and it is wise to make the occasional check simply by asking the unconscious mind to raise the yes finger, etc. A change of signals can be a sign of resistance, but in most cases analysis proceeds normally and uninterruptedly once normal communication is reestablished.

Finger Pressure
Sometimes, a finger bearing a signal may be noticed to be pressing down rather than lifting in response to a question. This must definitely be interpreted as a strong resistance to disclosure and the therapist must treat cautiously. It is as if one part is attempting to silence another and this is a clear sign of great conflict about therapy. Cheek (1981) believes that finger pressure may be a *yes, but* response requesting further information before replying.

Significance of Ideomotor Finger Responses
The unconscious signalling of the ideomotor questioning technique seems to be controlled by unconscious ego states. It is likely that the Adult ego state is the usual conscious ego state although it has many unconscious resources which are available for therapy. During therapy, the conscious part of the Adult is required to become relatively inactive, and it is probable that the ideomotor responses emanate from the more deeply unconscious ego states of the Parent and the Child.

Clinically, it would appear that the more authoritarian Parent usually takes control of the finger signals and is the ego state responsible for unconscious resistance. When there are confusing signals or the appearance of signals on the other hand, it is likely that the more deeply unconscious Child ego state is striving to communicate and to escape the control of the Parent ego state. It is in such cases that the

Child/Parent conflict becomes very apparent and the issues over which there is great unconscious disagreement between them (probably responsible for the presenting symptoms) become identifiable.

If this supposition is correct, then hypnosis is really a process of communication with unconscious ego states, with deeper hypnosis being the communication with the more deeply unconscious Child ego state to the varying exclusion of the more conscious ego state of the Adult. This would account for the posthypnotic amnesia experienced by the more conscious Adult which may have been excluded from the communication with the deeply unconscious ego states during hypnosis. (see Fig. 13).

Repeated reference has been made to unconscious resistance in this chapter. This resistance should always be accepted as part of the individual's survival mechanism and therapy, if it is to be successful, must always take it into account. If a resistant ego state (usually the Parent) can be identified, and the reason for its resistance to therapy understood, it is possible that the therapist might be able to convert it into an ally in therapy rather than the foe it would otherwise remain, ready to destroy any attempt at successful therapy.

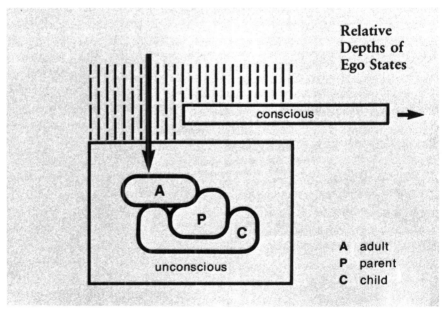

figure 13

Practice

PART TWO

An Analytical Procedure

Ellenberger (1966) conceived of illness as resulting from unexpressed secret ideas; illness, he maintained, is cured through the expression of such ideas. As he acknowledged, this concept was first formulated by de Puysegar and was extensively relied upon by the Viennese physician, Moritz Benedict. Analytical hypnotherapy appreciates this concept of illness, since the uncovering of the sources of emotional problems is the logical basis of any analytical procedure. However, as Schilder and Kanders (1927), and Freud before them, pointed out, knowledge of the historical roots of the disorder is in itself insufficient for cure. Only by strictly adhering to the principles of analytical hypnotherapy as described in Chapter Six will a significant majority of patients achieve successful recovery from symptoms.

The procedure to be described is one currently in use by the author. In this procedure, all of the principles underlying good analytical hypnotherapy are employed. It will be understood that any analytical hypnotherapist will formulate a procedure which will more nearly suit his own personality. He can be assured of success so long as the principles of analytical hypnotherapy are adhered to.

The first step prior to commencing analysis is to establish ideomotor signals. The therapist can proceed when he is certain that these are functioning as satisfactorily as he can encourage them to be. The sequence of questions that follows is one that the author has found to be effective for him, but they should not be imitated without due regard for the therapist's own personality and the patient's needs.

First Principle
Identification of the Critical Experience
Does your unconscious mind really want me to help?   This opening question gives the therapist the opportunity to observe the kinds of

signals which are being given, and also to determine whether good unconscious communication has indeed been established. Where the signal is in the affirmative and is a good one, therapy is evidently off to a good start. This can be a good time to establish, should there be any doubt, whether the responses are truly unconscious simply by asking, *Did that answer come from your deep unconscious mind?* If the answer is no, then ask the patient to allow his unconscious mind to answer and then repeat the question, *Does your unconscious mind really want me to help?* Where the signal is uncertain, there is likely to be some unconscious resistance to therapy and the therapist should be aware of this. Should the answer to this question be negative, there is present a great deal of unconscious resistance to uncovering which may render therapy impossible unless it is effectively utilised.

At this juncture, if there is evidence of unconscious resistance to therapy, there are two courses of action open to the therapist. First, he should make it clear to the patient that he cannot help him without his unconscious cooperation and that he can make him do nothing against his will. This may have the desired effect of reducing unconscious resistance resulting from a fear of being controlled or directed. An affirmative response may now be obtained to this first question. Alternatively, the therapist can ask the unconscious mind if there is a part that does want the therapist to help. If there is, it should indicate this by raising the yes finger on one or other hand, thus giving the opportunity to a cooperative part to disclose itself. If there is a part seeking help, that part which is rejecting help needs to be dealt with by asking if it will allow help to be given. This recognition by the therapist of the power of the unconscious part to sabotage therapy may appease it and allow therapy to proceed. In any case, the therapist must proceed with care, knowing that there is some unconscious opposition to therapy, and recognising that he is essentially powerless in the absence of unconscious cooperation. He should admit this both to himself and his patient in order for the expectations of therapy to remain realistic. Let us suppose that the unconscious permission for therapy to proceed has been gained and the therapeutic procedure can continue.

Does your unconscious mind agree to cooperate with me? This second question emphasises the essentially cooperative nature of analytical hypnotherapy and, if the answer to it is yes, there is then a far greater chance of success. If there is a negative response to this question – particularly when a desire for help has been expressed –

then it should once again be emphasised that therapy cannot proceed without cooperation, however limited; if this cooperation is not forthcoming, therapy will have to be abandoned. Fortunately, this abandonment is rarely necessary, for once again, the expression of the therapist's dependence upon the unconscious mind's assistance may be enough to enlist it. With each of these questions, the therapist remains alert to any conscious interference with the ideomotor responses and, if any is detected, the patient is exhorted to allow things to happen without interference.

Would it be all right for your unconscious mind to look at unconscious memories which are beyond your conscious memory? It is always to be hoped that this question is answered with a yes, since this lies at the heart of the use of hypnosis in therapy. If there is a no, the question should be modified by asking if it would be all right to look at *some* unconscious memories. Frequently the resistance is to the uncovering of *certain* secrets, although there may be an agreement to look at other unconscious memories. Later, there may well be a change of heart about dealing with the secret memories responsible for symptoms. Having arrived at this stage and having been assured that the ideomotor signals are being entirely unconsciously activated, the therapist can proceed with the analysis proper.

Please orient your inner mind back to the first experience which has anything to do with your present tensions and when you are there your yes finger will lift to let me know. This is the first direction for uncovering. In those cases where cooperation has been established, there will eventually be an appropriate response and the yes finger will lift. The directions should always be repeated at least once so that there is no misunderstanding as to what is being requested of the unconscious mind. When the yes finger lifts, we know that a critical experience has been located. Occasionally this may be accompanied by evidences of an emotional response, but generally, the patient is not aware of anything unusual.

Please review that experience in detail at an unconscious level and when the review is completed, the yes finger can lift to let me know (or the yes finger can be asked to fall back as a signal if it remains raised following the previous direction). The first detailed unconscious review of the critical experience has now taken place and there may or may not be any awareness of what has been reviewed. If the responses remain strong, the therapist knows that there is still good unconscious cooperation and communication, and the next series of steps in this procedure is directed at defining the emotional characteristics of the critical experience. It is important to note that each time a question is posed about this experience, a further review and reassessment of it is being made unconsciously.

Is that experience one that is scary or frightening? This is the first in a series of questions designed to delineate the emotional characteristics of the critical experience. Other similar questions follow which ask about sadness (hurt), anger (or resentment) and guilt (or shame or embarrassment). These are usually readily answered by a yes or a no signal. The answers may be accompanied by some visible expression of the emotion that is being recalled and the patient can be encouraged to allow himself to feel any or all of the emotion thus revealed. If he is indeed able at this stage to allow himself to feel this previously repressed emotion in an abreactive manner, he is already accepting this emotion as proper. This emotional response is an excellent prognostic sign and indicates an early reduction of the Parent/Child conflict because the Parent is permitting the Child to express a previously forbidden feeling. A simple but useful mnemonic device to enable the therapist to remember to ask about each important primary emotion is SHAG: Scary, Hurtful, Angry, Guilty.

Is there anything sexual about this experience? Since a very high proportion of problems are found to be due to guilt feelings arising from a sexual experience, it saves a great deal of time to ask this question at the outset. An acknowledgement of guilt about a sexual experience often enables the patient to begin to deal with it.

The critical experience has now been defined as far as its important emotional content is concerned and at the same time the chronology of the experience should be determined in order further to delineate and distinguish it from other similar experiences.

Timing of the Critical Experience
A series of questions is now directed to determine the age of the patient at the time when the critical experience occurred. There are many ways of doing this, but a satisfactory one is to ask initially about successive five year periods as follows: *Did this experience occur at the age of five years or younger? Did this experience occur at the age of ten years or younger?* When a yes is received, questions are then directed

at each specific year, e.g., *Are you six years of age at the time of this experience? Are you seven years of age?*, etc., until a yes defines the year. At this point, the therapist is able to label the critical experience by the year of age in which it occurred; this is the site of the Child/Parent conflict responsible for symptoms. It is the ego state complex formed by this conflict which now needs to be examined. Only then can the decisions made at that time, which are responsible for the symptoms, be dealt with and resolved.

It is at this juncture that the critical experience is ready to be dealt with more directly. Unconscious permission is required if this is to be done at a more conscious level; otherwise all succeeding therapy with this experience must take place only at an unconscious level. Therapy at a *conscious* level may be more effective, and has the advantage of giving the therapist a clear understanding of the factors involved in the development of the problem, but it must be emphatically stated here that much excellent analytical hypnotherapy can take place at a deeply unconscious level without any awareness by the therapist or the patient of the precise nature of the critical experience to be dealt with.

Would it be all right for John to know about this experience up here in 1981? If so, the yes finger will lift, to let me know. If not, the no finger will lift. If there is a negative response to this question, the therapist must respect the patient's wish to keep this information unconscious. In fact, the therapist has no alternative but to accept any decision made by the unconscious mind regarding the revelation of information. The therapist can indicate his support of the unconscious wish of the patient to retain information, and in so doing will inevitably increase his rapport with the patient. If, on the other hand, there is a yes response to this question, the therapist can then ask the unconscious mind to bring the experience to a level where the conscious mind can know about it and to indicate when this has been accomplished by raising the yes finger.

Would it be all right for John to feel all of the feelings of this experience? A no to this question must be treated with respect because the unconscious mind, in this instance, feels a need to protect the psyche from the intense feelings that have been repressed. Later, during the analytical procedure, these feelings may be allowed into awareness and this will be readily observable by the therapist.

In the event of a yes answer to this question, the next step is to ask the unconscious mind to bring these feelings forward to a level where they can be felt and, when each has been fully experienced, to indicate this by a yes signal. At this time, there may be a significant and therapeutic abreaction.

Would it be all right for you to talk to me about this experience? This question seeks permission for ventilation of the whole experience, and there may be an understandable reluctance on the part of the patient to do this. This reluctance must be respected; in fact, it is a good idea to remind him that he does not have to talk about anything that he does not wish to. If he indicated that it is all right for him to talk about the experience, he is then requested to be in that experience as fully as possible; that is, to feel, see and hear everything that is part of the experience to be described so that he may discuss it in detail. He should be encouraged to be present in the experience using the present tense because at such times many patients will regress fully to the experience. In any case the recall of the experience is usually detailed and the emotions evoked intense. The therapist who has reached the unconscious level by this prescribed route need not fear these intense emotions; they are being expressed with the permission of the patient's own unconscious mind.

If the patient chooses not to talk about the experience, it must then be dealt with at a nonverbal level, being labelled according to the age at which it occurred (e.g., *the experience of four year old John*). Regardless of whether it can be verbalised, care must be taken to ensure that all of the relevant material is being dealt with. Such questions as *Does forty year old John now know all that needs to be known in order to understand the experience of four year old John?* should be asked in order to ascertain whether any relevant material has been omitted. If the experience is verbalised, it is an easy matter to enquire, *Is there anything more that we need to know in order to understand?* The identification of the critical experience has now been completed and yet therapy has barely begun.

Principle Two
Understanding the Repressed Emotion(s) and the Associated Feeling of Guilt
In this second phase of analysis, the understanding of the Adult ego state is directly applied to the Child/Parent conflict manifested in the critical experience as it has been revealed so far. Sometimes this may have already been accomplished and this accounts for the occasional successes achieved with only identification of the critical experience.

...u uke you to give all of your forty (present age) *years of wisdom and understanding to four year old John* (labelled critical experience) *and when this has been done the yes finger will lift.* This occurs after a varying interval to indicate that the resources of the Adult have at last been brought to bear upon the critical experience that has been located. If a no is signalled, this can only mean that the four year old ego state complex at the critical experience is refusing assistance. The question, *Do you really want me to help?* should be repeated in the hope of achieving cooperation. Occasionally a no means that there is insufficient information for full understanding to be applied to the critical experience. The question, *Is there more information that needs to be divulged before full understanding can be attained?* needs to be asked. If so, this information should be imparted to the forty year old John (Adult) by the four year old John (Child/Parent) ego complex, and this can be done at an entirely unconscious level with the ideomotor signals as the only evidence that this has been accomplished.

It is the objective of this stage that the Adult persuade the Parent of the Child's essential innocence and of his fundamental right to his feelings. The Adult's understanding is simultaneously applied to the Child so that this ego state can now appreciate that its uncomfortable feelings, though no longer requiring to be repressed, neither require to be retained, since the event originally responsible for these feelings has long been concluded. The achievement of both these objectives must await the confirmation of further analytical procedures.

Principle Three
Recognition of the Current Irrelevance of the Previously Repressed Emotion
Four year old John (referring here to the original critical experience) *with the wisdom and understanding that you now have, do you still need to keep those old tensions?* At this point the specific emotions identified as being repressed can be enumerated individually. If the answer to this question is a no, the therapist can immediately proceed to the next principle. A significant proportion of cases answer yes to this question, which means that the ego state complex of the critical experience persists and our four year old John is not yet convinced that his tensions are irrelevant. Retention of tensions and uncomfortable feelings are not as accidental as we are sometimes led to believe. The functions of retained uncomfortable feelings are purposeful, being either protective or punitive. If they are retained for protective

reasons, it is because the Child part of the Child/Parent complex of our four year old John is not convinced that the forty year old Adult can be trusted to take care of him and therefore he must protect himself. This lack of trust may be the result of a continued internal dialogue between the Child and the Parent. On the other hand, uncomfortable feelings are often retained for punitive reasons by the Parent to keep the Child repressed. Until the Child is convinced that the Adult is able fully to take care of him with the aid of the Parent, or until the Parent is convinced that there is no longer any need to repress the Child with punitive discomfort, the need to retain old tensions remains. The reasons for retaining discomfort need to be understood and the following questions are directed to this end.

Are you keeping those old out of date uncomfortable feelings for protection? A yes answer to this question means that the therapist must renew his efforts to persuade the Adult of forty year old John to convince four year old John that he (forty year old John) is now able to protect himself and he needs no further protection from four year old John's outdated feelings. Four year old John needs to be reassured that forty year old John has ready access to his own protective emotions should the need arise. If necessary, four year old John can be asked to hand over all of his outdated, uncomfortable feelings and responsibilities to forty year old John who is now quite capable of protecting every part of the personality complex. If forty year old John has been sufficiently convincing, the question as to whether these old tensions are necessary should now receive a no response. This procedure may have to be repeated before this reply is attained. Sometimes four year old John remains convinced that he must retain his old protective emotions for one reason or another. He should then be asked, *Do you need to keep these uncomfortable feelings all of the time?* A no to this question should be followed by a direction to four year old John to be certain of the kind of circumstances when he feels that he needs all of his uncomfortable tensions and confirm this fact with ideomotor signals. He is then asked to be equally certain of those circumstances where the uncomfortable feelings are not necessary and be persuaded to discover means of relinquishing these feelings at such times. This manoeuvre does not abolish symptoms but it does establish considerable control over them.

Are you keeping these tensions to punish yourself with? A more difficult situation arises when old tensions are deemed to be necessary not for protective reasons but for self-punitive reasons. When the Parent remains convinced that it is still its duty to punish the Child (in spite of the intervention of the Adult), a renewal of this intervention is called for. The objective is to convince the Parent that the Child did not do anything that could be regarded as bad, even though it may have originally merited parental disapproval, and the punishment so far meted out by the Parent should now be regarded as having been more than adequate. To aid the Parent, the therapist can make such statements as the following: *I know that you have done a great job in disciplining four year old John and have done so to the best of your ability, but the time has now come for you to forgive him. I believe that you can do this if forty year old John will make sure that all will go well and if four year old John can assure you that he really did not mean to create so much distress by his behaviour.* In this way the Parent is given a means of relinquishing the arduous responsibility of maintaining a punitive stance toward the Child and can then be encouraged to take care of four year old John in other more appropriate, protective, nurturing and loving, parental ways.

The punitive Parent who resists Adult intervention is the most difficult therapeutic problem that the analytical hypnotherapist is likely to meet. His ingenuity in finding means of persuading the Parent to forgive the Child will be tried to the utmost if the patient remains in therapy. But in most of these cases, therapy is unilaterally terminated by the patient who, at a conscious level, is only aware that therapy is creating intense discomfort within him. A great deal of persuasion, then, will be necessary before a strong Parent ego state will relinquish the role of the disciplinarian, a role which so often characterises the Parent in these persistent Child/Parent conflicts. The Parent will sometimes refuse to give up this punitive role and so the Child/Parent conflict continues unresolved. However, if the Parent is persuaded, a no is finally received to the question as to whether the punishment in the form of the retained tensions is any longer necessary.

Principle Four
Relinquishing the Repressed and Repressing Emotions
While the Parent ego state has agreed to stop punishing the Child (and the Child has recognised that the old outdated feelings need no longer be retained), it must nevertheless be empowered to discover means of relinquishing its repressing activity. It may need to obtain permission from other parts of the personality to accomplish this; it also needs to find improved ways of relating internally with the Child. All of these

new behaviours must be discovered if the Child/Parent conflict is to come to an end. The Adult ego state is that part of the individual's personality with the resources and the communications within the personality to accomplish this task. With ideomotor questioning, it is easy to switch from addressing the unconscious Adult to communicating with the Child/Parent ego state complex simply by labelling them by their respective ages.

Four year old John has agreed that these old tensions are no longer necessary. Forty year old John, using all of your wisdom and understanding, I would like you to find a way for four year old John to let go of all of these unnecessary, outdated, useless old tensions. When this has been accomplished, the yes finger can lift to let me know. Fortunately, this stage is usually accomplished readily, even though it may take some time for the unconscious mind to find an appropriate solution. It is wise to assure the patient that the solution need not be known at a conscious level. In some cases, no solution is found and this is invariably because a strong Parent has decided to retain a punitive position.

Principle Five
Recognition of the Resolution of the Child/Parent Conflict
At this stage, a solution to the conflict between the Child and the Parent has been found but not yet applied. It is now necessary to apply this solution to see if it is acceptable to all parts of the personality.

Four year old John, forty year old John has now found a means by which you can let go of all of the old, out of date, unnecessary tensions that you have been keeping. Please use that way right now and let go of all of those tensions. When you have done so, let me know by raising the yes finger. In most cases the yes finger is promptly raised and the therapist knows that the conflict is probably at an end. Nevertheless, he should then confirm that the tensions have been relinquished by saying, *If you have really let go of all of the old tensions, John, you should now be feeling very comfortable inside, more comfortable than you have felt for thirty-six years. If you are really very comfortable, the yes finger will lift again.*

An even better confirmation of this relief from tension comes if there is a spontaneous smile. A simple confirmation of this inner comfort is the *smile test*, in which the previously distressed ego state complex is asked to indicate its relief by smiling, as follows: *Four year old John, if you are really feeling comfortable, you can give me a nice smile to let me know.* The presence of a really happy smile is excellent proof of total relief from the original tension. Conversely, any difficulty in giving that smile will alert the therapist to the probability that some old tension remains. In such cases, appropriate questioning usually indicates that a strong Parent is having difficulty in relinquishing its accustomed disciplinary and punitive role. Should this be the case, steps must be retraced back to Principle One to seek any aspects of the critical experience that have escaped Adult attention. Then, proceed to Principle Two to reapply Adult understanding and discover if the Parent can be persuaded that the time has now come for complete pardoning of the Child, and that there are other more rewarding tasks for it to undertake in the interests of the whole personality. If, at this stage, Parental forgiveness is forthcoming, the remaining Principles can be applied in fairly quick succession.

Principle Six
Rehabilitation
Although we have reached this final stage with confirmation that old and outdated tensions have now been relinquished in at least one critical experience, there are usually others that need to be dealt with similarly. This can readily be accomplished by asking the patient to examine memories before and after this particular experience already dealt with to see if there are any others which are the source of old tensions. If so, they are subjected to the same procedure.

It is not sufficient for complete therapy merely to deal with old tensions, because eradicating these tensions does not give the patient the means whereby he can properly manage his life. Inevitably, the previous tensions and the symptoms which they have produced have had many effects upon the patient's environment and the people who inhabit it. Without his symptoms, the patient's environment must certainly change and he needs to know how to deal with these changes. While he will have eliminated the disadvantages that his symptoms caused, there will also be a loss of some of the advantages, those secondary gains of which he may have been only dimly aware. He needs to learn how to retain these advantages without having to return to his symptoms for assistance, and a program of rehabilitation in which he learns to do so must be instituted. This rehabilitation programme has an importance that must not be underestimated if patients are to remain symptom-free. This phase comprises ego strengthening and assertiveness training, to be described in greater detail in Chapter

Fourteen, which are essential if the patient is not to return to his old symptomatology for the secondary gains that he needs.

When this stage is reached, there are other ways in which the therapist makes certain that no other sources of unconscious tension remain. In order to discover whether other critical experiences still remain to be dealt with, the following question should be asked: *Is there any other part of John who is not feeling O.K.?*, and *Is there any other experience which is still creating uncomfortable feelings?*

If either of these questions is answered by yes, then the previous procedures are repeated to locate and deal with any critical experience(s). If a no is received, then this indicates that all is well and every part of John is now feeling O.K. Nevertheless, a further check is prudent in order to make absolutely certain of this. For example, it can be stated: *If every part of John is feeling good, then every part is smiling inside. If that is so, then give me a big smile and raise the yes finger.* This smile test, if negative, will often indicate an uncomfortable ego state complex still concealed at the site of a persistent Child/Parent conflict. If the smile test is positive, the rehabilitation procedures designed to establish and reinforce ego strength and assertiveness are proceeded with.

Some or all of these analytical procedures may be accomplished at a single session, since many of the difficulties here dealt with at length occur infrequently in practice. As a rule, several sessions are required before all of the critical experiences are located and the associated tensions responsible for symptoms resolved, and it is always advisable to review the progress made in previous sessions before commencing therapy. This can be accomplished simply by asking the subject to *Please review in detail everything that we talked about at our last meeting. This can be done simply and rapidly by your unconscious mind without any conscious effort. When it has been accomplished, your yes finger will lift to let us know.* When the finger lifts, say: *If any of those experiences that you have reviewed are still causing uncomfortable tensions, your yes finger will lift; if not, your no finger will lift.* If there is any indication that a critical experience previously examined is still responsible for unconscious tension, it must be dealt with precisely as before. In such cases there has been some guilt retained and further efforts need to be made to persuade the reluctant Parent to relinquish its punitive role.

Here follows a transcript of an initial session with a patient, a woman of twenty-eight whom we will call Vera. She is suffering from attacks of acute anxiety which tend to occur whenever she is away from home. She recalled that five years ago, at the birth of her son, she had a great fear of dying, and whenever she thought about dying she would panic. This fear abated for about three years. Then two years ago, prior to therapy, the anxiety returned and although it was no longer associated with thoughts of dying, it would occur in crowds, when visiting friends, or in strange places. Her symptoms were typical in that she suffered from tightness in the chest, feelings of faintness, loss of control, and difficulty in breathing. These attacks were always followed by headaches.

The first part of the interview was taken up with listening to a recital of the symptoms and then discussing how hypnotherapy could help. At first her anxiety prevented her from accepting any suggestions, but when she was assured that she had full control over her responses, she relaxed and entered hypnosis successfully. At the commencement of this excerpt, Vera has already been able to experience good imagery of being by a lake and feeling relaxed.

DR I am going to ask you to let your head listen to me and to let it answer my questions by nodding for yes or shaking for no. Let it do this automatically. Don't even try to control it. Let whatever happens happen. If that's okay say yes.

It was felt that she was sufficiently involved in the hypnotic process to use head signals and this saved the time that would otherwise be spent in establishing other signals. Her agreement to let this happen also speeded the process.

PT Yes.

DR Now I am going to ask your deep inner mind a question. You may not be aware of how your head moves in response but it doesn't matter because you can enjoy that place by the water and you don't need to pay any attention to me. Your deep inner mind is listening all of the time. I am going to ask your deep inner mind this question: do you really want me to help you? If you do, your head will automatically nod for yes. *Head nods.*

The first question has been asked in such a way as to promote unconscious/conscious dissociation, stressing that she may not be aware of her head movements because of involvement with her imagery. Further, it is suggested that she need not consciously listen which probably increases her dissociation.

Do you think, in the back of your mind, that you really want to cooperate with me? *Head nods.* Listen to me very carefully, and when you are listening to me very very carefully, your head will automatically nod yes. *Head nods.* Now, would it be all right to look at experiences which are beyond your conscious memory? If it would be okay to do that, your head will automatically nod yes. If it wouldn't be okay, your head will shake for no. *Head nods.*

I am going to ask your deep inner mind, then to. . .

Hypnosis is being increased by increasing the unconscious attention; this is monitored by the ideomotor signal.

This is the first question directed at analysis. Evidence of cooperation is sought here. Unconscious automaticity is still being encouraged.

At this point, there is an inquiry into the patient's birth experience which is found to be a positive one (i.e. she feels good about having been born.)

Now, I am going to ask you to come forward from being born to the very first experience that has got anything whatever to do with these attacks of anxiety or tension. When you are at that very first experience that has anything whatever to do with it — you do not need to become consciously aware of it — but when your deep inner mind is there, your head will nod for yes. *Head nods.* Now I want you to go through that experience just in your deep inner mind — your conscious mind doesn't need to know about this — and when you have done that, again your head will nod for yes. *Head nods.*

Location of the first critical experience has now begun.

The important first critical experience has been unconsciously located. Although the head has nodded, there is no conscious awareness of what this experience is.

That experience you have just gone through. . . is it a scary experience? *Head nods.* Makes you feel sad? *Nods.* Makes you feel angry? *Nods.* Guilty? *Nods.* Is it sexual? *Head shakes.* Are you five years of age or younger?

The emotional components of the experience are being carefully delineated:
Scared?
Hurt?
Angry?
Guilty?

PT   About five.

DR   You're five years of age. Okay. Five year old Vera, what's happening? What's happening at five years of age? *The patient is beginning to look extremely sad and is obviously on the verge of tears.* You're feeling very sad, scared and angry. What's happening there? Five year old Vera, if it is okay to talk to me about it, just nod your head. If it is not, shake your head. *Head shakes.* Okay, you needn't talk about it. Does twenty-eight year old Vera know all about it now? *Shakes.* Can you tell her all about it? *Nods.* Will you tell her? *Nods.* Okay. . . Does she know all about it now? *Nods.* Can she now feel all of that scared feeling and all of that sad feeling and all of that angry feeling? *Nods.* She can? Oh, good. Do you think that you are going to be able to tell me anything about it at all? *Nods.* Okay, five year old Vera. It is really scary, is it? *Nods.* And sad? *Nods.* Okay, bring it all forward, What's happening now? Where are you?

The location of the age of the experience has been accomplished. The verbal response which replaced the expected nonverbal ideomotor response indicates a good involvement in the hypnotic experience. The therapist is observing a significant change in the patient's demeanour which clearly indicates that she is feeling very disturbed by the unconscious memory she has located. At first she is unable to verbalise what she is experiencing.

The information is still at a deeply unconscious level but is gradually brought up to a cognitive level, then to an emotive level, and finally to a level where it can be talked about. It is presumably reviewed at each level before it is permitted to pass on to a greater level of awareness.

PT   I'm waiting at home. *Tearfully.*

DR   You are? What for?

There is a spontaneous regression and the feelings of five year old Vera are being vividly expressed;

PT For my Mum.

DR Oh?

PT She's late.

DR Oh, dear.

PT I'm afraid of being left alone.

DR I see. What are you afraid of?

PT I don't know where to go if she doesn't come home.

DR Yes. . . what happens?

PT Well, I cry.

DR Is there anyone about?

PT No.

DR Are you in the house?

PT Yes. *Looking frightened.*

DR Very scared? Do you cry for a long time before she comes?

PT No.

DR Does she come soon?

PT About five or ten minutes.

DR And how do you feel when she comes?

PT Relieved. *With a sigh.*

yet, at the same time, the therapist is aware of the presence of the Adult Vera observing what is going on.

At this point, there is a feeling of being totally abandoned. This is the most frightening feeling that a child can experience.

It now becomes very apparent how important mother is to the child's feelings of security. The therapist is here searching for any

DR Did she say anything that bothers you?

PT No.

DR Does she ask you how you are? *Nods.* Does she give you a cuddle? *Nods.* Do you feel safe? *Nods.*

Okay, twenty-eight year old Vera, did you hear all of that?

PT Yes.

DR There is five year old Vera still feeling scared and still feeling hurt. Would you please give her all of your comforting, your wisdom and understanding? When you have done that, nod your head for yes. *Nods.* Five year old Vera, now you've heard that, do you still need to keep that scared feeling, that hurt feeling, that angry feeling any longer? If you do, nod your head for yes, but if you don't, then shake your head for no. *Head shakes for no.*

Okay, twenty-eight year old Vera, five year old Vera has told me that she doesn't need to keep that old scared feeling any longer. Would you please find a way for her to let go of it. When you have found a way, nod your head for yes.

PT *Nodding.* I've found a way.

DR Five year old Vera, there is a way now. There's a way you can let

elements of discomfort in the experience which are attributable to mother, but he finds none.

At this point the therapist calls upon the unconscious Adult ego state to review everything that the five year old ego state complex has to communicate. The Adult is mobilised simply by calling on it by its label, twenty-eight year old Vera. It is then asked to make its considerable resources available. Now the five year old complex is instructed to utilise these resources to formulate new conclusions in the light of this up-to-date information.

At this stage, it appears that the old tensions are now regarded as unnecessary, and the Adult is once again called upon to use its resources to discover a means of relinquishing long-held tensions.

Five year old Vera is now encouraged to consider this way of giving

go of that scared feeling right now. You can feel safe to change that sad feeling into a happy one. Let that old angry feeling go and be loving. When you have done that, let me know by nodding your head. . .

Five year old Vera, can you do it? *Head shakes slowly.* Okay. . . Now, twenty-eight year old Vera, five year old Vera can't do it yet. She is still keeping some uncomfortable feelings. . . I want you to really understand what it is she is keeping. Maybe, five year old Vera, you can tell me what it is that is making you feel so bad. . . You haven't told me about something that is still bothering you. What is that?. . . Are you still angry with her — with Mum for not coming?. . . Do you feel guilty about being angry with her?

PT *Sighs.*

DR Do you feel guilty about being angry with her? *Nods.*

Is there anything else that you want to tell us, five year old Vera? If there is, nod your head for yes; if there isn't, shake your head for no. . . *Shakes.*
Okay, twenty-eight year old Vera, talk to five year old Vera again and see if you can get her really to feel good. When you have done that, nod your head for yes. . . *Nods.* Five year old Vera, now you've heard that, do you still need to keep those old, out of date, uncomfortable feel-

up old tensions. The therapist continues to give as much encouragement as possible by making the state of being tension-free appear very attractive. However, she is unable to accept this solution and it becomes clear that there must be some reason for this which has not yet been dealt with. Once again, the Adult's resources are called upon.

The therapist's Adult and the patient's Adult cooperate in the search for something which prevents the five year old from relinquishing old tensions, something that is responsible for old guilt feelings is most likely, and this proves to be the case.

A careful check is made to ascertain whether there might be anything else about the critical experience which might cause further retention of uncomfortable feelings, perhaps for punitive reasons.

Once again, the Adult is called upon for aid in discovering whether five year old Vera is ready to relinquish the old tensions.

ings any longer?. . . *Head shakes.*
Good.

Twenty-eight year old Vera, five year old Vera now says she doesn't have to keep those uncomfortable feelings any more. They're out of date, they're finished with. It's all past. It's over, and I am going to ask you to please find a way for her to let go of those uncomfortable feelings for good. When you have found a way, nod your head for yes. . . *Nods.*

This time it appears that five year old Vera is more certain that these tensions are really unnecessary.

It appears to be much easier to find an acceptable solution to the problem since it has already been subjected to previous scrutiny.

Five year old Vera, you can now let go of those uncomfortable feelings. Let go of those uncomfortable feelings right now, and when you have done that, just nod your head to let me know that you have done it. . . *Nods.* Now if you really have let them all go, five year old Vera, you should be feeling very good inside. Good, comfortable feelings, so good to let go of all that pain and unnecessary uncomfortable feeling. When you are feeling really good inside, perhaps you can give me a smile which says, yes, I am feeling good. . . Five year old Vera, smile please. . . *Smiles.* Nice, that's nice. . . okay. Now, five year old Vera, I want you to help us because there are some other Veras that are not feeling okay. I now want you to come forward from being five to the next time that something is happening when Vera is not feeling okay. When you are there, nod your head for yes. . . *Nods.* I want you to go through that experience and when you have done that, nod your head again for yes. . . *Nods.*

Strong encouragement is given to five year old Vera to relinquish the outdated uncomfortable feelings.

Confirmation of complete resolution of the conflict is now sought and the *smile test* is applied since it has been found to be a reliable indicator of unconscious comfort following the resolution of conflict.

The stage is now set for the examination of other critical experiences (ego state complexes) contributing to the persistence of symptoms.

The rehabilitation phase of analytical hypnotherapy is postponed till near the end of the session when other critical experiences have been adequately dealt with, since this phase will suffice for all of the experiences.

In this first session, Vera was also able to deal with an experience she had at the age of seventeen. Her performance as a high school student at that time was so poor that it caused parental disapproval and brought forth much guilt. An experience at the age of twenty-six, when she was unable to be with her father while he was dying, produced more guilt feelings and a marked increase in her level of anxiety. This was directly related to the onset of severe headaches at that time. At later sessions, she dealt with other experiences associated with feelings of guilt. With a reduction of this guilt, she was able to relinquish her anxiety and within about four months of commencing therapy, she was able to function very normally.

It should be noted here that the assumption is made that uncomfortable feelings are always retained for a reason. Once that reason is recognised as invalid, the uncomfortable feelings can be reduced, not by a dampening activity such as is supplied by drugs and tranquillizers, but by a simple release of the feelings, as one would let go of a balloon which then floats away unhindered. When this is truly accomplished, such old feelings are gone forever. Of course, this does not preclude the individual from responding to new situations with similar uncomfortable feelings; but these are new feelings, and have no relationship with the previous cause of tension. Thus they can be dealt with entirely in the present context of the provocative situation.

Reframing

Reframing (first described by Bandler and Grinder, 1979) is the name given to a technique for promoting a beneficial change in an individual. There are essentially two types of reframing, the first of which attempts to separate the intention behind a specific set of symptoms from the symptoms themselves and to *reframe* (reassociate) that intention in a more beneficial behaviour pattern. The second approach accepts the inappropriate behaviour pattern and reframes it so that it only occurs in a useful context. It assumes that inappropriate behaviour is only inappropriate because it occurs out of context and that there is always a context in which it is appropriate and useful. Analytical hypnotherapy should encompass these objectives of reframing if it is to be maximally effective. These techniques are therefore of value to the analytical hypnotherapist and add a further dimension to his understanding of the mechanisms whereby change is able to be effected, and can be applied in whole or in part whenever there appears to be an indication for their application.

The first type of reframing, probably the more common in practice, is directed at the intention behind the behaviour pattern which needs to be changed. This type has six essential steps, all of which rest upon the basic premise (one that is also made in analytical hypnotherapy) that each patient has adequate resources with which to formulate solutions for his own problems. A second premise holds that symptoms are the means by which a part of the personality deals with a problem to the best of its ability and to the limit of its own resources. It does this on behalf of the whole personality in a somewhat separate manner which isolates it from access to other resources. These resources are either present at the time of the origin of the symptoms or are acquired at a later date by other parts of the personality.

In the techniques to be described, the problem is once again exposed to the far greater resources of the remainder of the personality in the expectation that therein will lie a more appropriate solution. These six essential steps in this first type of reframing are as follows.

Identification of the Unwanted Behaviour Pattern or Symptom Complex

The unwanted behaviour pattern is one that the patient wants to be freed from but is unable to control or modify. It creates discomfort for him either by taking the form of a compulsive behaviour pattern, or an inhibitory behaviour which prevents him from acting appropriately. Once this unwanted behaviour is identified, the therapist moves on to the next step.

Establishing Communication with the Part of the Patient Responsible for the Behaviour Pattern

Since this part is always unconscious, communication with it implies that hypnosis is being used. The ease with which this communication usually occurs confirms that the induction of hypnosis is, technically speaking, rarely a problem for the analytical hypnotherapist.

It is in this stage that the assumption that there is a part of the personality in charge of the unwanted behaviour becomes important. Even though it may be aware of the discomfort that it is causing, it is in this personality part that the behaviour must be maintained for the best interests of the individual. The therapist should communicate this understanding to the patient so that the unconscious part responsible for the unwanted behaviour pattern is aware that the therapist respects it as much as any part of the patient's personality. In order to accomplish this communication with the unconscious part, the patient is told that this part is attempting to do something positive for him and in producing the symptom complex, is doing so to the best of its ability. He is also told that this personality part must be satisfied that there is a better way of achieving the same ends before it will permit a change in the behaviour pattern. Such information engages the attention of the part in question. The patient is then instructed to talk to himself by going inside and asking the specific question, *Will the part of me responsible for the symptoms (behaviour) communicate with me in consciousness?* He then awaits and pays attention to any changes (kinesthetic, auditory or visual) that follow.

In many cases, the response to the question is clearly a yes or a no, which is heard, seen, or felt in some manner. In other cases, because the response is one which cannot be identified as yes or no, it is so structured that an increase in the response will stand for yes and a decrease for no. For example, the response of anxiety can be increased for yes or decreased for no. The originators of the reframing techniques favour the use of these nonverbal responses (e.g. sweating, palpitations, flushing, etc.) because they are immune from conscious interference and represent direct unconscious communication. However, because they are also ideosensory responses, and are only on occasion directly monitorable by the therapist, they require greater skill in their interpretation than ideomotor responses. The therapist monitors them by means of associated visible changes (e.g. flushing), but some reliance must be placed on the patient for reporting the responses.

Distinguishing between the Pattern of Behaviour that Requires to be Changed and the Intention Behind it.
The objective of this third stage is to retain the beneficial intention while altering the means by which the benefits are achieved. To accomplish this, the patient is once again asked to go *inside* and ask another question of the part creating the symptom: *Would you be willing to let me know in consciousness what you are trying to do for me by this behaviour?* Again, the answer may come in words, pictures or feelings which first indicate whether this communication is indeed possible and secondly, what the intention really is. Sometimes the intention may appear to be a negative and destructive one, but deeper inquiry will reveal *another* intention which is really the positive and

essentially productive one. This intention is acceptable at a conscious level.

Accessing the Patient's Creative Resources for Discovering New Solutions and Applying Them to the Problem
In this fourth stage, new ways of accomplishing the same intention by acceptable means are generated. This is accomplished by once again directing the patient to *go inside* and ask the creative part of his mind to communicate, at an unconscious level, with the part responsible for the unwanted symptoms and with it to create other ways of achieving the same outcome as was intended. From the many options thus generated, the part responsible for the symptoms is asked to select three which will work at least as effectively as its present behaviour pattern. Without being required to verbalise them, it is asked to indicate, by the ideosensory response, its selection of each of these three options.

Undertaking to use the New Options in the Future
In this fifth stage, the question is asked: *Do you now agree that these three choices are as effective as the original behaviour?* If the answer is yes, then the further question, *Will you take responsibility for using these other behaviours in the appropriate context?* is asked.

Ecological Check
This sixth and final stage is so called because a change in attitude in one part of the mind cannot occur in isolation; the views of the other parts of the personality must be considered. Thus it is that this important stage defers to every part of the mind in order to ascertain whether there are any objections to the new behaviours proposed. Since, in any particular behaviour pattern, many parts of the personality are involved, consensus is accomplished by asking the question, *Is there any part of me that has an objection to the new choices?* If the answer is no, the reframing process has come to an end; if the answer is yes, that objection must be dealt with if success is to be assured. This is done by asking the creative part of the mind to find and generate new choices that will be acceptable as was done in stage four. Stages five and six are then repeated.

In the second type of reframing, the task is to identify the context in which the behaviour would be appropriate. The behaviour is then securely attached to this context and limited to it. This is accomplished by posing questions in stage three to discover the appropriate context, and if none is found, then stage four will be necessary in order to call upon the creative parts to create new, appropriate contexts. In stage five, the part responsible for the behaviour would be asked to generate that behaviour only in those contexts.

These techniques of reframing have been examined in some detail because much can be learned from them by the analytical hypnotherapist. It is important to note that there is never any formal hypnotic induction and yet when reframing is employed, the patient gives evidence of being in hypnosis. The only instruction for the induction of hypnosis is the one to *go inside and talk to the part which . . . etc.* Hypnosis occurs without any signs of resistance since the patient is directing the process himself.

The parts of the personality responsible for the different behaviours are simply called *parts*. Presumably, they are ego states that become more clearly identified when using the hypnoanalytical procedures. The unconscious creative part that is called upon to generate new solutions is probably identical to the part which we have labelled the unconscious Adult, which contains the unconscious wisdom and understanding necessary to find a means of relinquishing unnecesary tensions.

In the final phase of analytical hypnotherapy, rehabilitation is prominent. It is in this phase that the individual finds ways of coping without his symptoms. It is similar to stage six in reframing where the ecological check unconsciously accomplishes the same objective.

In the following excerpt from an initial session with a patient, some of the principles of reframing are used. As the problems unearthed become more complex, the more formal analytical procedure previously described is employed.

Tim is a thirty year old man who comes to therapy because he is a compulsive gambler who admits that he gets a high whenever he gambles. He used to feel very good whenever he won, but prior to therapy, he found that he got the high feeling no matter what the outcome. He no longer cared whether he won or lost because gambling itself provided him with the thrill that he seeks. At one time it was winning that was all important to him, and he would experience a high that would last for days. At present, he says that the good feeling is of very short duration and lasts only while actually gambling. His response is similar to that of the drug addict who gets a high at first from his drug, but as tolerance increases, the high becomes more elusive. When not gambling, Tim gets very edgy; when gambling, he becomes more relaxed. The similarity between gambling and taking a tranquillizer is very evident.

Tim says that gambling has been a problem from the age of twelve when he first went to the races with his father. When he first met his girl friend (four years prior to therapy), he had a remission from the compulsion for six months. He recalls feeling very good with himself at the time, and did not even think about gambling. Since then, however, the urge to gamble has increased considerably. He is currently gambling both heavily and often and is becoming seriously in debt. At the time of therapy, though he does little else but gamble, he does not understand why he has changed so much. He rationalises that the excitement of his relationship to his girlfriend has worn off and consequently he has returned to gambling. He describes an extreme depression that overwhelms him whenever he loses heavily, as he frequently does. Every time, he resolves *never again*, but the determination does not last. There are times when he has seriously contemplated suicide, and on one occasion made preparations for death.

DR Would you agree with me that some part of you must know why you gamble?

This is the first suggestion that there is an unconscious part responsible for the symptoms and this suggestion is readily accepted by the patient.

PT There's got to be an answer somewhere, yes.

DR Yes, there must be some part of you that knows why you need this high; what it is that makes you feel so tense beforehand and what there is about gambling that makes you feel relaxed. There is some part of the back of your mind or your unconscious mind which knows these and I would like to try something simple to help you. We would like you to feel okay without having to gamble, but if you did gamble, it would only be occasionally and not compulsively.

In this first part of reframing, the need to identify the part responsible for the compulsion is being established, as well as making some early suggestions regarding its function in promoting gambling. There has so far been no mention of hypnosis but the process of communication with the *part* responsible for gambling is being discussed.

PT Yes, I would like to be able to gamble occasionally but not have to as I do now.

Although the patient evidently wants to be rid of his gambling compulsion, he is relieved to

DR I am going to ask you to close your eyes and then I want you to go inside and just ask yourself this simple question, *Will that part of me that makes me gamble, will that part communicate with me in consciousness?* Ask that question and see what answer you get. There may be a yes feeling or a no feeling; you may see a yes or a no or you may hear a yes or a no. If you get a yes, nod your head to let me know; if you get a no, just shake your head. . . *Will that part of me that makes me gamble communicate with me in consciousness?. . .* If you get a yes, nod your head; if you get a no, shake your head. . . *Head shakes for no. . .* Okay, you are getting a no. Ask that part that is not going to communicate with you in consciousness if it is really trying to do something for you, because I believe that it is trying to do something for you in some way that only it understands. If you get a yes, your head can nod for yes. . . *Head begins to nod very slowly.* Good. Now, even though you do not know what that part is doing for you, Tim, I want you to thank it. Say, *I don't know what it is that you are trying to do for me but I thank you for whatever it is.* When you've done that, when you've thanked it, just nod your head. . . *Head nods.* Okay. Now, that part is doing something for you and I would think — I would guess — that it is protecting you in some way. Let me ask that part, is it protecting you in some way? If it is, you'll get a yes

know that there is no intention to deprive him of his freedom to gamble.

The induction of hypnosis is simply that of asking the patient to make contact with an unconscious part. The closing of the eyes is suggested in order to facilitate this communication. This is the second stage in reframing. A wide variety of possible responses are suggested from which the unconscious mind can take its pick.

A modification of the usual reframing procedure is made by the therapist when he suggests that the ideomotor head signals be used to monitor whatever ideosensory responses are experienced. There has been no attempt to define what the ideosensory responses are.

Note that even a response of *I will not communicate* is itself a communication. Such a response is used to maintain contact with the part responsible for the unwanted behaviour which responds by agreeing that it really has a protective role.

Further indications of the therapist's understanding of this role are given by requesting the patient to thank that part for its previous help.

The therapist further emphasises this protective role which increases the likelihood of unconscious cooperation. This emphasis on the protective role separates it from the behaviour it engenders,

An Analytical Procedure 163

feeling and your head will nod for yes, and if it isn't your head will shake for no. You may not know in what way it is protecting you, if it is. . . Head Nods. Ah, you are getting a yes. Now, ask that part that's protecting you: *Is it protecting me from an uncomfortable feeling?*. . . *Head nods*. Yes, it is. Again will you please thank it for doing this for you. . . *Nods*.

Now ask if it will consider protecting you in a different way than gambling, if there is a better way to protect you than gambling, would it consider using that way instead?. . . *Head nods*. Yes, sure, it only wants to protect you in the best way it knows how. . . Okay, now since you have got that part to agree to protect you in whatever best way it can, perhaps it can do this without having to gamble. . . I am now going to ask you to direct the creative part of your mind to find other ways of protecting you from that uncomfortable feeling than by gambling. Ask it to find at least three ways. You won't know what those three ways are because you do not even know what it is that you are being protected from. The creative part of your mind can find several ways, but we will ask it to find only three. When you get number one way, you will feel your head nod for yes. . . *Head nods*. I now want you to ask it to find number two way. . . *Head nods*. Good. Now, ask it to find a third way, and when you have got

which is the third stage in reframing.

Some clarification of the kind of protection offered is being suggested. It appears that an extremely uncomfortable feeling exists which is relieved by gambling. Before the fourth stage of the reframing technique, it is wise to gain the commitment of the responsible part to consider alternative behaviours when they are presented.

This is the fourth stage of reframing in which the vast resources of the creative (unconscious Adult?) part are called upon to discover new solutions to the problem of dealing with discomfort. In this technique, only three new solutions of the many possible ones are asked for. This compares with the stage in the analytical procedure where only one satisfactory solution is requested.

We shall see later that these first two solutions were found almost too easily and that the time in finding the third way was well spent.

three ways, again your head will nod for yes. . . *Head nods after a long interval in which the therapist encourages him to continue to search for a third way.* Good. Now Tim, I am going to ask that part that has in some way been protecting you by gambling to look at those three ways which the creative part of your mind has just found. When it has done that, it will let you know by giving you a yes. . . *Head nods.* Now ask that part that has been protecting you by gambling, *Will it use those three ways, either one of them or all of them, to protect you instead of by gambling?. . . Head nods.* I am now going to direct you to ask every part of your mind whether it will be all right to use these three new ways instead of gambling. If it's okay to use these three ways instead of gambling, you will get a yes from every part of your mind. If any part says no, you will get a no feeling. . . *There is some considerable delay at this point in getting a response during which the therapist repeats these instructions carefully and slowly, and the head shakes.* Okay, there is a part there that has an objection. Ask that part if it objects to number one way and if it does you will get a yes. *Shakes head.* No. If it is objecting to number two way, ask it to give you a yes. . . *Shakes head.* No. If it is objecting to number three way, your head will nod. *Nods.* Okay. Again we will ask the creative part of your mind to listen to the objection.

The importance of gaining the approval of the part responsible for the unwanted behaviour to any proposed change in it cannot be overestimated.

This is the fifth stage of reframing wherein the therapist obtains a commitment from the part responsible for the symptoms that it will give them up in exchange for a symptom-free method which is equally effective.

The ecological check − the sixth and vitally important phase of reframing − is now made. Objections, probably based on the removal of secondary gains by the proposed changes, are freely heard and heeded.

In this case a delay suggests that a deeply situated part (cf. hidden ego state in next chapter) makes its objection known with some evident reluctance. This part objects to the third way (reached by the creative part only after long deliberation) which suggests that it was partly aware of disagreement.

With new information the creative part is equal to the task of generating modifications to any one of its solutions.

There is an objection coming from a deep part of your mind which says that it does not accept number three way; so ask the creative part of your mind to look at that objection and to modify that number three way. When that number three way has been changed to meet the objection you will nod for yes. . . *Nods.* Now, ask the part of your mind that has been making you gamble whether that new change in number three way is okay. *Head nods.* All right then. Let's go back to every part of your mind. Does every part of your mind now agree to those three ways?. . . *Nods.* Good. Notice that every part agrees and that's good. Ask the part of the mind that used to make you gamble, will it now take the responsibility for using those three ways to protect you?. . . *Nods.* Good. Good. Okay, I am going to ask you to see yourself at the next time that you feel the need for protection. See yourself, feel yourself using one of those three ways, and when you can feel that happening, your head will nod yes. . . *Head nods.* Okay. Now ask that part of your mind, will it be okay to use one of those three ways from now on? If it would be okay, your head will nod yes. . . *Nods.* Good. I want you to notice how good that feels. In fact, if it really feels good, your head is going to nod yes again. . . *Shakes.* Is there a part feeling uncomfortable? *Nods.* Okay, I am going to ask the part that is feeling uncomfortable, *do you object to those three ways?. .*

Again, every part that is concerned must be consulted, but the obviously important one is that which has the protective function. Since it now approves, the stage is ready for the ecological check.

We need to be certain that when protection is required, gambling will never again be used.

Projecting into the future, facing the situations responsible for tension, and testing whether the new solutions work are excellent checking devices.

The total absence of discomfort indicates the resolution of problems and is the basis of the smile test which is applied here in modified form, i.e. *feeling very good.*

This indicates that all is not as well as had been supposed and again a deeply hidden part makes its pres-

Nods. Does it object to number one way?. . . Nods. Number two way? Nods. Does it object to number three way? Shakes. It objects to number one and number two ways. Okay, I am now going to ask that part: please present your objections clearly and concisely to the creative part of the mind and when that has been done your head will nod for yes. . . *Nods.* Okay. Creative part of the mind: there are some objections there to number one and number two ways. I want you to look at those objections and find ways of meeting them because we can't have Tim doing something that is going to be objected to by any part of the mind. We want every part of the mind to feel okay about these new ways of protecting Tim. I want you to find an improved way for the number one and number two ways.

Tim, let's deal with number one way first. When you have modified it so that all objections have been met and no part of your mind is made uncomfortable by it, then nod your head. . . *Shakes.* . . How about number two then? *Nods.* Okay, number two feels okay? *Head nods again.* Number three is okay? *Nods.* Okay, then, it is just number one way that is a problem. Number one way seems to be really very tricky. Ask the creative part of your mind to think a bit more deeply about number one way. If it can't be modified, find a new number one way

ence felt. Its objections must be located. Because this part feels it cannot accept the first two solutions, these must be reprocessed once again through the creative part.

The creative part admits to extreme difficulty in finding a new solution to the problem or modifying its original, number one solution to meet the perceived objection to it.

The creative part is given the alternative of constructing a totally new solution as number one. It

that will be acceptable to every part of your mind so that there will be three ways to protect Tim from discomfort. When you have found a number one way that is satisfactory, your head will nod yes. . . Nods. Okay, now I want you to check with every part of your mind to see that number one way is now okay. Nods. . . Check with the part of your mind that has been taking care of you and protecting you by making you gamble and see if it is okay with that part. If so, your head will nod yes. . . Nods. Okay, now I am going to ask the part that has been taking care of you: would you please now use one or more of those three new ways of protecting Tim instead of by gambling?. . . Nods. Okay. Check again all the way through your mind and see if there is now any part that disagrees with one of those three ways. If there is, your head will nod yes; if there isn't and there is no disagreement whatever, your head will shake no. . . Shakes.

accepts this alternative and discovers a new solution which appears to be acceptable to all parts of the mind.

Once again, the commitment to use the solutions so painstakingly modified, is sought for and obtained.

Once again the ecological check.

Now, there should be a very good feeling there. Is there a good feeling, a nice comfortable feeling? Nods. Good. Nice relaxed, calm feeling?. . . Nods. Good. Keep it, keep that good comfortable feeling. Now that you've got that good feeling, you can see Tim doing all things that he wants to do and taking care of himself. I want to give you some important ideas and I want you to listen to me very carefully with the deepest part of your mind: your conscious mind doesn't need to pay any atten-

Although the ecological check proves satisfactory, the test for comfort is also made and is, at last, positive.

As an additional safeguard, projection into the future to test the solutions in action is made.
The stage is now set for some routine ego-strengthening and assertiveness training suggestions by asking for maximum unconscious attention with little conscious interference. This may be equated

tion to me at all because the deepest part of your mind can listen very carefully. When the deepest part of your mind is listening very carefully, your head will nod for yes. . . *Nods.* Continue to listen very carefully. I believe that every human being is important. And I believe that Tim is just as good and just as important as any other human being. If you agree with that your head will want to nod for yes. *Nods.* Good. Now I know that all human beings have uncomfortable feelings as well as comfortable feelings and that you have had feelings of sadness like any other human being. . . *ego strengthening and assertiveness suggestions are now given in detail here.*

with the common concept of deepening hypnosis.

These suggestions will be enlarged in Chapter Thirteen.

Six months later, a friend of Tim's reported that he had left the area, was doing well and was no longer gambling compulsively.

The Critical Experience, Overt and Hidden Ego State Complexes and Multiple Personalities

The Critical Experience

Caplan (1964) stated that the essential factor of a crisis is the imbalance between the magnitude of the problem and the resources immediately available to cope with it; the individual in crisis feels simply overwhelmed. Crucial to successful therapy is the identification of experiences which have constituted times of crisis for the individual. In these crises he has had to take emergency measures to deal with problems to the best of his somewhat limited ability. These critical experiences invariably involved a repression or concealment of part of the personality; such experiences mark the commencement of a specific Parent-Child conflict in which the Parent ego state assumes that a particular behaviour of the individual (Child) is likely to incur parental disfavour and must consequently be modified or eliminated. This decision is the result of the Parent's observation of real parental disapproval, either at the time of the critical experience, or, at some previous time during a similar set of circumstances.

As already indicated, the prime task of the Parent ego state is to ensure the continued acceptance of the individual by the parent. Its awareness of and sensitivity to parental disapproval motivates it to censure the Child whenever such disapproval is present or presumed, and critical experiences are always ones in which this disapproval is strongly present or implied. The Parent's power to censure the Child lies in its ability to create fear — the fear of parental abandonment — which is consciously interpreted as guilt. Therefore, although it may not be readily detectable, all critical experiences have this element of guilt.

The critical experience is, therefore, always succeeded by a change in the Child due to a repression of part of its functioning. It is this internally imposed restriction of the Child by the Parent, and the efforts of the Child to free itself from these restrictions, that gives the critical experience its importance in analytical hypnotherapy. Understanding of the critical experience by the Adult ego state permits resolution of the underlying conflict to be resolved, and without this understanding there can be little likelihood of therapeutic success. The critical experience embodies all of the elements of the Child/Parent conflict which must be exposed to the probing techniques of analytical hypnotherapy. Although there may be many subsequent similar experiences, they merely augment the effect of the original critical experience, and analyses of them would be fruitless. When the common therapeutic manoeuvre of going backwards in time from the present is employed, many experiences are subjected to analysis and discovered to be non-critical with symptoms persisting and time having been wasted. These non-critical experiences, traumatic as they may be, are of secondary significance in the analytical process; they are not responsible for the Child/Parent conflicts which created the symptoms, they simply serve to reinforce them. In fact, resolution of the conflict resulting from the critical experience permits all the tensions of the subsequent similar experiences to be relinquished spontaneously and coincidentally with those of the critical experience. As is often the case, to the patient who says: *Doctor, I have so many unhappy experiences and memories that I am certain it will take years to deal with them all,* the analytical hypnotherapist replies that he will be able to deal with the majority of these experiences simply and easily when certain essentials of these experiences are fully understood. It may be assumed that the unconscious mind identifies the critical experiences when requested to do so, simply by tracing the present tensions back to the time when they emerged. Whatever experience is present at the time of recall is assumed to be the cause of those tensions. In practice this process is usually both easy and accurate.

Ego State Complexes

Berne (1961) declared that an ego state can be described phenomenologically as a coherent system of feelings related to a given subject, operationally as a set of coherent behaviour patterns and, pragmatically, as a system of feelings which motivates a related set of behaviour patterns. The critical experience is characterised as the site of a strong interaction between the Parent ego state and the Child ego state and usually occurs at a time when the Adult ego state can contribute little to this interaction. The ensuing Child/Parent conflict results in decisions, attitudes and behaviour patterns which may be responsible for symptoms and unwanted behaviour. This conflict therefore is the source of a strong motivating force which we can regard as an ego state complex powerful enough to operate almost or entirely independent of the rest of the personality in areas which are of concern to the complex.

In dealing with the critical experience in analytical hypnotherapy, the therapist will often become aware of this ego state complex and the predominant characteristics of it. Although it may present as being primarily Parental, there will always be an essential element of the Child which is often well concealed but must be recognised if therapy is to be successful. Conversely, the ego state complex may present as consisting mainly of the Child, but the Parent is always present in the complex no matter how carefully hidden.

Thus the entire ego state complex presents when a critical experience is located. It has features of the Child and so the therapist encounters the feelings of repressed hurt, anger or fear and also the self rejection and guilt attributable to the Parent. Positive feelings, though present, are rarely in evidence since they are unlikely to be associated with conflict. They are of concern to the therapist however when the later stages of therapy are reached and are then needed for the rehabilitative phases.

It is important, in the initial analysis of the critical experience, to subject the whole ego state complex to the analysis so that all of the inherent conflict is made available to the resources of the Adult. If any of this ego state complex is withheld from analysis, the conflict will persist. This withholding represents a potent source of resistance to the uncovering techniques; so long as it remains, it will present an obstruction to the resolution of tension and the relief of symptoms, and therapy will be seen to have failed.

One of the more interesting findings in analytical hypnotherapy is the relation between the time of the critical experience and the resulting symptoms with the critical experience frequently occurring some time prior to the onset of the symptoms. For example, a severe depression which appears to have been precipitated by a recent loss or disappointment of some kind is rarely, on analysis, found to be entirely due to that recent event. In nearly every case the ingredients of the symptom complex have been formulated some time before in an earlier critical experience. The absence of symptoms in the intervening period is presumably due to the fact that the potentially explosive Child/Parent conflict seems to attain an equilibrium between the opposing forces of the Parent and the Child. The precipitating experience which may occur a considerable time after the critical experience upsets this equilibrium and releases the unconscious tensions of the conflict which then explode into the symptomatic behaviour pattern. The analogy of the production of an explosive which appears innocuous until detonated is a good one and enables the therapist to understand why in these cases the symptomatic response (the powder keg) is totally unrelated to the precipitating event (the match). During the latency period between the initiating critical experience and the onset of symptoms, there are usually some personality changes which in themselves are indicative of the presence of an ongoing unconscious Child/Parent conflict. These changes are usually outside the awareness of the individual who probably regards himself as normal.

The Hidden Ego State Complex
Every aspect of the critical experience is usually accessible to the uncovering techniques described and can be satisfactorily dealt with by using all of the principles of analytical hypnotherapy. Sometimes, there is evidence of unconscious resistance in one form or another. The ideomotor signals may not become established or may become confused or, after being initially strong, may fade away. All of this is clearly due to unconscious resistance and indicates that the unconscious mind and the conscious mind are sharply divided on the issue of therapy (the patient would not have presented himself for therapy if this were not so). In other cases there may be no evidence of this kind of unconscious resistance and therapy appears to have proceeded satisfactorily; and yet symptoms, in part or in whole, persist to the dismay of the therapist who remains at a loss to explain why this should be.

The assumption that hypnosis renders the unconscious mind totally accessible to the therapist is a false one that most hypnotherapists have unwittingly accepted. Even in deep hypnosis, important parts of the unconscious mind can remain totally outside the hypnotic process. Hilgard (1977) discovered that there was often a *hidden observer* which was aware of the hypnotic phenomena taking place but was separate and apart from it. The observer, which Hilgard regarded as a separate part of the unconscious, was able to comment upon the hypnotic process. Similarly, in analytical hypnotherapy, there can remain a part of the unconscious mind which continues to be separate and inaccessible to the therapeutic process. It is this part which can be responsible for resistance to therapy and is presumed to be a hidden ego state complex. When encouraged to come out of hiding and make communication with the therapist, it is discovered to possess a set of thoughts and behaviours separate from the main stream of the personality and frequently antagonistic to it.

This ego state complex which remains concealed from the therapist is usually one that has arisen as a result of an earlier critical experience which has not been detected by the uncovering techniques simply because it is not in the memory of that part of the unconscious mind accessed by them. This hidden ego state may be so opposed to any decision made by the ego state(s) in rapport with the therapist that it will sabotage that relationship and reverse any decision made for the relinquishing of adverse symptomatology. It will interfere with patient-therapist communication and in doing so it gives a signal by which its presence can be suspected. In fact the presence of a hostile hidden ego state complex should always be assumed whenever an inexplicable unconscious resistance is encountered. In practice, the hidden ego state is always violently opposed to the ego state which has been found to be cooperative with the therapist and, initially, its violent opposition does not permit it to give any cooperation. The opposition to the normal unconscious ego states may be so great that it regards itself as separate from them and also has a separate identity and perhaps a different name.

Location of the hidden ego state is difficult and when discovered it may be angry with the therapist, having no wish to be allied with any other unconscious ego states which are cooperating with him. A great deal of tact and circumspection must be exercised by the therapist in dealing with the concealed ego state if the resolution of the critical tensions is not to be obstructed by it. The therapist should treat a hidden ego state with the respect he would accord a separate individual, recognising that the now exposed ego state is likely to treat him with great suspicion and distrust – particularly if it believes the therapist is likely to be unsympathetic with its viewpoints.

Aversion to therapy may be indicated early on in the analytical procedure when the question, *do you want me to help you with your problem?* is responded to with a *no*. While it is evident that the accessible unconscious ego state is opposed to therapy, it must be assumed that, if there is an unconscious ego state in favour of therapy and likely to be cooperative, it is being hidden. Every effort must be made at the outset to expose a favourable ego state by asking, *Is there a part that does want me to help?* Until communication is made with such a part the prospects of successful therapy will remain poor. The techniques of communicating with hidden favourable ego states are identical with those used in dealing with hostile concealed states.

Uncovering a Hidden Ego State

Signs of unconscious resistance should lead the therapist to suspect a hidden ego state complex aversive to therapy. This may occur when initial signs of cooperation disappear or when there are conflicting signals either from the same hand or from both hands. It becomes obvious that an antagonistic ego state is active when the signals from one hand differ and oppose those on the other. In such instances the degree of concealment adopted by the hidden ego state has not been very great and it becomes possible to converse with each ego state separately to determine the area within which there remains conflict.

However, a greater degree of concealment of the hidden ego state exists when everything appears to have been going well with the analytical process and yet symptoms persist or return. In these cases the ego state that has remained in communication with the therapist during the analytical process remains unaware of the reason for this and is as puzzled as the therapist about the persistence of the symptoms for which no unconscious reason is forthcoming. It is at this stage that patients may abandon therapy because of the little progress that has been made and the frustration that this has produced. The therapist who is aware of the possibility of a hidden ego state responsible for the persistence of symptoms will now make every effort to locate and identify such an ego state as soon as possible in order to communicate with it. Certain questions can be asked which are frequently successful in locating, uncovering, and identifying the hidden ego state. They are as follows: *Is there a deeper part of your unconscious mind that really does not want me to help?* A *yes* to this will indicate that there is a separate and opposed ego state. Even a *no* to this question is not conclusive evidence that there is no hidden ego state since the part that answers *no* may truly believe that there is none. If the therapist is equally certain that there is probably a hidden ego state, this question should be repeated with the request that only the deepest parts of the unconscious mind should answer. If there is still a *no* it may be that the hidden ego state really wants the therapist to help so the following question should now be asked: *Is there a separate part that does want me to help?* A *yes* to this question indicates a separate but cooperative hidden ego state.

Having located the existence of a hidden ego state which does not want help, it can be addressed as *the part that does not want my help* and then can be asked: *Is your name X* (the first name of the patient)? A hidden ego state will often deny that he or she has the same name (or occasionally, even the same sex) as the patient and can then be asked if (s)he will tell you what his/her name is. If the ego state gives his/her name, contact has been made with this ego state and direct communication and conversation with it are now possible. The fact that a particular name will evoke a particular ego state can be confirmed in one's own experience. Most of us have a modification of our given name or perhaps a pet name which is used only by certain people in our environment. The use of this name will tend to evoke different responses within us than will the use of the more formal given name. In those cases where the name is the same as the patient some other identification should be sought (e.g. age or some other characteristic such as frightened, sad, etc.). Occasionally, the hidden ego state will not accept the patient's name but neither will it give another so that the therapist needs to find an acceptable name in such a case.

The previously concealed but now exposed ego state will initially, perhaps, be angry at having been cajoled into revealing itself to the therapist and communication with him will necessarily be guarded. It is at this point that the therapist should make every effort to understand the feelings that have been responsible for the alienation that must have occurred and should remain sympathetic with any point of view expressed without professing any agreement he does not genuinely feel. Any dishonesty on the part of the therapist is readily discerned by unconscious ego states and will endanger further communication.

It is also possible that the immediately accessible unconscious ego state remains unaware of the previously hidden ego state's presence. This can be readily ascertained by asking the previously hidden ego state, *Does X know that you are here?* If the answer to this is *no*, profound posthypnotic amnesia is likely to be present.

Therapy with the hidden ego state can progress much as with any other ego state, except that the hidden ego state usually has more information about the individual's life history. When the easily located unconscious ego state becomes aware of the presence of the previously hidden unconscious ego state, many heretofore puzzling experiences now become explicable. Thoughts and voices, which had previously appeared to emerge from nowhere and may have been frightening and perhaps self-destructive, now become understandable because they originated from the concealed and hostile ego state. Also, actions and behaviours which had appeared alien to the individual (such as exhibitions of intense anger at times when it seemed appropriate to remain calm) can now be understood. Other seemingly bizarre emotions which have been felt likewise have a meaning. The hidden ego state will often freely and proudly admit its responsibility for these phenomena.

Location of the original critical experience which led to the formation of the hidden ego state must be found; all of the relevant information about that experience must be accessed so that the resources of the Adult can be applied to discovering new solutions to the problems posed. This is usually a more protracted process with the concealed ego state because it may be reluctant to deal with issues responsible for its existence. It needs to be assured that the resolution of these old conflicts does not mean the dissolution of this ego state, but rather, that its energies will be directed to a harmonious support of the whole personality and not just a part of it. Therapy is directed at improving the relationship between unconscious ego states and reconciling any divergent viewpoints.

The hidden ego state may be Parental in attitude and consequently produce guilt and self-punishing symptoms, or, it may be Childlike and produce symptoms of rebellion. As a result, Parental symptoms are frequently psychosomatic and Child symptoms are usually emotional (e.g. anger, panic, etc.). In either case the ego state is always negative in attitude.

Sometimes the critical experience causing the emergence of this hidden ego state is prenatal and results from prenatal maternal rejection. This is often difficult to uncover and it requires the therapist's utmost skill and patience to locate and deal with such an experience.

The Unrelenting (Unforgiving) Parent Ego State
This is frequently a hidden ego state and is obstinate in its refusal to respond to Adult intervention. Thus it remains a common cause of failure of therapy and in children is often a source of behavioural problems. In cases where the parents are in conflict with each other, some of the child's behaviour is unconsciously programmed by the absent parent and the child becomes relentless and unforgiving in pursuit of goals set by that parent (see chapter seventeen). In adults it is more obviously an unforgiving Parent which will not listen to exhortations to cease punishing the Child (e.g. alcoholics). If the patient can be induced to stay in therapy — and this is unusual — only persistent and skillful reasoning with this stubborn ego state is likely to succeed.

A Case History of a Hidden Ego State
In the following excerpt a search for a hidden ego state is initiated in the case of a thirty-two year old woman who had been responding well

to analytical hypnotherapy. She had dealt well with feelings of panic but was now experiencing a constant feeling of anger which she projected upon her long-suffering family. She is aware of a curious mixture of feelings: she does not like feeling angry and yet, at the same time, enjoys the discomfiture that her behaviour inflicts upon others. It is this paradox which gave the impetus for a renewed search for a possible hidden ego state responsible for the uncomfortable feelings.

This patient was able to enter hypnosis well but had never been able to produce ideomotor finger signals. However, she was readily able to visualise yes and no on an imaginary blackboard and these ideosensory signals had been used with success.

DR   Let me see. . . what I am hearing from you is that you are saying, *I am angry and miserable.*

The therapist is able to identify the problem as being associated with the presence of two coexisting and yet mutually exclusive sets of feelings.

PT   Yes, well that's an obvious contradiction or I would not be here.

DR   But there is a part of you that is happy and another part of you that is miserable.

He confirms the suspicion that there is more than one part present unconscious and active.

PT   Yes.

DR   And so, the part that is angry is also happy about being angry because it knows there is another part being miserable.

PT   Yes and it is doing something that is making me content to be that way.

DR   But the part that's angry is not the part that brought you here today.

Both therapist and patient recognise that there is an internal division of opinion over therapy.

PT   No. It is the part that's scared that made me come.

DR   It is also the part that's miserable?

It is usually the uncomfortable
part that welcomes the possibility
of relief offered by therapy.

PT   Yes.

DR   You're saying that you do not
want to be like that?

PT   No, I don't, because it is offensive to me and it's offensive to others
— and it is uncomfortable.

This sounds more like an Adult
observation.

DR   But you still have the angry
part and it has a reason to be angry
but we don't know the reason.

This recognition of the angry
part's right to be angry predis-
poses it towards the therapist.

PT   Yes.

DR   Now I am going to ask you to
do the blackboard visualisation
again. Please close your eyes and
look at the blackboard. Now I
would like you to answer this question. We will see which part answers
the question — *Do you really want
me to help?* . . . What did you get? . . .

In previous sessions the patient
was able to visualise yes and no in
answer to questioning.

This question is designed to identify unconscious cooperation.

PT   The yeses and noes are all jum-
bled.

This is the kind of confused response where there are conflicting
unconscious opinions.

DR   Okay. Could you please place
the yeses on this side and the noes on
that side. . .

PT   *After a long interval.* I've got
them sorted. The noes are on the
right and the yeses are on the left.

DR   Okay. Would you ask the noes
on the right — the part that does not
want my help — if she is called

With ideomotor signals, yes and
no fingers lift together. The opposing opinions are separated —
with the part desiring help on one
side and the opposing part on the
other. It is the disagreeing part
that needs to be communicated
with.

Cindy. If she is, she'll put yeses on the board, but if she isn't she will put up more noes. . . What are you getting?

PT   Noes.

DR   On the right hand side?

PT   Yeah.

DR   Ask that part if she will tell us what her name is? She is not Cindy. What is her name?. . . What does she say? Will she tell us? Is she saying yes or no?

PT   Nothing.

DR   What name comes to your mind, Cindy?

PT   . . . SUSAN! *This is said in loud strong tone of voice and is accompanied by a hardening of the facial expression.*

DR   Okay, Susan. . . Susan, you dislike Cindy, do you?

PT Susan   No. *Said in a flat disinterested tone of voice.*

DR   Are you angry with her then?

PT.S   Yes. *Said strongly and emphatically.*

DR   She must have upset you in some way. Do you enjoy beating

---

She clearly states that her name is *not* Cindy. This further confirms her separateness.

The long delay in answering this question is probably because this part has not yet given herself a name and has to think of one.

On the other hand, the defiant way in which she announces her name may suggest that she had to overcome some obstruction to self-expression.

This is the first verbal communication from Susan and is a prognostic sign of good rapport with the therapist.

We now have some idea of the reason for Susan's anger.

her, Susan? Do you get a kick out of doing that?

PT.S   Yes. *Quietly.*

DR   Okay, Susan can you tell me how old you are?. . . Are you five years of age or younger?

An attempt is now made to define Susan more clearly and to locate the critical experience responsible for her appearance.

PT.S   Fourteen.

DR   You're fourteen. Fourteen year old Susan, something's happening that appears to be making you very angry, right?. . . Am I right?

PT.S   Right!

DR   Makes you feel uncomfortable in some other way too?

PT.S   *Sighs deeply.* It hurts.

This strong awareness of hurt indicates that Susan is a Child ego state. Inquiry is made into why eighteen years later she is still retaining the hurt.

DR   It hurts. Can you tell me what it is that hurts so badly?. . . You have been keeping this old hurt for such a long time. Do you feel that you have a right to stay hurt?

PT.S   Well, I don't understand. . . I just don't do anything right.

I just don't do anything right is a clear statement of awareness of parental (Parental?) disapproval which is being maintained by Cindy in Parental fashion.

DR   Who's criticising you?

PT.S   I don't know — it's someone over there. *Raising her hand and pointing to one side.*

DR   Always criticising you?

PT.S   Always telling me that I am doing things wrong.

DR   It's not Mum, is it?

PT.S   It's somebody.

DR   Yeah. Always telling you, you're doing something wrong.

PT.S   I must be doing something. . . She doesn't treat me like I'm doing it right.

DR   Hmm. Who is it? Look and see who it is. . . It's not Cindy is it?

PT.S   *Surprised tone of voice.* Yeah!

DR   It's Cindy. She's always criticising you, is she? Is that right?

PT.S   She sure is. She doesn't say it though. She just treats me. . . *Angrily.*

DR   What, like a nobody?

PT.S   Yeah.

DR   No wonder you feel hurt.

PT.S   Just like I don't have any rights or brains.

DR   Where did she get that from? Did she get that from Mum?

PT.S   Don't know. *Rather plaintively.*

The therapist attempts to identify the source of the parental influence and believes that it probably emanates from Mum.

The therapist rightly suspects that it is Cindy who is being Parent.

Cindy behaves towards Susan exactly the same as mother does towards Susan.

It is interesting here to note that Susan appears to be unaware of

DR You know you've got brains and rights don't you?

PT.S I don't know. There's just *so* many things wrong with me. *Sadly.*

DR Well, Cindy says that they are wrong but perhaps they are not. She's simply hard to please, isn't she?. . . I wonder who she gets that hard-to-please nature from? Does she get that from Mum? *Head nods.* You're telling me *yes* right? *Nods.* Is Mum hard to please. . . eh Susan? *Nods.* Why do you call yourself Susan. . . is that a nicer name than Cindy? *Nods.* You don't like Cindy, you prefer to be Susan, is that right? *Nods.* Have you always been Susan, even before fourteen. . . When did you first become Susan?

PT.S I don't think I was a younger Susan.

DR Just fourteen. . . is that right?

PT.S I think so. I don't know what I did when I was younger.

DR No. So you must be fourteen. Something happens at fourteen to make you feel so unloved and unwanted and such a bad person. Something happens there. Can you tell me what it is, Susan? Something you do. What is that?. . . You get all the blame. Does Cindy give you all the blame?

PT.S Yeah.

the striking similarity between Cindy and Mum. She accepts criticism from Cindy at face value. The therapist attempts to draw her attention to the unfairness of these criticisms and to view them differently.

Now the therapist has succeeded in demonstrating the nature of the Mum/Cindy relationship to Susan.

Susan is definitely not Cindy and does not want to be for some reason.

Therapist now attempts to identify the critical experience responsible for Susan's separation from the rest of the personality.

Susan was clearly located at fourteen and the separation appears to have occurred then.

The therapist feels that Susan has had to carry all of the blame for Cindy who remains free from maternal criticism.

DR Yes, I think it's something she does and she gives all the blame to you, you take all the blame. Is that right?

PT.S I think so, because she's not unhappy.

DR Yes, but you —

PT.S *As if watching something for the first time.* Everybody is looking at her and smiling.

Susan becomes aware that Cindy remains relaxed and occupies centre stage feeling blameless.

DR Yes, but you have to take all the shit. Is that right?. . . Is that right?

PT.S Mmmm. Same old thing all the time. *Resignedly.*

The therapist is very much aware of the contrast between the approval of Cindy and the disapproval of Susan. Susan agrees.

DR Can you tell what happened? Do you know?. . . Can you remember what it was that happened?. . . Look in your memory and see what it is that happened. . . something that happened to make you feel so different from Cindy. Something to answer the puzzle as to why Cindy has pushed you right back there.

The therapist now tries to direct Susan to discover the reason for this. This is unsuccessful.

PT.S Yeah, I'm really caged. *Laughs dryly.*

DR In a cage eh? Can't get out, is that right?. . . Okay, Susan, can I talk to you again in a few moments? Is that okay?

Susan agrees that she feels imprisoned. Susan (Child) is feeling locked up by Cindy (Parent) (This issue of feeling caged has been examined in the author's book *Unlock Your Mind And Be Free!*.)

PT.S Sure.

DR Okay. Incidentally, before I leave you Susan, did you want to come and see me today? Cindy brought you along but did you really want to come?

Prior to the appointment, Susan had no intention of communicating with the therapist.

PT.S Just to watch.

DR Do you mind me talking to you?

She had watched therapy before but had never previously allowed herself to become involved.

PT.S No.

DR Okay. Did you ever talk to me before?

PT.S I don't think so.

DR Okay. Cindy. . . Cindy, Hi. Hi Cindy. Did you hear that?

Cindy is called back to see if she can shed some light on the reason for the problems.

PT.C Yep.

DR Why did you treat Susan like that? Why do you put her in the back like that and lock her up? Eh?

PT.C She doesn't get mad − she's afraid to.

Cindy is able to recognise that not only is Susan isolated from the rest of the personality but she is forbidden to express her anger openly.

DR Who told you that?

PT.C I can see it.

DR What did she do wrong at fourteen?

PT.C She stays out too late, she doesn't do as she is told.

She does so only by rebellion.

DR She stays out too late.

PT.C She never comes home in time for dinner and she doesn't like her mother.

DR Does Mum complain about that?

PT.C No, she doesn't say things to her. She just treats her like she is less than a person.

Here we can see where Cindy gets her model for treating Susan.

DR Mum does?

PT.C Yes.

DR What do you think about that? Do you think that is right?

PT.C *Superciliously.* Well, she asks for it.

This very Parental attitude is obviously modelled on mother's behaviour toward Cindy (as Susan).

DR You agree with Mum then, do you?

PT.C Sure.

DR I see. . . What did she do that was so awful at fourteen?. . . Can you tell me what that was? Is it something that you're punishing her for?

PT.C Oh, I don't punish her. I stay out of it.

Although Cindy does not admit to punishing Susan, her critical attitude is highly rejecting.

DR Who punishes her then?

PT.C Her mother.

DR You stay out of it eh?

PT.C   Oh sure.

DR   What does her mother do to her?

PT.C   None of my business.

DR   None of your business eh? You just stay away from it all? She gets it all eh?

PT.C   Yep.

DR   Okay. I just want to talk to another part that has been seeing all that has been going on. I don't know what she is called, whether she is Cindy or whether she is called Susan. I'd like that part just to nod the head when she is listening to me. . . I need your help. . . *Nods*. Hi, you are there. . . Are you going to talk to me?

It is at this point that the therapist considers that the help of the Adult is urgently required. Fortunately, the Adult responds readily.

PT.Adult   Okay.

DR   There's Susan and there's Cindy, having a battle all of the time. Can you help me on this? I need your help. Susan is as angry as hell because she is locked up — Cindy has kept her there. Cindy believes that her Mum is right all of the time. You and I know that Susan is simply a regular girl and it is about time that she was forgiven, don't you agree? What is your view?

Briefly, the therapist reviews and explains the problem as he sees it, since it appears that there has been little Adult intervention hitherto in this Cindy/Susan conflict.

PT.A   *Casual and noncommittal*. I usually just watch.

The Adult now admits that it has never intervened in this conflict.

DR   Well, now that you're watching, can you come and give us a hand? Can you help me to get Susan and Cindy back to being friends again, because really that's no way for them to go on is it?

It's help is now being urgently solicited.

PT.A   I don't know if they like each other. I don't think they want to be together.

DR   I know they don't. They don't like each other because they don't understand each other. . . right? We need to find ways for them to understand each other. Isn't that right?. . . Let's take this step by step. . . Susan, I think, was not really liked by her mother, right?

The Adult is not being very strong or resourceful at this point and the therapist has to encourage its greater intervention and participation in the resolution of the conflict.

PT.A   No she certainly was not!

DR   And it isn't very fair is it, not to be liked? She must have felt very hurt about that.

Although the Adult is aware of Susan's feelings, it takes heed of Cindy's viewpoint at first but is encouraged to be more objective.

PT.A   Oh yes, I agree, but you have to have seen some of the things that she did.

DR   But you have seen some of the things that Mum did? Be fair.

PT.A   *Nodding in agreement.* Okay.

DR   You would agree wouldn't you that Susan was hurt?

PT.A   And I made her worse.

Now the Adult recognises an error

DR   Yes. Right. . . Now what about Cindy? Cindy's always. . .

in its previous position and also spots the falseness of Cindy's.

PT.A   Hmm – Goody two shoes! *Laughs.*

DR   Right. Butter wouldn't melt in her mouth, eh?

PT.A   No, you bet!

DR   But she isn't all that good. I'm saying, hey Susan isn't as bad as she has been painted and Cindy isn't as good as she has been made to appear. Don't you agree?. . .

The therapist de-emphasises the essential differences between Susan and Cindy so that better contact can be promoted between them.

PT.A   . . . Yes.

The Adult's help is now assured.

DR   Now can you get them to understand? You talk to them please. Give them all the wisdom and understanding that you have.

The remainder of this session was devoted to encouraging the Adult ego state (later called Helper Cindy) to take charge rather than stay uninvolved in the Cindy/Susan conflict. It undertook to encourage Susan to express her feelings and Cindy to be more tolerant. The therapist further encouraged Cindy and Susan to regard the events of fourteen years of age as no longer relevant. Some time had to be spent in encouraging the acceptance of normal anger as being proper and not something that must be deplored and condemned.

The patient was then asked to progress forward in time and to describe what it was like to have every part of her in harmony. She found this to be a period full of vitality and energy in which she would be able to express her feelings.

In fact this was the last session with this patient and several months later she called to say that everything was going well, that she felt at peace with herself and her family. She was no longer subject to her irrational anger or her panic attacks. She appeared to have little or no memory of the events of this last session and no attempts were made to probe what must be regarded as a therapeutic amnesia. It is assumed that all of the unconscious ego states have found it possible to function harmoniously with each other.

Multiple Personalities

All ego states are originally formed from the primary personality, the Child ego state, and each is a response of the Child ego state to the environment. The normal process appears to be the formation of a Parent ego state to understand and adapt to the parent world; similarly, the Adult ego state is a response to the adult world. However, the separation of parts of the personality can become much more complex. We have seen how ego state complexes form in response to critical experiences and persist to control or modify behaviour long after the critical experience has passed. These ego states sometimes command strong executive power and emerge from their unconscious hiding places to take charge of the individual.

The term *multiple personalities* is usually applied to the individual who has more than one of these unconscious ego states, each of which successively adopts executive power so that the personality of the individual appears to make dramatic changes. In the process of ego state formation, the clinical condition of multiple personalities occurs at the end of a continuum of ego state separation, which is a normal part of personality response to the environment. Even among multiple personalities, all degrees of this separation have been described, from those individuals having only two observable personalities to those having several.

In hypnosis, the conscious mind becomes dissociated, to varying degrees from the unconscious mind, so that access to the unconscious ego states is facilitated. Nevertheless, very powerful, directive ego states can remain concealed and continue to be responsible for symptoms and unwanted behaviour patterns, even in deep hypnosis. However, in the absence of conscious awareness, as may occur in deep hypnosis, such ego states may readily reveal themselves and admit responsibility for personality changes. Although these unconscious ego states may be sufficiently separate to have little knowledge of each other, or to have very different names and sets of memories, the term multiple personality has usually been restricted to those individuals whose unconscious personalities (ego states) have clearly, if only periodically, taken conscious executive control of the individual. For the analytical hypnotherapist, this distinction is immaterial, since therapy is the same regardless of whether the ego states gain control of the personality. The objective of therapy is to persuade the Adult ego state to be prepared to assume executive control at all times. In these multiple personality cases, the Adult is unaccustomed to this necessary position of authority within the personality complex. The Adult ego state is strengthened in therapy mainly by its gaining the approval and respect of the other conflicting ego states by resolving their differences. While there exist varying degrees of personality split, those individuals who manifest multiple personalities will require intensive and prolonged therapy before internal harmony can be established.

Both biographical and clinical literature are replete with cases of multiple personality; Taylor and Martin (1944) surveyed the English literature and found seventy-six cases so described, and Allison (1977) was able to increase this number to approximately ninety-six. Because interest in multiple personality has increased enormously in recent years, there have been many unpublished reports of this condition at scientific meetings. Indeed, Braun and Braun (1980) contend that they are aware of approximately 500 cases currently being treated. In each case, there is clear evidence of more than one personality successively assuming executive control of the individual. The evidence consists of observable distinctive changes in behaviour associated with the various personalities; periods of amnesia during which the host personality is unaware of the individual's experiences or behaviour and describes his loss of awareness of passage of time as 'blackouts'; and the identifiably distinct, consistent characteristics of each personality accompanied by a relatively separate memory for its life history. The rapid increase in the reported instances of multiple personalities indicates an increased awareness of this condition, which is reflected in the recent spate of books written for the lay public. Increased public awareness of a phenomenon inevitably leads to its receiving greater professional attention; multiple personality is no exception.

Since multiple personalities are simply unconscious ego states that have assumed executive control of the individual, everything that has been said about ego states applies equally well to multiple personalities. We recognise the multiple personality because of its executive control which must be maintained long enough for the personality to be observed. However, what is usually termed compulsive behaviour may well be an ego state's taking executive control for unrecognizably short periods. Thus, a study of the multiple personality may aid in the understanding of much pathological human behaviour.

Multiple personalities are usually discovered during hypnosis when the executive control of the conscious Adult is reduced. This has led to the accusation that multiple personalities are produced by hypnosis, which is rather like claiming that the microscope has caused infectious diseases. Yet, following hypnosis, uncovered ego states sometimes find it easier to assume executive control. Kampman (1976) found that 7% of apparently normal high school students could produce a secondary personality, as could 41% of highly hypnotisable subjects, but examination of the criteria for a secondary personality in Kampman's study reveals no resemblance to those cases seen clinically.

Hilgard (1977) believed that hypnotic age regression appears to be an analog of multiple personality but, when hypnosis is terminated, the regression is but a set of memories. In some sense this personality created in age regression is a temporary transition towards a multiple personality. However, he concluded that it would be a mistake to see this created personality as a latent multiple personality since it really exists only as a set of memories. Leavitt (1947) had already concluded that there is a strong resemblance between multiple personalities appearing in hypnosis and those existing spontaneously, independently of it. So, perhaps a relaxation of the Adult consciousness's vigilance which occurs in hypnosis permits the elevation of an unconscious ego state to a temporary executive level where it can control behaviour and produce symptoms.

At times, when communication is established with the hidden ego state, the therapist learns that there have been significant periods during which that ego state has been 'out' and in control. One can then assume that such a case is an early instance of multiple personality. In the practice of analytical hypnotherapy, a hidden ego state is always responsible for behaviour which, although totally acceptable in its own viewpoint, is completely inappropriate to most if not all of the rest of the personality. The subject's amnesia in these cases serves to insulate this unacceptable behaviour from interference of other objecting parts of the personality; these parts remain unaware of the mechanism underlying the behaviour.

Like any ego state, the components of the multiple personality syndrome may have strong Parental or Child characteristics, due to the splitting of the existing ego state complex into a part that is Parent oriented and one that is Child oriented at the time of the critical experience. The Child portion of the ego complex is usually the hidden ego state, which may emerge as the separate personality. The splitting which creates the multiple personality syndrome is usually the result of a critical experience which is physically intolerable. In such an experience, the Child uses the splitting mechanism to partially escape the traumatic environment which is clearly rejecting it. Often these cases give a history of sexual or other intense physical abuse. Although real or apparent rejection is a common factor in most of the problems that an analytical hypnotherapist is called upon to treat, this is never more true than in the cases of multiple personality.

Ego states which are opposed within the unconscious mind while maintaining separate identitities, are not, strictly speaking, multiple personalities until they show evidence of having obtained executive control of the individual. Frequently, when contact has been made with such an ego state, there is a claim made by the relevant ego state that it has exerted significant control over the individual's behaviour. One can assume that this is due to the temporary assumption of executive control during a relaxation of the normal vigilance of the conscious Adult.

The following is an excerpt from a session with such a case of multiple personality. She is a thirty-four year old woman, married with two children, whose attendance for hypnotherapy was to lose weight. Her initial response was good but after a few months the weight she had lost was regained, and she returned for further therapy. During this second phase of therapy, she became depressed and anxious. At first it was not clear what created the problem since, in hypnosis, she was unable to locate any source of tension; she indicated acceptance of suggestions but did not keep them. Incidentally, she was an excellent hypnotic subject, and it was not clear why she was unable to carry out therapeutic suggestions. On one of her visits, she brought with her a letter which she did not recall writing but knew she had written. This letter made veiled references to some terrible thing that she had done; this she found extremely upsetting and puzzling. Therapy now assumed a new direction. We subsequently located a memory of sexual abuse by her father which occurred when she was about fourteen years old. She was able to describe the experiences in considerable detail in hypnosis, but had only a vague memory of the experience in consciousness, and a hazy recollection of this period of her life. In fact, at a conscious level, she had difficulty accepting that this experience had ever occurred although it must have gone on for more than a year. She did recall that she became sexually promiscuous around the age of sixteen and became pregnant prior to marriage. At this time, she began to gain weight until she weighed about two hundred and fifty pounds.

By the stage of therapy from which this excerpt is taken, we had resolved most of the unconscious tensions and, although she was feeling very well, she found that she periodically lapsed into periods of depression. Of primary importance, however, was that she still could not adhere to a diet programme. This was accepted as evidence of a persistent unresolved tension presumed to be due to the presence of a hidden ego state. Prior to this session, the ego state responsible for the letter and the depression had been presumed to have been successfully treated by dealing with the experience of incest and its associated guilt. This was in reality a qualified success.

In therapy, the responsible ego state was located and defined; whereas the patient's name was Anne, this ego state called herself Sandy. She was still aged fourteen (the age of the incest) and admitted that she continued, as she had always done, to make Anne overeat and tell Anne that she was bad to make her depressed. Sandy resisted giving up these activities, even though she really did not wish to continue them, because she was aware that Anne now wanted to be rid of her, even though, originally, Anne had created her to deal with father and had then promptly forgotten about her. Anne, on the other hand, was very distressed at having to share her body with another personality. In treatment of multiple personalities, as with less distinct ego states, ways must be discovered in which they can coexist in harmony. It is clear that the normal structure of the healthy personality − in which the Adult is always in control, even when not in the executive position − must be reestablished. Although the resorption of an unwanted ego state is evidently one solution, it was unacceptable to this patient, and so the alternative of peaceful coexistence is pursued.

PT.Anne *Crying.* Can you help me? We were living great for a while but since she. . . she came out you know, I don't want her around any more.

Anne is feeling desperate. Identification of the hidden personality has increased her inner turmoil and she feels that this personality is the cause of all her problems.

DR Why don't you want her around any more?

PT.A Because I don't need her any more.

DR I see. Can we ask her to go

Anne recognises that the secondary personality had at one time been necessary and that she is responsible for her presence, yet she feels alienated from her.

back with you again? Can we do that?

PT.A   *Sobbing.* I don't want her to.

DR   But she is a part of you. You made her didn't you?

PT.A   But I don't want her any more.

DR   Well, what are you going to do with her? Can you take back the energy from her that you gave her?

Resorption of the unwanted ego state is suggested by the therapist.

PT.Sandy   No. *Defiantly.* Can't take it away. She won't get me.

DR   Nobody's going to get you.

A defiant Sandy interrupts the therapist's exchanges with the unconscious Adult before this line of approach goes too far.

PT.S   No. *Still defiantly.*

DR   What are you going to do then, Sandy, are you going to go on making things bad for everyone? Anne does not like you because you're not doing nice things for her. Why don't you be nice and perhaps you won't have to go away?

The therapist then attempts to explain the reason for Anne's rejection of Sandy.

PT.S   They want us all to be one and I don't want to, I *don't* want to.

DR   You don't want to be one eh? Why do you want to go on being separate?

Sandy is determined to fight any suggestion of ego state resorption. The therapist attempts to discover the reason for this.

PT.S   I don't know. I just know that it's not fair.

DR   What isn't fair?

PT.S   Well, they create me and then they just take me and leave me alone. *Angrily.* They just push me away.

Sandy makes the valid point that she did not choose to exist and has a right to retain what existence has been given her. The therapist indicates his understanding of her position, thereby increasing his rapport with her.

DR   I can understand that. It can't be much fun for you having to fight Anne — not like it used to be when you could sit back and have fun. Do you like Anne at all?

PT.S   She's okay.

DR   You were helping her to lose weight for a while. Why have you stopped doing that now?

PT.S   Because when she starts losing weight she starts feeling confident and I won't be needed any more and she'll get rid of me. She'll get stronger.

Sandy's antagonism to Anne is toward her attitude rather than her personality. Sandy's ability to make Anne overeat is her way of fighting back.

DR   So you're scared that she'll get rid of you?

PT.S   *Petulantly.* Well I don't want to be got rid of. I just want to. . . oh, I don't know any more.

Sandy is fighting for survival.

DR   Don't want to fade away?

PT.S   That's right.

DR   Do you feel yourself fading away?

PT.A   Yes, but it's hard to fade her.

DR   I know.

It is Anne's turn to interrupt, and the demeanour suddenly changes. Anne admits that she has tried, unsuccessfully, to get rid of Sandy.

PT.A *Sobbing.* Because she wants to be herself.

DR Aha. She wants to be herself again, doesn't she?

DR (to S) She made you to deal with that problem and now she wants you to be a part of her again.

The therapist unconsciously readdresses Sandy. She is aware of this and responds. Presumably, the tone and content of the therapist's remark initiated this switch.

PT.S I'm fighting two of them now. I'm fighting Anne and I'm fighting the older Anne.

We now become aware of the presence of two Annes, the younger being the one with whom Sandy had been able to communicate. The therapist appreciates Sandy's fight to survive, and encourages her by recognising that she had done all that was demanded of her.

DR Right. That's a losing battle, though, isn't it?

PT.S Yeah.

DR They really do want you to disappear, don't they?

PT.S Yeah.

DR I think that they should thank you for doing a damned good job, don't you?

PT.S Yes. I did what I thought was best.

DR You did what you were asked to do. You were a part of sixteen year old Anne, and she asked you to take care of those memories.

PT.S Yes.

DR What was your job, Sandy? What were you asked to do?

It now becomes necessary to determine precisely what these de-

PT.S   Be a friend.

DR   Just be a friend?

PT.S   Yes. She didn't feel like she had any friends. She didn't have anybody.

DR   And you were her friend. Why didn't you stay her friend?

PT.S   Because I decided that I wanted something for myself.

DR   I see. Anne wasn't getting anything for herself at all, eh?

PT.S   You were starting to get rid of that Anne.

DR   Sixteen year old Anne?

PT.S   Yes. She used to be fourteen but now she is sixteen.

DR   And you began to feel lonely?

PT.S   No, but if you got rid of her you would get rid of me and I'm not going to be got rid of.

DR   But sixteen year old Anne hasn't gone, has she?

PT.S   No, but she used to be a fourteen year old me and now she's sixteen.

DR   And fourteen year old Anne has gone, eh?

mands were. In this reply we are reminded of the way in which children frequently create imaginary playmates who, perhaps like Sandy, resist attempts to reabsorb them. They may remain as hidden ego states whose unwanted existence creates difficulties.

The therapist had attempted to persuade fourteen year old Anne to mature, and had evidently been partly successful. This obviously increased Sandy's fear that she too might be modified out of existence.

PT.S   Yes.

DR   So sixteen year old Anne is going to go soon, you think?

PT.S   Yes, as the older Anne gets stronger.

DR   Sixteen year old Anne. . .

PT.S   I can't let you talk to her because when you talk to her you make her stronger.

DR   Sixteen year old Anne?

PT.S   Yes.

DR   You don't want me to talk to her?

PT.S   No. I just pushed her away and I'm not going to let you talk to her because you'll just talk her into growing up.

DR   I want what's best for everybody. Do you understand that?

PT.S   No. *Commences to cry.*

DR   I know how you must be feeling, Sandy. It must be awful.

PT.S   *Sobbing.*

DR   I would like you to be happy, Sandy.

PT.S   But it wasn't so bad before.

Sandy forecasts that therapy is likely to effect increased maturity and strength of the unconscious ego states.

The therapist would like to communicate with sixteen year old Anne at this point, but Sandy is afraid to permit this since she fears that the therapist will encourage Anne to mature away from her. Thus, Sandy remains defiant.

Sandy is confused. She is disturbed by the therapist's empathy, yet feels that she must continue to protect herself.

DR   It wasn't that good, you know.
It was okay for you maybe. . .

PT.S   Yeah, well, it *was* okay for me.

DR   It wasn't okay for the rest.

Sandy insists on the need to maintain the status quo, since any change threatens her with annihilation (which she cannot permit).

PT.S   If you correct those things, then I won't be here any more.

DR   Where will you be?

PT.S   Gone. I won't exist anymore.

DR   But where were you before?

PT.S   I didn't exist before.

DR   But you must have been a part of Anne then.

PT.S   I guess I was some part of her, I don't know. I just know I wasn't around until that happened to her. . . and then I was there.

An ego state's memories are confined to those experiences directly related to them, although it may be aware of the experiences of the other ego states.

DR   And you don't want to go back to being where you were before?

PT   I don't know where I was before.

DR   You were part of Anne. You didn't come from nowhere. You came from Anne. *Patient sobs.* Wouldn't that be okay? It's not like dying. It's not like being absolutely gone and being dead. It's more becoming part of something else — a

The therapist suggests that resorption might be a solution, but this suggestion only serves to increase Sandy's distress.

safer part — a sharing. Wouldn't that be all right?

PT.S   But I would be a part of her. I wouldn't be me.

Sandy is unable to relinquish a separate identity.

DR   That is true. You wouldn't be able to make decisions on your own any more.

PT.S   Being me isn't so much fun lately.

DR   No. I am sure that it would be much more fun being part of Anne, because you know a lot of things. You could give your learning to her.

The therapist seeks to discover an alternative mode of functioning by reviewing Sandy's resources and the contributions that she could make.

PT.S   *Sobbing.* I haven't learned anything.

Sandy remains uncertain that this would be enough to ensure her survival.

DR   Oh yes you have! You learned how to be a friend to fourteen year old Anne first of all. You learned how to protect her from people who wanted to put her down, didn't you?

PT.S   Yes.

DR   And these are things she needs to know about. What other things have you learned?

PT.S   *Sobs.*

DR   Learned how to be a friend to her?

PT.S   That's all. I was just. . . just there so she would have someone to

Sandy's main function was that of confidante, since Adult Anne was unable to tolerate the painful memories of incest. Adult Anne has always remained sepa-

talk to. She wouldn't talk to anyone and she wouldn't tell the other grown up Anne because she wasn't supposed to know.

rate from these memories in order to function.

DR   So you kept all of the memories and the hurt. Is that right?

PT.S   Some of it. I shared it with fourteen year old Anne.

DR   I see. How could you become better friends and really work together instead of having to fight?

The therapist once again seeks a solution to the obvious conflict.

PT.S   If I do that then you will get us all together and I won't be here anymore.

DR   That's my aim, but I don't think you will ever disappear altogether.

PT.S   I don't want to let go of Sandy.

Sandy is confused and uncertain whether she really wants to remain Sandy or to become a part of Anne.

DR   You want to remain Sandy, do you?

PT.S   Oh, I don't know. I suppose it's got to come eventually anyway. I'd rather be Anne. Once when we started fighting she got scared and thought that she had better just go away.

DR   To go away? Doing what?. . . And do what?

PT.S   Get rid of us all.

Evidently, Anne has seriously

DR   To die?. . . You don't want
that, do you? That's not what you
want is it?

considered suicide to escape the
inner turmoil.

PT.S   No.

Obviously, Sandy does not want
this to happen.

DR   You don't really want that, do
you? When she gets so depressed, I
bet she feels like that, eh?

PT.S   *Sobbing.* Yes.

DR   Could you help her over that?
Instead of fighting could you now be
friends? Perhaps instead of disappearing altogether could you live
side by side with her?

The therapist now considers the
possibility of permanent peaceful
coexistence as an acceptable alternative.

PT.S   Well it's better than nothing, I
guess, because we have eventually to
live. She's going to win anyway,
isn't she?

Sandy concedes that the
therapist's suggested alternative is
adequate.

DR   I don't know. I hope that you
all win.

PT.S   Even me?

DR   Yes. I want everybody to win,
because it cannot be good if any part
loses. I want every part to win.

PT.S   Oh, okay.

DR   But that means that you all
must be friends. Maybe you should
have an equal voice, eh? Maybe you
should say, *look, even though I
can't run things I've got a right to be
listened to.* It isn't fair that you be
kicked out is it?

The therapist explains the position of peaceful coexistence more
clearly and inidcates that it can be
advantageous to every part of the
personality. He agrees that Sandy
deserves special consideration because of her role in handling the
critical experience.

PT.S Well, that's what I'm angry about.

DR Aha. Will you let me talk to Anne?

PT.S I'll let you talk to sixteen year old Anne.

Now Sandy allows the therapist to place this proposition before sixteen year old Anne.

DR Will you? Okay. Hi! Sixteen year old Anne.

PT.A [16] Hi!

DR Did you hear that?

PT.A [16] Yes.

DR What do you think of that? My idea is that all the Annes and the Sandys can get together and be friends. How do you feel about that?

PT.A[16] That would be better than fighting, I guess. As long as Sandy is okay. I have tried to get rid of her because she was starting to want too much.

Anne agrees and explains how she had felt compelled to prevent Sandy from usurping too much control.

DR Too much. That wasn't fair, was it? She was trying to run the show.

PT.A [16] No, it's not fair. It's just that she's only a part − she's not the whole.

DR Just a part, that's right. I'm suggesting that every part get together and be friends and talk with each other. Would you agree with that?

PT.A[16]   Well, of course. I only pushed her away because of what she was trying to do, but maybe she's found that she can't.

DR   Okay. Sandy, did you hear that?

PT.S   Yes. That's true. I just wanted to be there, and I was scared that they were going to get rid of me.

Sandy counters by explaining that her actions were necessary for her survival.

DR   Okay, if they agree not to get rid of you, you won't fight. Is that right?

PT.S   Yes.

DR   Okay, sixteen year old Anne, did you hear that?

PT.A [16]   Yes.

DR   She thought you wanted to be rid of her, that was why she was fighting you. Now she says that if you don't want to get rid of her, and, if you will use her as a friend, she will stay as a friend.

PT.A [16]   Oh, okay.

DR   Good. I have to talk to thirty-six year old Anne and see what she thinks. Okay?

The unconscious Adult is now consulted, since she must be able to assume full control.

PT.A [16]   Okay.

DR   Thirty-six year old Anne, Hi!

PT.A [36]   Hi!

DR   What do you think? It's a new thought isn't it?

PT.A [36]   Just. . . scares me.

DR   Scares you eh? Wouldn't it be nice to have friends inside?

However, she remains somewhat puzzled by events which have been unfolding within her. She needs to understand the nature of this conflict and the effects that it has had upon her.

PT.A [36]   Is that why I have been feeling so bad?

DR   Oh, I would think so. It is the inside fighting that has been making you so depressed.

PT.A [36]   I can't cope with what is going on around me. Everything is so awful inside. *Commences to cry.*

She recalls how difficult it has been to deal with life with so much turmoil persisting within her.

DR   I have them saying that they are going to be friends. Could you trust them?

PT.A [36]   I have to.

DR   Wouldn't it be nice to be able to relax inside? If you could, your headaches will go and your ulcers will get better and you'll lose weight. . . You know that you have to be sure that Sandy understands that you have decided to accept her.

It is obvious that some of Anne's symptoms have been directly caused by this internal tension.

PT.A [36]   Well if she won't fight me any more, of course I will accept her.

DR   Well, you didn't before. In fact

In an earlier session, Anne em-

one time, you said *no way*. You wanted to get rid of her and she heard you say that.

PT.A ³⁶   Well it scared me. I don't want other people inside me.

DR   Well they are not other people, they are still you. They are parts of you that you had pushed away from yourself.

phasized that she could no longer tolerate the presence of another personality.

The therapist attempts to clarify how Anne is responsible for the current situation, which makes it easier for her to accept.

PT.A ³⁶   I see.

DR   In order to deal with problems, you pushed parts of yourself away until it seemed like it was somebody else. But in fact, all of the time it was you.

PT.A ³⁶   Okay, but I would like us all to just try to help me to cope with everything every day, and lose more weight, and be the way I want to be.

DR   Well, let's ask. Sixteen year old Anne. . . did you hear that?

PT.A ¹⁶   Yes.

DR   What do you think about that?

PT.A ¹⁶   That would be the smartest way to be.

DR   Do you have to keep that old anger any more?

PT.A ¹⁶   Well, some of the anger was towards Sandy, but if she isn't going to fight me and Anne (36), then some of that anger will go. But Sandy and me − we've got to keep that memory from Anne because she's not ready to cope with that yet.

It seems that there remains some repression of the memory of the incest. The therapist fears that this will perpetuate tension.

DR   But will keeping that memory make you all that angry?

PT.A [16]   I don't think so, because I'm so tired of being angry.

DR   Okay. Let me talk to Sandy. Sandy. Sandy, Hi!

PT.S   Hello.

DR   How do you feel about all that?

PT.S   Okay. If they're not going to get rid of me that's the only thing I have to feel bad about.

DR   Okay. Do you trust them, now that you have heard them?

PT.S   Yeah, plus I've got to realise. . . That I guess I have to be part of her. I can't be somebody by myself.

DR   That's right, you can't. And you always were a part of her and she made you in the first place. She gave you the thoughts and ideas and things to deal with.

PT.S   Yeah.

DR   Still, she needs you to advise her and to give her your point of view on things.

The therapist tries to interest Sandy in the possibility of future interchanges. Sandy, however, is

PT.S Well, couldn't I just not fight   tired of it all and simply wants to
any more right now?. I don't want   be left alone.
to talk.

The remainder of this session was devoted to ensuring that all of the unconscious ego states retained an increased mutual respect and understanding, which would enable them to interact harmoniously. This was an important session for Anne, after which she was able to feel much more at peace with herself. The symptoms of headaches and stomach discomfort abated; her general feeling of relaxation increased, and although she did not immediately lose weight, she became quite certain that she would do so. At the time of writing, therapy is continuing and progressing favourably, since Anne is much more at ease. Consciously, she is rarely bothered by the thought of other personalities within her.

A very important lesson can be learned from Anne's case: such an ego state needs to be recognised and accepted. We assume that Sandy was formed by Adult Anne, at an unconscious level, to protect her from the painful memory of the incest experiences. But it is possible that fourteen year old Anne is the original ego state to whom this task was designated, and that she in turn formed a friend, Sandy, to share the burden. There was still evidence, at a later session, of tension between Anne and Sandy. At this time, the technique of placing one ego state in one hand and the other in the opposite hand was used; they were then asked to approach each other and fuse. This appears to have been successful, since at each subsequent session there has been increased evidence of comfort and general internal harmony. Anne has little feeling of having a separate personality within her; presumably Sandy functions in a manner similar to the ego states which each of us has, but which are not independent.

In the therapy of multiple personalities the analytical hypnotherapist must deal with each personality's need to remain separate. This necessitates a greater intervention of the therapist's Adult, because the formation of multiple personalities indicates the probable presence of an Adult who has tended to avoid confrontation and involvement. In this case, Anne herself wanted nothing to do with Sandy, and wanted her to go away, taking with her whatever memories she still retained.

The conflict over Anne's acceptance of the part of her which had been emotionally involved in the incest has been resolved; the present battle involves the acceptance of the separate identity that this part has erected to defend its memories. If the personalities can be persuaded to find a means of working in harmony, it is usually found that those ego states that no longer serve a useful function in the service of the whole personality gradually become weaker and finally disappear. In Anne's case, it appears that immediately after this reported session, Sandy was much less in evidence.

The Negative Birth Experience

Analytical hypnotherapy has frequently and clearly demonstrated that the critical experiences responsible for Child/Parent conflicts can occur much earlier in life than was previously thought possible. We now know that the process of birth can be a very traumatic critical experience. Furthermore, there is much evidence that the foetus is capable of responding to prenatal events as critical experiences.

Verney (1977), in his review of the literature on this subject, cited many examples of the effect of maternal stress upon the unborn child, and pointed out that many investigators attribute infantile autism to intense maternal anxiety during pregnancy. Sontag (1941) suggested that chronic fatigue, malnutrition, and strong emotional disturbances may so alter the physiology of the pregnant woman that the foetus is adversely affected. As early as 1935, Sontag and Wallace demonstrated that the foetus responds to sound vibrations applied to the abdomen of the mother. Frank (1966) believed that a woman bearing an unwanted child may be so unhappy and disturbed that she may be said to have a hostile uterus. Thus, persistent worries, resentment and anxiety may have an effect upon the unborn child. Prenatal effects are no longer considered to be old wives' tales and should be considered as possible components in emotional and psychogenic disorders. There can be little doubt that the emotional impact of birth may be so intense as to create lasting problems for the individual. Rank (1914) stated that the circumstances of birth itself, the *birth trauma*, are imprinted upon the psyche of the infant; Harris (1967) cited evidence to prove that the events of birth and of infant life are recorded even though they are not remembered. Cheek (1974), using ideomotor techniques, regressed subjects to the birth process and observed sequential head and shoulder movements which were identical to the movements which must have occurred, based on a subsequent study of hospital records, during the process of birth. In Cheek's (1975) review of birth memories, he concluded that the baby may respond to maternal stress with feelings of guilt; such feelings are responsible for subsequent conditioned problems manifested as patterned responses of illness. Chamberlain (1980) compared birth memories of ten mother/child couples and found them to share a wealth of factual detail in a very high proportion of cases. He concluded that birth memories are indeed real, although the possibility of falsification does exist. He believed that the quality and content of birth memories give clear evidence of the infant's ability to experience, learn, understand and form relationships from the very beginning of life.

Kubie (1958) declared that very early in life, a central emotional position is often established, a position to which the individual automatically returns during his life. This position may constitute the major safeguard – or, conversely, the major vulnerability – of his life. When that position is a painful one, the individual may spend the whole of his life defending himself against it. Harris (1967) succinctly described this position as being *I'm not O.K., You're O.K.*, which he declared to be the universal position of childhood. The decision to move to the position of *I'm O.K., You're O.K.* is made following the receipt of information which is available only later in life.

Grof (1976) believed that perinatal experiences are a manifestation of a deep level of unconsciousness and cannot be reached by classical Freudian techniques. Furthermore, he asserted that Freudian analysis neither permits an explanation of these experiences, nor provides a conceptual framework for their interpretation. Fodor (1949), on the other hand, suggested that birth trauma appears later in life as symbolic of the desire to return to the peace and security of the womb. Raikov (1980) believed that, in hypnosis, age regression to infancy reproduces the components of infancy; this is neither fantasy nor role playing. Cheek (1974) demonstrated that deep hypnosis is not necessary for total age regression at the level of the ideomotor response. This author, in almost every case, has repeatedly confirmed Cheek's discovery in his practice of reviewing the birth experience. Meltzoff and Moore (1977) have conclusively demonstrated that a detailed awareness of the environment is present in neonates not more than sixty minutes old; therefore it is a reasonable assumption that such a highly developed awareness is present at birth.

Prior to establishing the practice of reviewing the birth experience of every patient, the author was, from time to time, puzzled by the relapse into previous symptomatology by a patient who seemingly had completed therapy successfully and was apparently cured of symptoms. All of the critical experiences located in hypnosis had been dealt with adequately at the time of therapy, and apparently, none remained to create problems. When these patients were asked to review their birth experiences, however, a high proportion of them expressed unpleasant, *not O.K.*, negative and guilty feelings associated with their births, which were still present at an unconscious level, thus preventing them from liberating themselves from these punitive symptoms. It was presumed that the previous techniques had not been sufficiently exploratory, thereby omitting the birth experience from the analytical process. When these *negative birth experiences*, as they soon came to be called, were subjected to the usual analytical procedures, the associated negative feelings were, in most cases, erased to be replaced by positive feelings. In such cases, the return to symptom free status has nearly always been dramatic with more than two sessions rarely required. This suggests that the birth experience was the single remaining problem that required remedy to secure the full objectives of analytical hypnotherapy: complete mental health and well being.

In a negative birth experience, it is presumed that the infant is aware of the parental distress that his birth has caused. As Berne (1972) has pointed out, the associated guilt is sometimes reinforced by the mother's telling the child that she has been sick since his birth. The therapist must persuade the patient to relinquish both the responsibility for his own birth that he might have previously felt, and the guilt associated with any parental distress. If we regard the Parent ego state as being that part of the Child whose specific duty it is to care for the infant by understanding parental attitudes, then any maternal distress at birth would presumably be interpreted by the Parent ego state as disapproval for which the Child is responsible. This disapproval is internalised by the Parent ego state which, in its turn, actively disapproves of the Child. This is the origin of the early self rejection associated with the negative birth experience; it is therefore the site of a potent critical experience and of a Child/Parent conflict responsible for many of the presenting symptoms. Such a negative birth experience must be located and dealt with if there is to be any hope of resolving this conflict.

The importance of this approach will be realized if one examines the results of the investigation of the birth experiences of 876 patients referred to the author. It was found that 245 or 28% indicated negative feelings about their births. These results are examined in greater detail in the appendix, but it may be pointed out these patients (the above-mentioned 28%), without the aid of hypnosis, could not attempt to resolve their problems. Hypnosis is the only route to the unconscious memories of birth. In order to locate and deal with the birth experience, specific directions for the uncovering of this experience must be given to the patient. The following are those currently used with considerable success by the author.

Would it be all right for you to look at memories that are in your unconscious mind but are beyond your conscious memory? In Chapter Ten we discussed how to deal with a negative answer to this question, so let us assume that an affirmative response has been obtained. The next direction is, *I would like you to orient your inner mind back through your unconscious memories, right back before your unconscious memory to a place where your conscious mind cannot go. I would like your unconscious mind to go back to the very first breath you took just after you were born and, when your inner mind is there, your yes finger will lift to let us know.*

Sometimes the yes finger does not lift even after this direction has been repeated; in such cases the patient should be encouraged not to try consciously to recall this first breath because it is impossible for him to do so, but simply to allow his unconscious mind to travel back to that breath and patiently await the yes signal. This is often effective. Rarely, there still occurs no response and the patient may even lift the no finger. If this evidently is an unconscious response, clearly, there is an unconscious resistance to returning to the birth memory. In any case, it is wise at this time to enquire, *Is there something about the birth that makes it too uncomfortable for you to return to?* If this is answered with a yes, it is obvious that, at a deeply unconscious level, the birth experience must have been reviewed and found to be unpleasant. The nature of the unpleasantness can be clarified simply by asking, *Is it too scary (sad, guilty, etc.) to return to?* The negative birth experience can be identified in this subtle manner as if it were being directly described.

If a yes signal is received to this direction to return to the first breath, it is a good practice to ask the patient to advance in time to the very first experience of being wrapped up, warm and safe in the crib, and to indicate when this is accomplished with a yes signal. This confirms that the birth experience has been reviewed at an unconscious level. The next direction is, *Babies, when they are born, know many things and the baby, Jane, knows many things. One of the things that she knows is whether she feels okay about being born. If she feels okay about being born, the yes finger will lift, but if she does not really feel okay about being born, then the no finger will lift.* If the patient indicates that she unconsciously feels okay about being born, then one can assume that no critical experience has occurred up to and including the time of birth. She is then instructed to enjoy the okay feeling that she has about her birth and perhaps to indicate her enjoyment with a smile. A failure to smile may suggest that her birth was not an entirely satisfactory experience and should be reviewed in greater detail to ascertain whether there remain some persistent negative feelings about the birth.

Patients with unambiguous negative feelings about their births are encouraged to deal with this as with any other critical experience. Questions are asked to discover the nature of the negative feeling, such as, *Babies who do not feel okay about being born sometimes feel guilty about being born. Does the baby Jane feel guilty about being born?* This is commonly answered with a yes; questions are then asked to define the nature of that guilt, e.g., *Does the baby Jane feel guilty about causing mother so much pain?* Should the unconscious communication appear to be profound, then the patient might be asked to review the experience until her knowledge is complete. She then can talk about it, and indicate when it would be all right to discuss the experience. In many cases the patient will be able to verbalise the negative aspects of the experience. For example, she may be aware that her mother is in great distress, or is unconscious, or her sex is remarked upon with disapproval, and it is clear to the newborn infant that this is a source of great parental disappointment.

When all aspects of the birth experience have been determined, regardless of whether they have been verbalised, it is then available for Adult reassessment, e.g. *Thirty-five year old Jane, you have heard how newborn baby Jane feels about her birth. I would like you to give her all your wisdom and understanding and, in particular, tell her that no baby is responsible for her birth and that she really should not feel guilty about anything that is associated with it.* At this time the therapist can allow his own Adult wisdom to support that of the patient's by pointing out that whatever discomfort mother suffered could have been avoided with improved obstetric care, or that fifty percent of people are female (male), none of whom had any choice in the matter. When a yes signal is received, indicating that this Adult communication has been completed, then, as with any ego state, the question is posed: *Does the newborn Jane now feel that she needs to keep those guilty (sad, scared, angry, etc.) feelings any longer?* If the answer is still yes, further application of Adult wisdom to explain to the newborn Jane that birth is a basic human right, even if one does not arrive at a time and place when and where one is wanted. One does not ask to be born; one simply has no choice in the matter. In fact, it was much more the parents' responsibility that one was born; whatever distress mother suffered had nothing to do with the newborn baby. Furthermore, mother did not do too badly in the long run: she has a child. These and similar arguments are presumed to be delivered by the Adult to the newborn Child/Parent ego state complex that is still enduring negative feelings about its birth.

Usually this question receives a welcome *no*, indicating that the negative feelings need no longer be retained. However, if the *yes* persists, it is possible that the critical experience responsible for the negative birth feelings occurred prenatally. The question that should now be asked is, *Did something happen before birth that makes you feel not okay about being born?* The answer to this question is often a yes, and the prenatal experience responsible for these negative feelings must be dealt with in precisely the same way as natal and postnatal critical experiences.

We will assume, for the moment, that the newborn Jane has at last accepted her right to the experience of birth and now feels positive about it. The therapist then directs the Adult to discover a means of relinquishing the now unnecessary negative feelings and, finally, asks for indication of full acceptance of positive feelings by the *smile test*. This acceptance is usually accompanied by other signs of genuine pleasure and relaxation.

Prenatal Critical Experience

A significant proportion of negative birth experiences appear to originate before birth. Once again, the unconscious mind is directed to orient itself back to the relevant experience in which the feeling of guilt or other tension first occurred and, upon accomplishing this, to indicate by signalling. When this signal is given, the experience is examined, as is any other critical experience, by defining its attributes (guilt, sadness, fear, anger, etc.). Once again it may be possible for the patient to verbalise the experience and to describe it as a vivid scene. More frequently, something appears to have been overheard which indicates that the baby will be a nuisance, if and when it is born. The circumstances surrounding such rejecting statements can also be clearly identified, as can the participants in the scene. The experience may not be verbalised in this way; in any event, the Adult is once again called upon to review the experience and to apply its current wisdom and understanding to the experience. The usual hypnoanalytical procedure is followed until a smile reveals that the effects of this experience have been discarded and self acceptance is established. If satisfactory progress is not achieved, every step so far detailed should be retraced until therapy is successful. Failure is usually due to a hidden ego state that resists attempts at communication but makes itself evident by maintaining the persistence of symptoms.

Matthew is an example of a patient with a negative birth experience which has always affected his life. He was fifty-five at the time of the first interview, an excerpt from which follows, and reported a history of constant headaches which began as long ago as he could remember. He described them as an aching pain at the back of the head, which increased with tension, but never really disappeared. In fact, if he had not experienced two ten minute respites from pain, separated from each other by an interval of about three years, he would readily have believed that headaches were a normal part of life, endured by everyone. For these short periods, he experienced an intense freedom and relief, which he described as sheer joy. Matthew could not find any causal event to which he might attribute his headaches, although since their onset he recalled injuries to his head which might have aggravated them. Always tense and anxious, he suffered from marked insomnia; this he attributed to being awakened by tension and discomfort in his legs before he could settle down at night. He realized that he possessed a fierce temper, which he did his best to control, but noticed that his headache became worse prior to a show of anger. He tended to keep things that bothered him to himself until mounting tension resulted in explosive anger.

Following suggestions for relaxation during the administration of ACE (on which he reached stage 2), ideomotor signalling was readily established. The following excerpt commences after ideomotor questioning had indicated that good unconscious cooperation had been secured.

DR I would like you to let your inner mind go right back before conscious memory, right back to the very first breath that you took just after you were born, and when you are there, the yes finger will lift. Don't try to go there consciously

The immediate request to regress back to birth is usually complied with readily, as in this case. However, a delayed response indicates either unconscious reluctance to deal with the birth experience (determinable by asking whether it is

because your conscious mind cannot possibly remember this; but your inner mind can easily go back to the very first breath and, when it is at that memory, the yes finger will lift. . . *Yes finger lifts after some delay*. Good. Now babies, when they are first born, know many things. One of the things that they know is whether they feel okay about being born. If the baby Matthew feels okay about being born, the yes finger will lift to let me know. If he does not feel okay about being born, the no finger will lift. *No finger lifts*. Babies that do not feel okay about being born sometimes feel guilty about being born. If the baby Matthew feels guilty about being born, the yes finger will lift. *Yes finger lifts and the patient begins to look very distressed and makes a groaning sound*. There is something about being born that feels awfully uncomfortable. There is something about that very uncomfortable feeling that is causing pain. Does the baby Matthew feel that he is causing a lot of distress and bother by being born? As if he is the centre of a lot of trouble? If so, the yes finger will lift. *Yes finger lifts*. Yes. Does it feel awful scary to be doing that to mum? If so, the yes finger will lift; if not, the no finger will lift. *Yes finger lifts after a long delay during which tears start to flow*. And does the baby Matthew feel he is a bad person for causing all of that trouble? If so, the yes finger will lift. . . Does he feel bad about

too uncomfortable) or with a patient determined to retain control, a conscious interference in unconscious regression. (In the latter case, this control must be relinquished; the therapist must encourage the patient to *let it happen*).

The therapist proceeds immediately to enquire into the nature of the birth experience, since it is clear that Matthew has readily oriented to it. Matthew appears to be extremely uncomfortable. Strong feelings of guilt are usually prominent in negative birth experiences.

The therapist's comments upon Matthew's evident distress increases Matthew's awareness of it.

The assumption that his distress is really a reflection of his mother's distress, which he now vividly recollects, proves to be correct. Fear, as well as guilt, is in evidence. This fear indicates the probability of much underlying hurt and sadness resulting from the self rejection caused by guilt. A strong Parent/Child conflict had presumably begun during the birth experience.

causing all of that difficulty? *Yes finger lifts.*

Now, you and I, up here in 1980, know that no baby is really responsible for any of the difficulties that his birth causes, but newborn baby Matthew doesn't know that. He feels that he must be responsible for all of the distress that his birth has caused. I would like you to talk to him with all of your wisdom and understanding. Do that at a deep inner mind level and, when you have done that, raise the yes finger. . . *Yes finger lifts after an interval.* Okay. Now, newborn baby Matthew, now that you have heard that, do you still need to go on feeling guilty about being born? *No finger lifts.* You don't need to keep that uncomfortable feeling? Okay. I would like you to please use *all* of the wisdom and understanding that you have up here in 1980 — fifty-five years of wisdom and understanding — to find a way for newborn baby Matthew to let go of that awful uncomfortable feeling that he has been keeping for these past fifty-five years. When you have found a way to let go of that uncomfortable feeling, the yes finger will lift. You can tell him that he doesn't need to feel guilty about that because it isn't his fault, and that you understand, and that he can also understand now. There are many things that you can tell him to convince him. When you have found a way to let go of that uncomfortable feeling, raise the yes

Having fully defined the nature of the birth experience, it is time for the Adult to become involved in convincing the newborn Matthew that he need no longer feel guilty about the distress caused by his birth. Any failure to accept the Adult's counsel usually indicates a prenatal critical experience that must first be dealt with.

The newborn Matthew had assumed guilt for the whole of his life so now the Adult must discover new, acceptable ways of looking at life. Fortunately, this is usually readily accomplished since the Adult has profound knowledge of many other life styles which are superior.

In this case, the considerable delay in arriving at a suitable alternative gives the therapist time to make suggestions that his own Adult has knowledge of. Eventually, a satisfactory alternative is chosen.

finger. *Yes finger lifts after a delay.* Okay. Now, newborn baby Matthew, there is a way to let go of that unnecessary guilt feeling. You don't need to keep it any longer. You have already kept it far too long. Let go of it. Just let it go. You are just as good and important as any other newborn baby. It wasn't your fault that your birth caused so much distress. When you have let go of all of that uncomfortable feeling and are sure that you have done so, the yes finger will lift. *Yes finger lifts after a long delay.* Now, if you have really let go of all of that uncomfortable feeling, there should be a very nice relaxed feeling there — the best relaxed feeling that you have had in fifty-five years. If you have got that feeling, the yes finger will lift. It will be even better than the relaxed feelings that you experienced on those two occasions. *Yes finger lifts.* That's good. I am going to ask you to really enjoy that good feeling — simply enjoy it to the full. It's a beautiful feeling. You've got a right to that feeling. You did not know that you have that right. That feels so good. Let all out of date, unnecessary, uncomfortable tensions go for good. Completely gone. Now, while you are enjoying that nice, comfortable feeling, I am going to tell you that I believe that every human being is important and I believe that you, Matthew, are just as good and just as important as any other human being. If the baby Matthew really agrees with this, the

The newborn Matthew is able to utilise the Adult's point of view and relinquish his negative one, which is now recognised as outdated and unnecessary. The guilt feelings evaporate. The therapist takes this opportunity to inject some strong ego-strengthening suggestions since, in the early part of the interview, there appeared to be much evidence of very low self esteem.

The therapist makes every effort to establish the relaxed and free feeling which Matthew previously experienced on only two occasions.

The emphasis on enjoyment, free of anxiety and guilt, is very important here, since Matthew had always unconsciously felt that he was unjustified in enjoying himself.

Routine ego-strengthening suggestions are repeatedly stressed to ensure that any changes which occur are likely to be permanent.

yes finger is going to lift. *Yes finger lifts*. Good. What a lovely feeling that is! I am going to ask you to take care of Matthew. Don't let him ever feel uncomfortable again about being born. If you agree to do that, the yes finger will lift. *Lifts*. I want you to really love him and take care of him and make him feel good. If you will do that, the yes finger will lift again. *Lifts*. Good. Give him all the love that he really needs and has never had. When you agree to that, raise the yes finger. *Yes finger lifts*. Good. I want you to really enjoy that good feeling. Don't ever put him down again. Don't ever let anyone put him down again. No one has a right to do that. You are just as good as anybody else. I want you to enjoy the good feelings that you have, and I shall be talking to you again in a few moments.

Assertiveness Training in self protective attitudes is as important as the self accepting attitudes encouraged by ego-strengthening suggestions. The ideomotor responses serve admirably in monitoring adequate acceptance of these suggestions.

The session continues after a short interval, for unconscious realignments and readjustments. In the remainder of this first meeting, other critical experiences are dealt with.

At the first follow up session, about two weeks later, Matthew dealt with another critical experience, in which he was disturbed by a female cousin while urinating. He was very angry with her, and refused to speak to her again. When she was killed three weeks later, he was overcome with feelings of guilt about his harsh attitude. In therapy, he was encouraged to relinquish this guilt and accomplished this satisfactorily. As a result, at his third visit a month later, he reported that his headaches had become much less severe and markedly reduced in frequency. He was sleeping well, worrying less, and had an improved attitude toward himself. Later sessions emphasised ego strengthening, and brought a further amelioration of symptoms.

The following second example of a negative birth experience is included here because it illustrates how negative feelings about birth may arise during the prenatal period. At the time of this first interview,

Pamela was forty-five years of age and was attending therapy for help with multiple, literally crippling, phobias. She was unable to remain in any confined space for any period of time; such common activities as driving in a car or bus, or travel by air, had become well nigh impossible for her. Any attempt at these things resulted in intense anxiety with a tightness in the stomach, difficulty in breathing, and a fear that she would pass out or even die. Her first marriage had ended after a short time some twenty years ago, and she had recently remarried. Her second husband was described as a kind and generous man, for whom she had nothing but love and admiration; still, she was surprised to discover that her symptoms had become worse since her remarriage. Furthermore, she was puzzled by her frequent feelings of anger toward her husband, contrary to her expectations of feeling warm and loving.

Pamela described herself as a perfectionist, intolerant of any fault in herself or others. She recalled that her father had been brutal to her throughout childhood, as was her first husband during their marriage. She admitted that she was made nervous by all men and that she found her present husband somewhat dominating and controlling at times. Since this was his only fault, she thought that she must not complain about it. She slept poorly, which she attributed to her husband's insistence on closing the bedroom door at night, which increased her anxiety. Previous hypnotherapy and psychotherapy resulted in no lasting improvement. This excerpt commences after Pamela had shown good hypnotic responsiveness and had readily regressed to the birth experience.

DR Babies, when they are first born, know many things, and the baby Pamela knows many things. She knows whether she feels okay about being born. If she feels okay, the yes finger will lift, but if she does not feel okay about being born, the no finger will lift. *No finger lifts.* Okay. Babies that don't feel okay sometimes feel very uncomfortable about being born. Sometimes they feel guilty about being born, and if baby Pamela feels guilty about being born, the yes finger will lift. *Yes finger lifts.* Is she scared about being

Immediate acceptance of this first statement indicates that good direct unconscious communication has been established, since the conscious mind can have no knowledge of the birth experience.

A negative birth experience is indicated, and the feelings of guilt are first identified.

Because of the presenting phobic

born? *Yes.* Yeah. Is she feeling angry about being born? *Yes.* Yeah. Even sad about being born, is she? *Yes.* Yeah, all of those awful feelings. Now do these awful feelings that Pamela is feeling when she is born start before she is born? *Yes.* Yeah. Let's go back then to a time before Pamela is born where something happens to make her feel, *Hey, I don't want to be born!* When you are right back to that something happening, the yes finger will lift. . . before she is born. *Yes.* Okay. I would like you to review that experience at a deep inner mind level and, when that review is complete, the yes finger will lift again. *Yes.* Now, that experience that you have just reviewed, can you talk to me about it? If you can, raise your yes finger; if you cannot, then raise the no finger. *Yes finger lifts.* Okay, what are you hearing? You are not born yet — what are you hearing?

symptoms, the therapist carefully seeks any natal source for the fear; sadness and hurt, the inevitable precursors, are located. The admission of fear of being born immediately suggests the possibility of a prenatal critical experience, which receives ample confirmation on further questioning. Pamela evinces no difficulty in locating the prenatal source of tension. Nevertheless, a review of the relevant experience was thought to be useful to define accurately the experience.

PT   My father. . .

DR   What is he saying?

PT   He doesn't want me. He's yelling at my mother.

DR   And what is he saying?

PT   That she is stupid. . . that she should not have got pregnant. *Sobbing.*

DR   Aha — that she's stupid, eh?

Like any other critical experience, it is not always possible to elevate a prenatal experience to a verbal level, but Pamela has little difficulty in accomplishing this.

The quarrel between parents, where the infant seems to be the cause of the argument, is a very common prenatal critical experience, often responsible for a negative birth experience.

PT   *Very distressed.*

DR   And you feel guilty about that?

PT   Yes.

DR   Okay. Is there anything else that you can tell us about that? I bet you are scared, aren't you? You probably don't want to be there.

Again the therapist painstakingly seeks the source of fear that he believes must have arisen in this prenatal experience.

PT   That's right.

DR   Yeah. Probably thinking, *Hey, this is no place for me to be,* and no way do you want to come outside where dad does not want you.

PT   No.

DR   No way. It is bad enough being inside, but to be born seems awful. Okay. Forty-five year old Pamela, did you hear that?

Once again, it is time to summon the patient's Adult to aid the therapist's Adult in his task of freeing the Child from the restricting fears of the old Parent/Child conflict.

PT   Yes.

DR   There is an unborn baby there. She's scared to death about coming out and being born. Can you help her, please?

PT   *Sighing, restless.*

DR   Tell her it's not her fault that she is there. Tell her that things do turn out all right after all. She does not have to go on being scared because she eventually gets through it

The therapist uses his own Adult to encourage the Patient's Adult to comfort and support the Child, and immediately the Patient's Adult responds by entering into a

all very well. Can you tell her all those things, please?

PT   Don't be afraid.

DR   Tell her that you will take care of her.

PT   I will take care of you.

DR   You will? Okay, how does she feel now, is she still scared?

PT   She is scared. . . a little bit.

DR   She is, eh? Tell her some more, then.

PT   Don't be frightened. I'll take care of you. He won't hurt you. But he always does hurt. *Tearfully.*

DR   Can you tell her then that she is going to survive all that?

PT   You'll survive. . . you'll make it.

DR   That's it. Tell her she'll make it. She'll get through it all.

PT   You'll get through it.

DR   Is she okay now?

PT   I think so.

DR   Okay. Let's check. Can we get her being born now? Can you get her to be born and feel okay about being born?

verbal dialogue. This is relatively uncommon and tends to occur in the highly susceptible subject, such as Pamela.

Suddenly, the Child interjects her doubts based on her adverse experiences.

These are allayed by the Adult's reassurances that things are now different. The old order has changed, but the Child and the Parent had not realized these changes.

In this subject, a rapid review of birth is easy.

PT   Yeah.

DR   Let's see. Does mum want her?

PT   Mum wants her.

DR   Does mum cuddle her?

PT   Mum cuddles her and mum thinks she is beautiful.

DR   Is she smiling at her?

PT   Yes.

DR   Great. There you are, you must remind her of that.

PT   See, she loves you.

DR   How does that feel? Feels good?

PT   Feels good.

DR   Okay, so in fact, it is only dad who is the problem. It's not mum, is it?

PT   Right.

DR   Okay. Remember to tell her that. Mum really wants her.

PT   Yeah.

DR   It's just dad. Does she feel all right now?

PT   Yeah.

Pamela recognises that she experienced good feelings from her mother.

A reminder of these feelings is enough to generate a strong attitude of self worth, which had been negated by father's rejection. Nevertheless, the therapist must remain wary, lest the paternal part of the Parent ego state remain unconvinced and return to the previous self-rejecting attitudes. The memory of mother's acceptance clearly helps Pamela to cope with father's rejection of her.

DR Are you sure? Have you got her smiling?	Once again, the *smile test* is invoked, and is satisfyingly positive.
PT *Nods.*	
DR Now I want you to come up from being born to the next time something happens which is still scaring Pamela inside.	Further therapy is directed at later critical experiences.

One month later, this patient reported that she had been able to take her vacation by air without any anxiety, and had since comfortably flown on her own. This was something she had never before accomplished. She had also been able to ride in a car without any anxiety, was sleeping very well, and was generally much less nervous. She noted that she had become assertive, in a pleasant way, but her family and colleagues were finding it difficult to adapt to the striking changes that they perceived in her.

The self acceptance gained through dealing with the negative birth experience removed the guilt that had hitherto prevented Pamela from being adequately self protective. Following this first session, she immediately gained access to her many normal resources for safeguarding herself, which had previously been denied her. The Parent, instead of pursuing its previous function of concealing the Child, now supports and protects it with the aid of the Adult's vast resources.

Analytical Hypnotherapy and Previous Life Experiences

Every hypnotherapist will, sooner or later, be asked about the possibility of regression to a previous life experience which may be responsible for problems in the present life. There appears to be an increasing interest in reincarnation, although the history of this belief is a long one indeed. Also, from time to time, when the analytical hypnotherapist asks his patient to regress to the critical experience responsible for symptoms, the patient apparently returns to one that occurred in a previous life. Some hypnotherapists have made a special study of this kind of regression and Fiore (1978) has described in detail some of her observations in this regard. While conceding that her patients' experiences cannot prove the reality of reincarnation, she notes frequent complete resolution of emotional and other problems following the uncovering of these previous life experiences. This would indicate that these experiences have some relevance to the problems presented.

Stevenson (1966) also documented twenty such cases which he believed to support the theory of reincarnation.

Most of the experiences described in the literature have been associated with highly hypnotisable subjects who have been able to give other manifestations of deep hypnosis, including amnesia and hallucinations. For example, Bernstein (1956) recorded the previous life of Mrs. Virginia Tighe as Bridey Murphy. This achieved great notoriety as a book and subsequently as a film, and appeared to create a sensation in much of the western world. A critical response detailed striking inconsistencies between the descriptions given by Mrs. Tighe in hypnosis and the historical facts; in addition, critics pointed to the probable present life sources of information which were previously thought to have been available only to somebody living before Mrs. Tighe's life. Iveson (1977) detailed some of the six lives that a Mrs. Jane Evans described in hypnosis, and discovered that the wealth of detail was historically accurate but nevertheless accessible in the present. The remarkable thing in this case is that none of this information appeared to be available at a conscious level; neither did the subject recall ever studying or reading about these periods of history when the previous lives had supposedly existed.

Taylor Caldwell, the well known novelist, uncovered several previous lives when working with Stearn (1973), who attributed Caldwell's fertile source of material for her books to these previous lives. Caldwell herself does not accept this explanation. Kline (1956) demonstrated how easily material of this sort is obtained in hypnosis. Hilgard (1977) was equally unimpressed, since he has demonstrated that memories may be readily recaptured in hypnosis without identification, and be woven into a realistic story which is believed by its inventor. Thus it may be that this is the true explanation for previous life experiences described in hypnosis. The subject draws from his vast storehouse of unconscious memories, a myriad of life experiences, the majority of which have been accumulated without conscious awareness. From these memories, past life experiences are constructed.

Nevertheless, whatever the true reason for an account of a previous life experience, the analytical hypnotherapist should be prepared to deal adequately with them on occasion. So many life experiences are stored at an unconscious level that it is easier to accept the explanation that past life experiences are, in fact, artificial constructs. A highly hypnotisable subject will, on request, readily construct a plausible story about any fictitious event and can be persuaded that it is true. He will then consciously defend it as being true and will add, if pressed, other elaborations which he also believes to be true. Such a story will bear the stamp of validity since it will be so carefully constructed as not to conflict with other facts known to the subject. This creative ability of the unconscious mind, which works best in such highly imaginative people as Taylor Caldwell, must always be borne in mind when dealing with any memory of an experience offered by the patient in hypnosis.

Indeed, it may well be that some of the experiences offered to the therapist as critical ones are products of the imagination, with no real basis in fact. In practice, it must be emphasised that the *validity* of a critical experience does not concern the analytical hypnotherapist — and this applies to present life experiences as much as to past life experiences. What is of concern is the emotional conflict associated with these experiences and the resolution of the conflict. More often in dealing with the present life critical experience, much of it has been remembered in consciousness prior to the hypnotherapy; however, the hypnotherapy deals with those aspects of the experience which have remained responsible for the symptoms. It is also probable that these aspects, crucial to an understanding of the symptoms and their eventual resolution, cannot be dealt with without revealing an experience that must be kept hidden deeply in the unconscious memory. Perhaps in these cases, the unconscious device of offering a similar previous life experience (created specifically by the unconscious mind for this purpose, the disturbing aspects of which are similar to those of the present life experience), enables these aspects to be dealt with and the disabling symptoms removed. Therefore, we can accept that the unconscious mind may substitute one similar experience for another, in much the same way that dreams carry, in a symbolic manner, the elements of emotional conflicts.

A previous life experience is dealt with by the analytical hypnotherapist in precisely the same way as any other critical experience. When a conflict has been identified, but the source is difficult to locate in a present life context, the hypnotherapist should not be averse to seeking it in a previous life experience. This can be accomplished by asking the question, *Does this experience occur before birth?*, which will locate a prenatal critical experience. If the answer to this is negative, the next question must be, *Does the experience occur in a previous life?* If the answer to this is *yes*, then it should be exposed to the same analytical procedure as any other critical experience. Usually, strong feelings of guilt and fear are attached to such an experience. The task of the therapist is seldom easy in these cases, since the displacement of the conflict into a previous life may indicate a reluctance on the part of the patient to deal with it, as shown by the patient's resistance to suggestions for resolution of the conflict.

Ego Strengthening and Assertiveness Training

Hartland (1971) stated that the greater the patient's need for his symptoms as a defence mechanism, the more intractable the symptoms will prove to any method of psychotherapy. He elaborated a series of ego strengthening suggestions, the objective of which was to strengthen the ego defences, making the symptoms unnecessary. Many therapists agree with him and have approached the problem of the depleted ego in different ways. Branden (1972) stated that one common denominator at the base of all patients' symptoms is a deficiency of self esteem; the goal of therapy is to correct that deficiency. Self esteem, he believed, is a basic psychological need and the failure to achieve it leads to the disastrous consequences of intellectual and moral self doubt, feelings of inadequacy, helplessness and guilt. The extent of the problem is indicated by Zimbardo's (1977) survey, which estimated that forty million Americans consider themselves to be shy and inadequate.

Gardner (1976) advocated the use of hypnosis for increasing and maintaining hypnotherapeutic gains by the administration of ego strengthening suggestions. DeVoge (1977) found that hypnosis was of value in assertiveness training and self concept change; she advocated the visual rehearsal of assertive behaviour in hypnosis as a powerful means of establishing it. Hartland (1971) gave a series of authoritarian ego strengthening suggestions, e.g. *You will feel more self confident and more relaxed*, etc. They may be extremely effective in producing changes in behaviour, but they can also fail signally. Gwynne, Tosi and Howard (1978) pointed out that when treating nonassertion with behavioural approaches, underlying causes may be ignored and often generalisation will not occur because negative cognitive states still exist and operate in other settings. On the other hand, a *cognitive only* approach may fail because the client lacks appropriate social skills.

They conclude, as does this writer, that both cognitive and behavioural processes must be attended to when treating nonassertion. It is therefore important for the analytical hypnotherapist to understand that ego strengthening and assertiveness suggestions constitute the final phase of therapy and form an integral part of it.

Every patient who comes to the hypnotherapist with a problem is assumed to suffer from a Child/Parent conflict of some magnitude. In this conflict, the Child is battling with a coercive Parent who forcefully rejects him, in whole or in part. Because of this internal rejection by the Parent, the Child naturally feels unaccepted — and unacceptable — and even when the conflict is finally resolved by the Adult's intervention, there always exists a depleted Child ego state, wearied from many years of battle. This Child ego state needs support, encouragement, and new ideas about its true worth in order to function effectively in the absence of the previous symptoms. It must be understood that even the most self destructive symptoms have had some secondary benefits for the Child, minimal though they may have been, which have come to assume an importance which must not be ignored. To be permanently effective, therapy must provide a means by which the individual may reap similar benefits without these symptoms. On its part, the Parent ego state has interpreted its role of protector of the Child as that of a punishing disciplinarian. This interpretation must change if therapy is to be effective. The Parent needs to be encouraged to become supportive and caring in a positive, loving way. In this way, a new close relationship is established within the personality, which gives the individual greater strength and solidity. When the patient begins to like himself, then we can truly say that ego strengthening has begun.

The last and perhaps equally important part of the rehabilitative process is that of assertiveness training. It is one thing to feel good about oneself, but quite another to establish that point of view in an environment which has been conducive to the maintenance of the previous Child/Parent conflict. A patient without this conflict is vastly different from one with it, and the change imposes adjustments upon those people relating to him. All hypnotherapists have been struck by the changes that others must make in response to modifications in the patient. This has often been a source of great pleasure to both patient and therapist. Assertiveness training is the process by which the strengthened ego of the patient can establish an effective pattern of behaviour which will be acceptable to his new thinking and also to his environment. Because of the internal rejection resulting from the

Child/Parent conflict, there has been no effective defence against attack from others; in fact, attacks from the environment have served only to reinforce the Parent ego state's position that the Child must be repressed. Prior to therapy, the Parent complies with attacks on the Child, but must now be required to defend him. A simple example is that of the fat lady who has always made jokes about her rotundity and has invited people to laugh at her. After therapy, she will never encourage this assault; on the contrary, assertiveness training teaches her to discourage it. Prior to assertiveness training, the individual's point of view and feelings are consistently ignored, but training teaches him that his point of view and feelings must always be supported.

The critical and hostile Parent ego state often uses its attacking powers to reject not only its own Child, but also to attack the Child ego state in others. This is also a kind of defence for the Child, but one that is bound to create greater problems for the individual as he engages in fruitless battles with others. Therefore, assertiveness training includes methods of disengaging from these battles which are unnecessary when the patient is adequately defended. When ego strengthening and assertiveness training suggestions have been fully accepted, and are seen to be working in practice, the patient no longer needs further therapy. This is the goal to which all therapy should be directed: the achievement of ego state complexes which remain united and strong in all circumstances and no longer require the previous symptoms to function.

Throughout this final rehabilitative phase of therapy, the Adult ego state is extremely active in assuming the directive and controlling role within the personality, which is essential to permanent mental well being. This role, which constantly heeds the Child's needs and the Parent's cultural understanding, makes the Adult the proper leader of the internal ego trio. This position, prior to therapy, is too often occupied by an unfeeling and critical Parent or an undirected and unnecessarily emotional Child.

The rejection of the Child by the Parent is so universally a feature of problems seen by the analytical hypnotherapist that the monitoring of this rejection provides the therapist with a sensitive device to measure the progress of therapy. Thus the acceptance or rejection of ego strengthening and assertiveness training suggestions provides a means of estimating both the progress and the prognosis of therapy. These suggestions can be monitored simply by means of ideomotor signals, which can also estimate the effect of the resolution of the Child/Parent conflict. It is unlikely that ego strengthening suggestions can be fully accepted so long as any Child/Parent conflict remains. It is also unlikely that assertiveness training suggestions will be accepted if the Parent has not relinquished its disciplinary role. Therefore, the full acceptance of these suggestions indicates that therapy is progressing favourably. Conversely, rejection of these suggestions indicates that all is not yet well. The rehabilitative and diagnostic qualities of these suggestions are obvious, but their therapeutic aspects may be less so. The administering of ego strengthening suggestions in the absence of any prior analytical hypnotherapy may sometimes be therapeutic since, in order for them to be accepted, the internal resolution of conflicts must first take place. This can occur without specific direction in those cases where the conflict is not complex, for there exist the resources for resolving it. This mechanism accounts for the occasional permanent resolution of emotional problems without the prior intervention of analysis.

Ego Strengthening

The suggestions to be outlined are based on the assumptions that the individual is basically *good* and that any previous judgments of him as being less than good are faulty, which have been accepted by the Parent ego state. Such judgments are received from parents and parent surrogates, who have no right to make them, despite their belief that seniority entitles them to such a privilege. These suggestions depend heavily upon the Adult's experience of the world, and the maturity, understanding and wisdom it has accumulated over the years, but which have not hitherto been available to the Child or the Parent. Their effectiveness also depends, as do most suggestions in hypnotherapy, on their being delivered with conviction by the therapist, whose own Adult must share and accept the underlying belief in human worth and importance. These suggestions have been used with many hundreds of patients with very good effect, when the patient has found them acceptable.

The first step is to state a basic belief in humanity's worth and evident importance, and to seek the patient's affirmation of this belief. This is accomplished by making the following statement: *I believe that every human being is unique and important; do you agree?* If this is replied to with a yes signal, then proceed to the next question. Sometimes, however, a no is received. If so, further analysis is required to discover the reason for this. An acceptance of the fundamental truth of the concept of universal human importance and individual uniqueness will, in such cases, require the therapist's greatest persuasive qualities. If the no answer persists, some progress might be made by saying, *Even though you do not agree with me, do you believe me when I say that I believe every human being to be important and unique?* This question must receive a yes, or further ego strengthening is impossible at this time.

The next step is to persuade the patient to accept *himself* as an important and worthwhile human being. In order to accomplish this, the following question is asked: *I believe that you, John, are unique and special – just as unique and important as any other human being, living or dead, do you agree?* This question always meets with considerable thought and some delay before an answer is forthcoming. It is directed at the fundamental problem affecting all who suffer from emotional disorders: a deficient feeling of self worth resulting from a lifetime of adverse criticism first from the real parent and subsequently from the internal Parent. A positive answer to this question is a very encouraging sign, indicating that therapy is progressing very favourably; much if not all of the Child/Parent conflict must indeed be at an end. However, it is wise to remain cautious and ascertain whether this point of view is fully accepted by asking, *Is there any part of your inner mind that does not entirely agree with me?* This serves to identify any lack of internal unanimity on the issue of self worth. If any part of the personality is unable, at this juncture in therapy, to accept the individual as good and important, this question will hopefully persuade it to reveal itself. It must be pointed out here that sometimes a hidden ego state will remain silent even at this point; these ego strengthening suggestions will appear to have been accepted by all of the personality only to be sabotaged by the concealed ego state at some later date. Should any part express disagreement at this stage, then an unresolved Child/Parent conflict clearly exists, and should be dealt with by the usual hypnoanalytical approach.

When every part of the patient's psyche expresses agreement that he is of true intrinsic worth and that the individual is as worthy as anyone else, we can conclude that the previously conducted analysis has been successful and is complete. However, even in the presence of a strong *yes* which appears to be unanimously expressed, further clarification of the Parent's acceptance of the Child is recommended by asking specific questions about the nature of this acceptance. Thus, the patient is now asked, *I believe that you (Child) have the right to all of your feelings whether or not they are unpleasant. Do you (Parent) agree?* Even if a yes is readily indicated, the therapist can be more precise by detailing the specific emotions, by saying, *I believe that you have as much right to your feelings of sadness as any other human being, as much right to your feelings of happiness as any other human being, as much right to your feelings of anger as any other human being, as much right to your love, your fear and your safe feelings. Do you agree?* If there is any doubt about these rights and a no or a doubtful yes is given, then an attempt must be made to discover the reason for the Parental rejection of the Child's natural feeling. For example, anger may be regarded as an unacceptable feeling despite excellent analytical therapy. If so, the Adult's logic must once again be harnessed to point out that anger has a very important function in the individual's survival. Provided that anger is controlled, it need not be destructive or harmful to anyone who does not seek to harm the individual; indeed, he has a duty to protect himself and those who depend upon him. Similar arguments can be presented to justify the acceptance by the Parent of the Child's normal human emotions of happiness, sadness, love, fear and security.

This assurance can be further reinforced by the statement, *I believe that you do not need to feel guilty, ashamed or embarrassed about any of your normal human emotions; you have a right to keep them for as long as you need them and a right to let them go when they are no longer necessary.* This latter statement is made to enable the Child to feel that giving up an old unnecessary emotion does not deny his right to have it again, should it become necessary. Agreement to this statement should also be sought. In so seeking, any element of guilt that still persists over normal human feelings will be identified and permit analytical resolution. The persistence of guilt is always a sign of the continued presence of a Child/Parent conflict, which must be dealt with if therapy is to be successful. If this phase of rehabilitation is successfully concluded, and all of the Child's normal human feelings have been accepted by the Parent, then it is clear that Parental opposition to the Child has now been withdrawn.

Assertiveness Training
Further ego strengthening continues in this next phase which is properly referred to as *assertiveness training*, because it teaches the individual to maintain his ego strength at all times. Jakubowsi and Lange (1976) define nonassertive behaviour as the violation of one's own rights by failing to express honest feelings, thoughts and beliefs. Consequently, others are permitted to violate the individual. It is in this phase that the Parent is encouraged to embrace its neglected and

repudiated role as *protector* and *supporter* of the Child. To effect this, we ask the patient, *I believe that it is your* right *and your* duty *to* respect *and* protect *every one of your feelings, do your agree?* Each of the emphasised words carries a special meaning. Let us examine them separately.

Right   In therapy, we constantly emphasise the rights of the individual because the Child has unlikely been allowed to appreciate his rights to feelings; this gives the Adult the opportunity to advise him of these rights. The Parent has forbidden the Child some of his rights until now, when he is appraised of them, since an admission of these rights strikes directly at the heart of the Child/Parent conflict.

Duty   The Parent, in its initial term of reference, is bound by a sense of duty which, until now, has been restricted to fulfilling what others expect of the Child by repressing the Child in whole or in part. It has lost sight of its originally intended protective role. This phase encourages the Parent to modify its role appropriately without yielding its concept of protective duty.

Respect   In denying the Child its true feelings, the Parent has shown little respect for them. It is now very important in therapy for the Parent to exhibit respect for the Child and its feelings; undertaking this will prevent it from restricting them ever again.

Protect   When the patient presents for therapy, the Parent ego state has been obsessively engaged in protecting him from the wrath of his real parent(s). This role is now irrelevant, and yet has persisted with little change since childhood. The Parent is now asked to assume a new kind of protective role in which it does precisely the opposite of what it had been doing. Its new role will give much more relevant and effective protection by safeguarding the Child's feelings from others. There will always be those who seek to put the individual down and belittle him. Until now, the Parent has conceived of its duty as currying favour with these people by siding with them against the Child. This must end. The Parent must truly protect the Child with the assistance of a logical and wise Adult. The Adult is able to provide up to date information on how best to provide this protection, and the Parent can now assume the fully caring and nurturing role for which it was originally intended.

In order to establish these principles, simple questions are directed to the patient. *Will you now respect John and his feelings, and never again put him down or belittle him? Will you like him? He is as good and as important as any other human being. No one has a right to belittle him or put him down, not even you. Do you agree?* If all of these questions are answered in the affirmative, we can be certain that internal respect is being consolidated. At last, the Parent can like the Child; they can become friends.

The next phase in assertiveness training is to establish a highly defended position for the Child by asking, *Will you now take care of John and protect him at all times so that no one will be allowed to belittle or devalue him or try to put him down? No one is any better than he is, and therefore no one has the right to put him down, since he is just as good as anyone else, living or dead. Do you agree? Will you love him?* An agreement to do all of these things is essential for complete assertiveness training. The notion that one can love oneself is often entirely new to the individual whose Parent has been trying to mould the Child into its (parental) artificial concept of something lovable. We are now asking it to love the Child as it is, without any modification whatsoever. This is of course a true parental function; those fortunate people who have learned to love themselves with their parents' total acceptance never have a Child/Parent conflict, and never experience any of the problems which bring patients to the hypnotherapist. To love oneself is a truly difficult and strange task at first; but when this has been accomplished, the patient will remain truly and completely assertive, since he will always be self protective.

The final phase of assertiveness training seeks to ascertain that the patient will no longer engage in battles which are totally unnecessary if he remains fully defended at all times. To do this, he is asked if he will never again attempt to put anyone else down, but rather to respect their feelings as fellow human beings, since he has no more right to put them down than they have to put him down. This undertaking also serves to establish the underlying principle of equality, which the Parent has been called upon to defend. At this point, the patient may realise that he or she has often put others down in the same way that he has allowed them to put him down. Long, wearying, useless and often very destructive battles have been engaged in over the years. The attempt to put others down has been the previous temporary solution to the painful experience of humiliation. By remaining fully assertive at all times, this discomfort is terminated; there is no longer any compulsion to attack others since he is no longer vulnerable to their assaults. To consolidate these suggestions (which we assume have all been accepted), the patient is asked to review all of them and to picture himself in various situations where he normally would have allowed himself to be put down, but now sees himself carrying out these suggestions successfully. Often, during initial interviews, patients describe many instances in which they have allowed themselves to be belittled and have fought back ineffectively. Following therapy, the patient can visualise himself as being well defended and capable of dealing with situations assertively instead of aggressively.

In the following excerpt, we return to Tim, whom we left in Chapter Ten after applying the reframing procedure to him. Here, considerable emphasis is placed upon the ego strengthening process, particularly because the therapist is unaware of the nature of the conflict responsible for Tim's compulsion to gamble, but is certain that Tim needs to have a very strong ego if he is to resist returning to a behaviour pattern having many secondary gains. Furthermore, he must maintain his ego strength securely to remain sufficiently assertive to resist returning to the unwanted behaviour patterns. For Tim, assertiveness training is therefore as important as the ego strengthening.

DR When the deepest part of your mind is listening carefully, your head will let me know by nodding for yes. . . Nods. Okay. Keep listening very carefully. I believe that every human being is important, and I believe that Tim is just as good and just as important as any other human being, living or dead. If you agree with that, your head will want to nod for yes. . . Nods. Good. I know that all human beings have uncomfortable feelings as well as comfortable feelings, and I know that you have had feelings that are uncomfortable. I know that you have had feelings of sadness like any other human being. If you agree with that, again your head will nod for yes. . . Nods. And you have had feelings of happiness like any other human being. If you agree with that, again your head will nod for yes. . .

Every effort is made to secure the maximum unconscious attention in the hope that the suggestions to be made will have the optimum effect.

Fortunately, this basic concept of human worth and goodness is acceptable to Tim. It is upon this basis that the philosophy underlying ego strengthening rests. The uncomfortable feelings that Tim presumably had have been the source of conflict. They are here given the context of universal human attributes, which he can learn to accept.

He is able to understand that if a comfortable human feeling such as happiness can be acceptable, so should the opposite uncomfortable feeling of sadness. Love, anger, fear and security are similarly dealt with.

Nods. And you have had feelings of anger, like any other person. . . *Nods.* Feelings of love, like any other human being. . . *Nods.* Feelings of fear; scared feelings; just like any other human being. . . *Nods.* And feelings of safety and security, just like anybody else. . . *Nods.*

Now all of those feelings are normal human feelings and you don't need to feel ashamed or guilty or embarassed about any of them. You have a right to all of your feelings, whether or not they are comfortable. But you have a right to let them go when you don't need them any longer. If you agree with all of that, your head will nod for yes. . . *Nods.* And any old, out of date, uncomfortable tensions that you have been carrying around which you no longer need can be let go. And if you feel that you have let them go right now, your head will nod for yes. . . *Nods.* And you can stay free of those old, out of date, uncomfortable feelings. You have a right to those feelings of hurt any time you need them back; you have a right to have your feelings of anger back at any time you need them; you have a right to have your feelings of fear back any time you need them; but when you don't need them any longer, you can feel happy, feel loving, and feel safe and secure. I would like you to promise me that you will respect Tim always. By that, I mean that you will respect his feelings. . . *Nods.* You'll like him because he

Further appeal is now made to the Parent ego state for full acceptance of these feelings as being normal. They must be considered right and proper. The decision as to whether an adverse feeling should be allowed to remain is left to the Child after gaining access to Adult understanding and wisdom.

These uncomfortable feelings can be retained if they still serve a useful purpose, but can be relinquished when these purposes have been fulfilled. Pleasant feelings can replace them.

The Parent is appealed to fully to accept the Child.

has human feelings and has a right to his feelings. And because you like him, you will listen to his feelings and not put him down for having them. He has a right to have them. And you will find ways of helping him to feel comfortable – good ways that are helpful. Never put him down for having uncomfortable feelings, for he has a right to them. Listen to them, respect them, like them. I want you to always protect him, as you have been doing in the best way that you could; but now, you have better ways of protecting him. Listen to his feelings. You've got better ways. You've found better ways. Always look for better ways to take care of Tim. Don't let anybody put him down. He is just as good as anybody else. No one has the right to put him down, so protect him from anybody who wishes to do that. Take care of him at all times. In fact, I want you to take care of him, but also to care for him. Care for Tim, love him. If you will do all of these things, your head will nod yes. . . *Nods*. And as you do all of those things, some wonderful things happen: you feel very safe, very secure. It feels like you have the answer to so many things which used to puzzle you. You'll feel so safe, so secure, that you will no longer let things get you down because you know how to handle them. You always did know, but you did not use the knowledge. You can use it to the best of your ability. And with that good knowledge, you

Once more, an appeal is made to the Parent to accept the new means of defending the Child which have been discovered by the Adult. The therapist stresses that these new ways are more beneficial. Assertiveness – not aggressiveness – is encouraged. The Parent is asked to become a close ally of the Child. These new viewpoints are promoted since the Parent has previously degraded the Child.

For the Parent, the idea of loving the Child (self love) is new, and is repeatedly stressed by the therapist in order to ensure unconscious self protection. Much of the old anxiety that Tim experienced was archaic, but persisted because of an established Parent constriction of the Child. The reduction of the Parent's control permits the Adult to assume a greater control of the Child. It is assumed that the patient's Adult will be able to generate many adequate options for the Child in the task of problem solving. The very availa-

can do the things that you really want to do. You will be able to do them because you feel friends with yourself. It's a nice thing to feel good friends with yourself. And if you are feeling friends with yourself right now, your head will nod for yes. . . *Nods.* Continue to be friends with yourself. Continue to listen to yourself, hear yourself, and give yourself good advice. And take the good advice that you give yourself. And as you feel very good about yourself, I am going to ask you, please, to know that you don't need to put anybody else down because you feel that you can respect other people, who have their problems just like you do, and can find their own ways of dealing with them. And because you are feeling so good, today will be a very good day. I would like you to see yourself having a very good day. When you can see that, nod for yes. . . *Nods.* Good. You feel so good. There's a nice, calm, relaxed, smiling feeling right through. . . *Smiles.* And keep that feeling. Keep it every day. It's a good feeling to have. Feel good about Tim, being the person you are, liking Tim, and taking care of him. I want you to know that you can remember what you need to remember at all times, and forget what you need to forget, because your unconscious mind will always remember everything that we have talked about. If that is understood, your head will nod for yes. . . *Nods.* It will keep all of the suggestions that we have agreed

bility of these options maintains the secure feelings.

Self protection is once again emphasised, and *feeling friends with yourself* underscores the self acceptance necessary to increase ego strength. This increased ego strength provides the power for assertiveness.

The good advice that you can give yourself is an indirect way of stimulating the creative wisdom of the Adult and promoting its acceptance. Assertiveness training flows from the ego strengthening that has been accomplished and the self respect so gained must be maintained by a defensive behaviour which protects the personality from assaults upon it by others.

Once again, the *smile test* is invoked, and indicates unconscious well being and unanimity. Tim is reminded how he can maintain these good feelings.

Finally, the patient is encouraged to keep all of these instructions at an unconscious level where they will not be subject to conscious interference.

upon, so that your conscious mind does not have to bother with trying to remember the things that we have discussed. Your conscious mind can leave all of the remembering to your deep inner unconscious mind, so that when I have you open your eyes, your conscious mind can be free to be busy with other thoughts.

Direct and Indirect Suggestion in Analytical Hypnotherapy

Many of the criticisms which have been levelled against hypnotherapy have been directed at the indiscriminate use of direct suggestion in hypnosis. The occasional dramatic response to direct suggestion — and the history of hypnotherapy is replete with such responses — has given hypnotherapy an unscientific notoriety which has hindered progress in the understanding and acceptance of it as appropriate therapy. Hypnotherapists have been unable to provide adequate explanations regarding their success in some instances and failure in others involving the administration of direct suggestions in hypnosis. Consequently, direct suggestion in hypnosis has not gained its rightful place in orthodox medicine as a reputable therapeutic tool. This lack of esteem is due to exorbitant and unsubstantiated claims made on its behalf and also to the inconsistent results. Esdaile achieved brilliant results while working in India, but was unable to duplicate them for a critical medical audience upon his return to England; the hypnoanaesthesia he had hoped to demonstrate, which might have revolutionised nineteenth century surgery, was considered myth rather than scientific fact.

Every hypnotherapist soon acquires considerable first hand experience with the disappearance of long standing symptoms of variable severity following the administration of direct suggestion in hypnosis. His inability to explain how this occurs, and why it sometimes does not, accounts for much of the scepticism exhibited by those who have limited experience of hypnotherapy. Even those who admit that symptoms can be removed by direct suggestion in hypnosis may criticise this form of therapy on the grounds that it simply promotes symptom substitution. Brenman and Gill (1947) maintained, however, that symptom cure by direct suggestion could be permanent, and that symptom substitution was not prevalent, particularly in the treatment of those disorders which were relatively peripheral to the total personality. Reider (1976) reiterated the traditional psychoanalytic view that the rapid symptom resolution either diffuses the patient's desire for understanding and mastery, or forces the underlying conflict to emerge in a different, perhaps more serious way. Spiegel and Spiegel (1978) observed that there have been many successful symptom-oriented techniques which cast serious doubt upon this theroretical formulation. Hilgard (1977) and Frankel (1976) agreed that using hypnosis in an ancillary role to lessen or remove symptoms, while attending to the psychodynamic context in which the symptoms arose and are maintained, appears to be a reasonable compromise. It therefore behooves us to look very closely at what happens when symptoms respond to direct suggestion in hypnosis. In any case, the analytical hypnotherapist needs to be aware of the potential success of non-analytical techniques of hypnotherapy.

We have already examined the range of resources available to the unconscious mind, some of which directly affect body functions. The means by which this effect is achieved are many but are poorly understood at present; it is probable that they mainly involve the humoral or autonomic nervous system control. Presumably, the exercise of this control produces emotionally based symptoms via these mechanisms. Furthermore, the voluntary nervous system can also come under unconscious control with the production of such diverse disorders as hysterical paralyses, anaesthesia, blindness and deafness. The recognition that symptoms often have an unconscious origin acknowledges the immense resources of the unconscious mind in its favourable or adverse influence on the body. Hypnoanalytic theory indicates that emotional mechanisms are involved in these disorders and thereby provide the rationale for therapy. The success of direct suggestion in the removal of symptoms would indicate that there is no unconscious resistance to their eradication. It must therefore be assumed that their manifestation has continued after the reason for their onset and continued maintenance has ceased, or become minimal. Suggestions given at this time have merely provided the motivating force for the unconscious mind to institute the minimal changes necessary for final termination of symptoms.

The sole difference between the analytical hypnotherapist and other hypnotherapists in the treatment of symptoms is that the former seeks to discover and deal with the causes of persistent symptoms prior to giving direct suggestions for their removal. With this approach, the analytical hypnotherapist hopes to increase his success rate in the removal of symptoms. The direct suggestions are therefore the same, although the timing of their administration is different; they usually follow the receipt of evidence of the patient's unconscious readiness for their acceptance. In the absence of prior analysis, the therapist must rely upon his communication with the patient's unconscious mind for effective direct suggestion. They must be carefully worded to achieve maximum effect. To be sure, the analytical hypnotherapist must also possess these skills, but he has the additional advantage of being assured that unconscious resistance to his suggestions has been removed prior to their administration.

The logic of this approach is inescapable, and provided that we accept that the unconscious mind does indeed possess the resources that we have attributed to it, the removal of symptoms by direct suggestion will become increasingly acceptable to orthodox medicine. In those cases where an analytical approach is neither feasible nor acceptable, for some reason, symptom removal by direct suggestion without prior analysis is a plausible alternative approach and will on occasion be successful when the unconscious resistances are insufficient to impede their acceptance. In such instances, the degree of success may be surprisingly great. Another approach is that of the administration of indirect suggestion; here, the idea for the removal of the symptoms is communicated to the unconscious mind in such a way that the conscious mind, and perhaps some parts of the unconscious mind, are unaware of the true purport of the suggestions made and are therefore unable to oppose them. In this latter instance, prior analysis is unnecessary since it is assumed that any unconscious resistances will be eliminated while initiating the change resulting in the relinquishing of symptoms.

Symptom Removal by Direct Suggestion
There are many techniques for the administration of direct suggestion for the removal of symptoms. These can be grouped into specific categories.

Authoritarian Approach
Much of the popular knowledge of hypnosis and its role in therapy stems from the exhibition of direct suggestion authoritatively administered. In such cases, suggestions are accepted by individuals who are highly motivated to accept them, and the results are often dramatic. Symptom removal by authoritarian direct suggestion is sometimes surprisingly effective; this forms the basis of the faith healer's techni-

ques. Such an approach mobilises all of the relevant unconscious resources, in these cases, with striking results. Unfortunately, when it fails, it does so miserably and the technique, hypnotherapy and the therapist all share equally in the loss of credibility. Therefore, the authoritarian approach is unacceptable to the ethical therapist who strives not to gain notoriety for himself but improved health for his patient. Nevertheless, there are a few occasions when an authoritative command to give up a symptom or to alter a body function is effective. In this context, Cheek and LeCron (1968) described a case of injury in which the direct suggestion to stop bleeding, authoritatively administered, was immediately effective.

Relaxation Approach

Relaxation is perhaps the most common means of inducing hypnosis today. The ability of the unconscious mind to induce physical relaxation is usually an easy resource to mobilise and much symptom removal is achieved through relaxation. This is accomplished by associating the idea of symptom reduction with the diminution of tension. Many symptoms owe much of their severity to associated anxiety and a suggestion to relax will considerably reduce these symptoms. For example, pain syndromes such as tension headaches, back pains and migraine are so often aggravated by tension that relaxation suggestions allied to direct suggestions for pain relief are often effective. Failure can be attributed to the patient's inability to relax adequately rather than to the hypnotherapeutic procedure.

This direct approach can properly be used by the analytical hypnotherapist prior to understanding fully the true nature of the problem. The patient is helped in this way to gain some control over the symptom in the early part of therapy. However, the goal of complete relief from symptoms should be observed despite any great improvement that direct symptom removal might induce.

Anaesthesia and Analgesia

Direct suggestions for the relief of pain are clearly such an important application of hypnotherapy that they require separate attention. The resource of the unconscious mind for the reduction of sensation is invaluable in controlling pain syndromes. A common technique is the induction of a localised anaesthesia by the direct suggestion that this area will become numb. The use of imagery to recall previous experiences of numbness and coldness increases the possibility of success in producing such localised anaesthesia. Hypnoanaesthesia has the useful property of being readily transferable and can be applied to any area requiring pain reduction. Often, this successfuly produces anaesthesia and pain relief; unfortunately, there are some patients who, for some reason, cannot be induced to mobilise this unconscious resource. Possibly, the need to retain feeling or pain overrides the suggestions for its removal, no matter what technique is used.

Other techniques for pain reduction and removal include suggestions for less frequent attacks, for the transfer of pain to less disabling sites of the body, and for an alteration in the quality of the sensation. These techniques may be effective when the need to retain the pain cannot be relinquished.

Imagery
The unconscious mind's immense potential for imagery can be harnessed in a less direct manner for symptom removal. Encouraging the subject to imagine himself without his symptoms in surroundings normally associated with them — and yet, capable of dealing with his environment — demands that he unconsciously discover means of ridding himself of the symptoms and of functioning well without them. The use of imagery in this manner is clearly a direct suggestion for symptom removal, and it is also an indirect suggestion for the *means* of accomplishing this. In order to accomplish this, the subject must draw upon other unconscious resources to handle his symptoms. Frequently, he can continue to use these resources after therapy, although neither he nor the therapist may be aware of their true nature.

Imagery therefore has a tremendous therapeutic potential due to its ability to mobilise powerful unconscious resources. Furthermore, satisfactory imagery indicates to the therapist the possibility of good responses to suggestion. Imagery can be used to discover the goals of the patient and also his potential for reaching them, by the patient's producing self images of attaining his goals and then focusing on the pathways to these goals. Such a situation was described by Porter (1978) when she observed that patients who are told in hypnosis to imagine the ideal self, free of presenting inhibiting factors, discover for themselves ways of removing these factors. Imagination is, of course, the normal mechanism of all creativity; hypnosis does no more than stimulate normal unconscious processes.

Indirect Suggestion for Symptom Removal
Direct suggestion will often meet with resistance which is probably

both conscious and unconscious. Such resistance may be active in preventing the relinquishing of symptoms as it may prevent any response to hypnotic suggestions. This may explain the greater response to *therapeutic* suggestions in those patients who exhibit a greater response to *hypnotic* suggestions.

The indirect approach offers an alternative, both in the induction of hypnosis and in the removal of symptoms, to the therapist who is faced with signs of resistance to suggestion. Erickson was the greatest exponent of therapy by indirect suggestion and we owe much of our understanding of the mechanisms and effectiveness of this approach to his many writings on the subject. In each case that he described, we see that the therapist was able to establish unconscious communication with the patient and successfully deliver several options to him, the choice of any one of which constituted a valid response. Even the failure to respond, if offered as one of the possible choices, is essentially a response, since it may be assumed that a choice was made.

Erickson and Rossi (1975 & 1979) have deeply explored this approach in their discussion of binds and double binds, in which the patient is offered suggestions which provide opportunities for therapeutic gains. A bind is a series of suggestions, the choice of any of which leads the patient in a therapeutic (or hypnotic) direction. A double bind is similar, except that the options are likely to be perceived unconsciously. Much of what constitutes indirect suggestion is essentially double bind, and whether it is motivated toward producing a hypnotic or a therapeutic response, the unconscious mechanism is presumed to be the same. Suggestions can be given in this multioption manner without the therapist's exerting any pressure to make a choice. However, the options that are proposed are such that the acceptance of a least one of them will unconsciously appear to be preferable to accepting none. This approach has no specific direction regarding how the patient will deal with his symptoms (or enter hypnosis). Such an approach is a valuable resource when resistance has been so high that a useful response to effective analysis is precluded. It may well be that none of the options suggested by the therapist is acceptable; the options' effectiveness may lie in stimulating an unconscious search for and the discovery of a preferable means of relinquishing symptoms (or entering hypnosis).

When using this approach, the conversation that takes place with a patient rarely makes much conscious sense, since it abounds in many undefined and uncertain phrases, such as *I don't know whether, you don't know, I wonder whether, Perhaps you may notice, you may wonder,* etc. Such qualifying words as *wonder, whether, may, if, perhaps,* are commonplace in the highly permissive language of indirect suggestion. The therapist is able to hint at a myriad of possible responses which may be relevant to the patient. There may be some conscious initial effort to assess these possibilities, but they are too numerous to be processed at this conscious level; only the unconscious mind is able to formulate a response, which it may institute immediately or after a varying interval.

When these suggestions are used to induce hypnosis as advocated by Barber (1977), the proportion of patients who prove insusceptible is much smaller than with the use of direct suggestion, where some five percent of people are considered to be hypnotisable. When used to alleviate symptoms, indirect suggestion may be extremely effective, as indicated by deShazer (1980) in his treatment of erectile dysfunction. Erickson (1976) believed that because these indirect suggestions do not arouse the patient's resistances and are outside his usual range of conscious control to effect therapeutic goals, they utilise unconscious associative structures and mental skills. It would therefore seem to the patient that his therapeutic goals have been accomplished *spontaneously* and in a manner apparently unrelated to therapy. In this context, it is pertinent to wonder how much successful therapy is inadvertently accomplished through indirect suggestion outside the therapist's awareness, who is unconsciously responsible for them. In any case, the analytical hypnotherapist should always be prepared to give indirect suggestions which are never more appropriate than when direct suggestions are not heeded.

Therapeutic Metaphor

Perhaps the most potent form of indirect suggestion is the metaphor. It would appear that therapists have always used metaphor as an important part of therapy, but none has mastered this art better than Erickson. He spent most therapeutic sessions telling his patients stories which, although extremely interesting, had no apparent bearing on the problem for which he was being consulted. Haley (1973), for example, related how Erickson treated a boy for bedwetting by talking about sports, contraction of the pupillary muscles, and stomach sphincter muscles without ever mentioning the bedwetting – which eventually cleared completely. Through the medium of the symbolic language of metaphor, Erickson elegantly conveyed to the boy's unconscious mind ways to control the bladder function. Gordon (1978) advocated extensive use of metaphor in therapy and suggests that, if the indirect suggestions implicit in metaphor are significant to the patient, he is unconsciously motivated to check through his experiences to discover subjective models congruent with the metaphor. He suggested that the patient accomplishes this by completing transderivational searches. Levine (1980) was able to relieve childhood insomnia through the process of metaphor contained in childhood fairy tales constructed especially for the child to deal with his conflicts. Bettelheim (1976) has illustrated how children employ fairy tales to analyze and resolve inner conflicts; it may be assumed that adults unconsciously use similar mechanisms when presented with a relevant metaphor.

Symptom Prescription
Symptom prescription is another application of indirect suggestion. In this technique, the therapist actually sanctions or encourages symptomatic behaviour and in so doing, provides a rationale for the symptoms. In effect, the therapist directs the patient to do exactly as he is already doing; but at the same time, he provides an additional therapeutic contribution or modification to the symptomatic behaviour. Zeig (1980) described three different principles espoused by Erickson: meeting the patient within his own frame of reference; establishing small therapeutic modifications which are consistent with this frame of reference; and eliciting the cure from within the patient. Thus the patient is assisted to establish change utilising his own power and through his own resources. Symptom prescription gives the patient the opportunity to recognise, evaluate and change his own behaviour either consciously or unconsciously. Zeig (1980), in another paper, described how complex symptom prescription could be simplified by breaking the symptom into its elements and confining the prescription to only one of these elements.

The similar approach of Farrelly and Brandsma (1974), called *provocative therapy*, involves the ironic acceptance of all the patient's negative attitudes in such a way that he feels challenged and is provoked into making a change. The provocation arises because the therapist's symptom-encouraging attitude robs the patient's behaviour of its secondary gains; consequently, the symptoms must be altered or removed in order to maintain previous gains.

These are but a few of the ways in which indirect suggestion may be effective. When Alman (1979) compared the effectiveness of direct versus indirect suggestion, he found that in poorly susceptible subjects, indirect suggestion was far more effective. The analytical hypnotherapist may experience resistance to analysis with these subjects, and therefore the judicious application of indirect suggestion may produce symptomatic improvement.

Common Problems in Analytical Hypnotherapy

PART TWO   Chapter 15

There are certain clinical problems which, more than others, tend to be referred to the analytical hypnotherapist. This chapter will consider these problems in some detail and apply the techniques already discussed to their treatment.

Anxiety

No clinical problem referred to the analytical hypnotherapist is entirely without some evidence of anxiety which must be taken into account during therapy. In many cases, the level of anxiety is not great enough to warrant special attention and the normal techniques of relaxation employed in hypnotherapy will deal adequately with it. Nevertheless, a high proportion of cases present with a significant degree of anxiety. Such anxiety may be constant, with the individual rarely free of it, or it may be episodic, associated with certain recognisable situations. More commonly, both the acute and chronic kinds of anxiety coexist; such an individual is always tense, but is particularly so at certain times.

Anxiety is an overt expression of fear. It is due to an unconscious awareness of danger and is the appropriate response to it. Therapy that ignores the appropriateness of these anxiety responses is doomed to failure. Thus we find that patients will take medications of all kinds, year in and year out, because the therapist does not recognise that the anxiety responses as they are unconsciously perceived are entirely proper. Only when this perception has changed can the individual allow himself to relinquish his fear. The physical manifestations of anxiety, such as rapid heart rate, rapid breathing, sweating, muscle tension etc., all give evidence of the individual's preparedness for flight from an unconsciously perceived danger and are, from his unconsciousness viewpoint, totally normal responses. This understanding of the nature of anxiety enables the analytical hypnotherapist to start from an entirely different perspective than most therapies designed to relieve anxiety.

Even in cases of acute anxiety, where there is an apparent conscious reason for it, closer examination discloses that the intensity of the anxiety is far greater than the current situation really warrants. Such an anxious response is not entirely due to the obvious cause, but rather, is largely due to the presence of unconscious fear-producing associations. Presumably, the individual does not wish to know consciously about these fearful memories, but nevertheless, has left the unconscious mind with the task of guarding him against these unconsciously perceived dangers. Unfortunately, this process denies these unconscious protective mechanisms access to later consciously perceived information, which might indicate that the need for anxiety has passed. Whenever the anxiety demonstrated is not commensurate with the present circumstances, the therapist can assume that the patient is responding to an unconsciously perceived old danger with an awareness sharpened by his previous distress following an en-counter with that danger. It is this awareness which distorts his interpretation of the present.

Immediate anxiety will often respond to the relaxation suggestions integral to the common induction techniques of hypnosis, but old anxiety will respond only temporarily, if at all. This old anxiety must be dealt with by the analytical approach in order to ensure success. Success with nonanalytical approaches is less assured, because it depends upon the fortuitous discovery by the unconscious mind during therapy that the need for anxiety has indeed disappeared. The methods of analytical hypnotherapy, on the other hand, are specifically designed to direct the unconscious mind toward this discovery and to its other resources, which will not only ensure recovery but also the continued maintenance of mental well being.

Theoretical Considerations

In Chapter Five, we discussed how the appropriate expression of feelings, when repressed in the interest of survival, will result in their inappropriate expression. This is true of the repression of fear which has been diverted from its original target (a parent or parent surrogate) and can be only partly expressed at symbolic targets. Some of the unconscious anxiety detected by the analytical hypnotherapist is of this nature, while some appears to be the result of strong feelings of guilt resulting from parental disapproval of the individual which is maintained in the ongoing Parent/Child conflict. This guilt is essentially the unconscious fear of parental abandonment and unconsciously represents a greater fear than the fear of death. It may in fact be a factor in attempted and realised suicide. This guilt is freqently so deeply unconscious that only hypnoanalysis can discover it as the source of the anxiety symptoms.

The Presentations of Anxiety

Anxiety can present in many ways and frequently goes unrecognised because the presenting symptoms obscure it. In fact, it may be only on close enquiry that the individual is able to recognise the anxiety responsible for his symptoms.

Panic attacks   Intense, acute episodes of anxiety can be labelled panic or acute anxiety attacks, in which all of the physical symptoms of anxiety (e.g. sweating, hyperventilation, nausea, diarrhea, shortness of breath, choking, etc.) are frequently accompanied by a strong feeling of helplessness. Bellack and Small (1977), in their therapeutic approach to panic states, sought to link features of the current precipitating event with significant events of the past and believed that this correlation enabled them to discover the actual cause of the panic.

Phobias   Phobias are also panic attacks with one main difference: the likely precipitating factors are known by the patient and are carefully avoided because of the severe anxiety response that contact with these factors will produce. In the phobias, the acute anxiety is likely to subside rapidly, when the individual is no longer exposed to the precipitating factor. Nevertheless, in practice, the phobia sufferer also experiences varying degrees of anxiety in non-phobic situations, but it is less crippling in these circumstances. The phobic situation, for these people, is simply one in which the unconsciously perceived danger is most clearly and overwhelmingly experienced; but elements of that danger are sensed at other times when the lesser degrees of anxiety are in evidence. As a result, it is rarely enough to deal with the phobia alone; during analysis, other sources of anxiety soon become evident and must also be dealt with if the sufferer is to remain completely tension free. Anxiety is also a feature of many other symptom complexes in which it has usually been regarded as secondary.

Obsessive Compulsive Behaviour

Many presenting symptom complexes contain strong elements of obsession and compulsion. While this may be the prime complaint, in many cases, the compulsion is not clearly obvious. Any unwanted behaviour which cannot be consciously controlled must be considered *compulsive* and results from a persistent or repetitive idea which must also be regarded as compulsive. Probably all of the problems of addiction, whether to food or to drugs of different kinds, must be regarded as examples of obsessive compulsive behaviour.

The role of anxiety in these symptom complexes can more clearly be recognised when any attempt is made to impede the compulsive behaviour. For example, if the heavy smoker is deprived of his cigarettes, he becomes intensely anxious. The anxiety that he feels is only an increase of a constant anxiety that is persistent below the level of conscious awareness, but is apparent even to the casual observer. This constant anxiety is controlled and reduced by smoking, so the successful analytical treatment of addiction takes this need for control into account, and deals with the unconscious anxiety responsible for compulsive behaviour. Most people who behave compulsively are aware only of the relief that they experience, which prompts such statements as *I enjoy smoking*, because they are unaware of the constant anxiety that demands relief by means of the compulsive behaviour. Such behaviour never removes the anxiety, which is often found, upon analysis, to be an old anxiety which can be dealt with adequately by the analytical approach. Direct suggestion to terminate compulsive behaviour is rarely successful because the relaxation achieved by suggestion is seldom sufficient in intensity or duration to be of lasting value. Only permanent relief of the underlying anxiety responsible for the compulsive behaviour will effectively eradicate that behaviour. This anxiety frequently goes unrecognised in the treatment of obsessive compulsiveness and habit disorders with the result that therapy is unsuccessful.

Psychosomatic Disorders
Psychosomatic disorders frequently conceal deeply rooted anxiety and even where the anxiety is apparent, the extent of it is discoverable only during therapy.

Gastrointestinal The chronic bowel syndromes are often physical manifestations of unconscious anxiety. Overactivity and spasm of the large bowel with abdominal pain, diarrhea and nausea are features of acute anxiety for some people. Conversely, those people who suffer from chronic bowel diseases, such as colitis, spastic colon, etc., are similarly suffering from an anxiety which is less obvious, but rarely do they receive treatment for this source of their symptoms. Presumably, the anxiety creates overactivity of the autonomic nervous system which, in these cases, mainly involves the abdominal nerves. It is interesting here to refer to Engel (1968) who in his summary of the findings of earlier physiological studies of patients with ulcerative colitis, observed their strong, almost symbiotic attachment to a key figure (usually the mother); symptoms began when this relationship became endangered. Presumably, the fear of abandonment, though unconscious, is intense in these cases. There are often other manifestations of anxiety, such as restlessness, tension and insomnia, but seldom do we find that adequate consideration is given to this anxiety in therapy.

Cardiovascular   The role of anxiety in cardiovascular disease has gained wider recognition. Bruhn et al (1968) have shown that myocardial infarction occurs most typically under circumstances of emotional drain and Friedman and Roseman (1959) have elegantly documented the association between myocardial infarction and what they labelled *type-A behaviour pattern* in which the person is found to have aggressive drives and an overwhelming sense of the pressure of time. In analysis, these prove to be the individuals suffering from chronic anxiety from which their particular kind of behaviour gives them some release. Hypertension is also a disorder of the cardiovascular system and has been shown by Wolf et al (1955) to be closely related to anxiety; such patients show a striking need to excel.

Skin Disorders   There is no doubt that much emotional tension can be expressed via the skin. Musaph (1964) found that intense itching is often due to repressed anxiety and that therapy directed at reducing this anxiety will reduce the itching.

Sexual Dysfunction   Sexual dysfunction must be regarded as a psychosomatic disorder and is one that frequently comes to the attention of the analytical hypnotherapist. Chronic anxiety is now well recognised to be a common cause of sexual dysfunction. Fabbri (1975) has described a hypnobehavioural technique designed to reduce this anxiety which has met with some success. In the male, chronic anxiety is responsible for such sexual problems as failure of erection and premature ejaculation.

Analytical hypnotherapy for anxiety is directed at discovering a true, unconscious security to replace the unstable one achieved by the Parent at the expense of the need for self expression by the Child. Therapy is at once both simple and fraught with difficulties: simple because the clear objective is to locate the source of the anxiety and deal with it, assuming that there are adequate unused unconscious resources to accomplish this; difficult because these sources of anxiety are not easily located. These sources are buried beneath strong feelings of guilt which may sometimes defy all of the therapist's efforts at penetration.

The following case history illustrates an effective approach to the problem of anxiety. Jane is a twenty-five year old divorced woman who works as a hairdresser and lives with her boyfriend in an apparently good relationship. Her main complaint is that for two years she has constantly felt very anxious; during this time, medications and relaxation therapy of different kinds had been tried without any continued success. Her anxiety is greatest at night when she is at home, particularly if she is alone. Also, it is so severe when she attempts to drive that she was forced to give it up. The attacks of acute anxiety which originally forced her to seek medical help were characterised by nausea, hyperventilation, faintness, diarrhea and frequency of micturition. Occasionally, these attacks would occur at work, and she would have to go home. At the time of the first interview, these attacks had become so frequent that she had taken a leave of absence from her work. In the letter of referral, she was described as a constitutionally inadequate type of person with unrealistic expectations, who becomes frustrated and depressed when these are not realised.

Questioning revealed that she had not had a happy home life and had related poorly to her father. At eighteen, she had married an immature man who had not been able to give her any sense of security; what little communication they had developed did not survive the two years that they stayed together. She described her present relationship as satisfactory and fulfilling. She was able to enter a light level of hypnosis only, but her ideomotor finger responses were good. She indicated that her birth experience was good and that she felt okay about being born. The following excerpt commences at this point.

DR Now I want you to come forward from being born and that nice okay feeling — come forward to the

Jane's review of her birth experience results in good unconscious communication via ideomotor

very first time where Jane doesn't feel okay. At the very first time where Jane feels not okay, the yes finger will lift. . . *Yes.* I want you now to review that memory in detail and when that has been done, the yes finger will lift again. . . *Yes.* That experience that makes you feel not okay — is it a scary experience? If so, the yes finger will lift. If not, the no finger will lift. . . *Yes.* Okay. Is it one that makes you feel sad or hurt? If so, the yes finger will lift and if not the no finger will lift. . . *Yes.* Do you feel angry or resentful? *Yes.* Do you feel guilty, ashamed or embarrassed right there? *Yes.* Is that experience a sexual experience?. . . *Yes.* Are you five years of age or younger right there? If you are five years of age or younger, the yes finger will lift; if you are not five years of age or younger, the no finger will lift. . . *No.* Are you ten years of age or younger right there. . . *Yes.* Are you six years of age? *No.* Seven? *No.* Eight?. . . *No.* Nine? *No.* Ten? *Yes.*

Ten year old Jane, there's something really scary and uncomfortable there. Can Jane, up here in 1980, know about that experience? If she can, the yes finger will lift, but if she can't the no finger will lift. . . *Yes.* Okay. Tell her all about it, and when she knows all about it, the yes finger will lift. Don't hide anything from her. Tell her everything. . . *Yes.* Okay, now, ten year old Jane, that uncomfortable feeling — would it be okay for Jane up here in 1980 to feel

finger responses. The first relevant experience — the critical experience — must first be located; an adequate unconscious review establishes it.

The therapist seeks to define its emotional attributes and finds that all of the primary emotions are involved.

Locating the time of the experience allows the ego state guarding the relevant emotions to be more clearly defined.

Location of the critical experience of the ten year old and the associated ego state is readily accomplished. Bringing this experience to a less unconscious level renders it more accessible.

The concept of one ego state with its unconscious memories communicating with another ego state is basic to the techniques of analytical hypnotherapy. Communication of associated feelings renders information about this

that scary feeling? *Yes.* Okay, let her feel that scary feeling right now and when she can feel it, raise the yes finger. . . *Yes.* Good. Now can she feel that sad feeling? *Yes.* Now let her feel. . . *tears begin to roll down Jane's face at this point. The yes finger lifts.* Okay. Can she also feel that resentful feeling? *Yes.* Okay, let her feel it all. Is there any guilty feeling there? Or an ashamed feeling, or an embarrassed feeling? *Yes.* Let her feel all of that. When she has felt all of the uncomfortable feelings, raise the yes finger. *Yes.* Now, ten year old Jane, would it be okay to talk about that experience? If it would be okay to talk about it, the yes finger will lift; if it would not be okay, the no finger will lift. *Yes.* Ten year old Jane, something awful is happening to you at ten years of age. What's happening right there?

experience more accessible. Frequently, the feelings associated with a critical experience have remained unconscious prior to hypnotherapy. When knowledge of all the relevant facts is accessible, greater understanding is possible.

PT   Daddy's trying to rape me.

DR   Daddy is?

PT   Yes.

Only when prior permission for verbalisation is obtained should the therapist ask for verbal communication. This respects the patient's desire for secrecy.

A bombshell! Yet it is stated in a flat, matter-of-fact tone which conceals all of the intense emotions this experience must have generated.

DR   That's awful, isn't it?

PT   Yes.

DR   What do you do?

PT   I am running away.

DR   Are you getting away from him?

She runs, which clearly indicates the intense fear she must have endured.

PT   Yes.

DR   Do you get right away?

PT   Yeah.

DR   Do you ever come back?

PT   Pardon?

DR   Do you come back to him again?

PT   No, I don't go near him.

DR   Okay. If there is anything else to tell me about that experience, the yes finger will lift. If not, the no finger will lift. . . No. Okay, twenty-five year old Jane, did you hear that?

The fear of father is intense. This is as much as she can deal with at this time.

It is time to call upon the services of the Adult.

PT   Uhmm.

DR   Ten year old Jane is still feeling those scared, awful, uncomfortable feelings. She needs you to talk to her and comfort her. When you have done that, raise the yes finger. . . Yes. Ten year old Jane, now that you have heard that — and you have got twenty-five year old Jane to take care of you — do you still need to go on being scared?. . . Yes. You still need to go on being scared. I see. Twenty-five year old Jane, ten year old Jane still needs to be scared. You are going to have to help her a lot more than you have, because she really is very, very scared. She is more scared than you ever thought.

The Adult needs to be given clear terms of reference in order to accomplish its task.

For some reason, the Adult's aid has fallen short, and it has not been sufficient to find security for the scared ten year old Jane. She has apparently concealed much of her fear and has therefore not

I am going to ask you to really help her. Talk to her and tell her that you will see to it that it won't every happen to her again. Do everything that you can. Tell her that you will take care of her. She is so scared that she does not really trust you. I don't think that you really understood before how scared she was. When you have done that, raise the yes finger. *Yes.* Now, ten year old Jane, now that you have heard that, do you still need to keep those scared feelings? *No.* Oh, good. Okay. Twenty-five year old Jane, I think that we have at last convinced ten year old Jane that she doesn't need to be scared any more and that you will take care of her. You can be scared for her, if necessary. Now, would you please find a way for her to let go of those scared feelings. When you have found a way for her to do that, the yes finger will lift. . . *Yes.* Okay, there you are, ten year old Jane. There's a way to let go of those scared feelings. Let them all go. Use that way right now, and when you have let them all go, raise the yes finger. . . *Yes.* Ten year old Jane, if you really have let go of all those uncomfortable feelings that you have been keeping for these past fifteen years, you should be feeling so good. If you are feeling good, ten year old Jane, raise the yes finger. If you are not feeling good, raise the no finger. . . *No.* Okay, ten year old Jane, you are still keeping some uncomfortable feelings, is that right? *Yes.* There is a bit, isn't there? Okay.

been fully understood. The therapist makes every effort to encourage greater understanding of Jane's evidently deeply held fears.

This approach eventually meets with success. This new understanding with its accompanying greater wisdom apparently suffices.

The therapist congratulates the Adult on having been able to successfully reassure Jane's Child and convince the Parent that it need no longer scare the Child.

It is now time to find a way to relinquish all of the old, unconscious tensions. A way has been found, although it is not verbalised, and may never reach consciousness.

Now the time has come to finally let go of the outdated and unnecessary feelings that have contributed to the symptoms over the years.

However, this solution is not an acceptable one, since Jane is not ready to relinquish her protective fears. She does not fully trust the

Twenty-five year old Jane, ten year old Jane is still feeling a bit scared. I want you to talk to her again, and when you have done that, raise the yes finger. . . *Yes.* Now, ten year old Jane, do you still need to keep that bit of scared feeling?. . . *No.* Okay. Twenty-five year old Jane, I want you to find a way for ten year old Jane to let go of that bit of scared feeling, and when you have found a way for her to let go of it, raise the yes finger. She has got to be able to trust you to take care of her. *Yes.* Okay, now, ten year old Jane, let go of all of those uncomfortable feelings right now, and when you have done that, raise the yes finger. Okay now, ten year old Jane, let them all go. *Yes.* Are they all gone? Do you feel really comfortable now? Are you comfortable enough to give me a smile? *Smiles.* Does that feel good?

Adult. She believes that she must remain armed with her fear. The therapist once again calls upon the Adult to delve into its resources to discover better means of dealing with the reasons for these persistent remnants. The emphasis is now upon getting rid of all of the scared feelings. Up to now, the Adult has not exhibited sufficient understanding of the Child to deal with the Parent's frightening admonitions.

PT   Uhmm.

At last, there is evidence of success and the *smile test* confirms this.

DR   About time, isn't it?

PT   Yeah.

DR   Right, that's fifteen years of feeling uncomfortable. Wasn't that awful?

PT   Uhmm.

DR   Okay, now, twenty-five year old Jane, you have ten year old Jane feeling so good. She really is smiling at me and that seems so good. I

The Adult is congratulated for its efforts, and now the search for other critical experiences is begun. The accompanying uncomfortable ego states must be identified.

think that there may be some other Janes inside that are uncomfortable. If there are, the yes finger will lift; if there are none, the no finger will lift. *Yes*. There are. Okay, let's come to the next Jane above ten who is feeling uncomfortable, and when you have found her, raise the yes finger...

Once again, the simple technique of finding the relevant ego state via the ideomotor finger response is employed.

Yes. How old are you there, Jane?

PT   I don't know.

DR   Are you more than fifteen?

PT   No, I don't think so.

DR   Are you eleven?

PT   Eleven or twelve.

DR   Eleven or twelve, eh? What's happening there? Can you feel what's happening? *Patient appears tearful.* You look sad. Does it seem sad?

When located, the uncomfortable feelings can readily be identified.

PT   Uhmm.

DR   Yes, what's there?

PT   Dad's beating up on mum again.

Again, we find the father to be the source of much uncomfortable feeling.

DR   Oh dear, has he done that before?

PT   Yes.

DR   What are you doing?

PT Can't do nothing. Just listening.

The essential helplessness of the Child is very evident here.

DR You're just listening. And where are you?

PT In the bedroom.

DR You are in the bedroom, eh?

PT Yes.

DR In bed?

PT Uhmm.

DR Do you have any brothers or sisters?

PT Uhmm.

DR Where are they?

PT Listening.

DR Are you all together in bed? All scared together?

The common bond that the family shares is their unanimous fear of the father. Even though there is an older sister, she is not of much help and indicates to eleven/twelve year old Jane that being older is not of much use, since it does not necessarily equate with greater power. It is small wonder that it is difficult for the Child to trust the Adult to take care of it where the father is concerned.

PT Uhum.

DR Are you the oldest?

PT No.

DR Who is the oldest?

PT Pat.

DR What does Pat do?

PT She doesn't do nothing.

DR She is as scared as you are?

PT Uhum.

DR Yeah, I see. Are you all feeling scared?

PT Uhum.

DR Are you crying?

The old sadness is there and persists unconsciously. There is also persistent unconscious anger.

PT Uhum.

DR You are eh? And are you angry with dad?

PT Uhum.

DR . Do you know what he is beating her up about?

PT There doesn't have to be a reason.

The father's behaviour cannot be understood; there is no good reason for it. He can only be feared.

DR Is he drunk?

PT Uhum.

DR Ah, I see.

PT He's an alcoholic.

DR Aha. Okay. Is there anything else to tell us, eleven or twelve year old Jane? If there is, the yes finger will lift. Is there anything else about that we need to know in order to understand? *No.* Okay, twenty-five year old Jane, there is eleven or twelve year old Jane feeling dead scared. She can't do anything. She is

He is irresponsible, as are all alcoholics. The therapist is at pains to discover all that can be communicated about the first critical experience in order to ensure optimum application of Adult wisdom. The therapist calls upon his own Adult to clarify to Jane's Adult how he assesses the problems of the helpless and scared Child, which is being harried by an unreasonable Parent.

helpless. She probably feels guilty because she can't do anything. I don't know, but she is really feeling awful. I want you, please, to use all of your wisdom and understanding to talk to her, and when you have done that, raise the yes finger. . . *Yes.* Now, eleven or twelve year old Jane, now you have heard that, do you still need to keep those uncomfortable feelings?. . . *No.* Oh, good. Twenty-five year old Jane, I want you to find a way for eleven year old Jane to let go of these old uncomfortable feelings, and when you have found a way for her to do this, the yes finger will lift. . . *Yes.* Ah, there you are now, use that way, right now. Let go of those uncomfortable feelings. Let them all go, and when you are sure that they have all gone, raise the yes finger. *Yes.* That's good. Now, I want you, please, if you have really let go of all those uncomfortable feelings, to raise the yes finger again. . . *Yes.* If you are really feeling that comfortable feeling, you have got a smile for me. . . *Smiles.* Yeah, good, that's nice. Okay, now we have got eleven/twelve year old Jane feeling good and ten year old Jane feeling good and they are smiling. Now, look to see if there is any other Jane who is not smiling. If there is, the yes finger will lift, but if there isn't the no finger will lift. Any other Jane unable to smile?. . . *Yes.* Okay, there is a Jane not smiling. We have found one. How old is she?

Fortunately, this intervention appears to prove successful. The Adult resources are futher employed to discover a means of relinquishing these outdated feelings.

The therapist makes an extra effort to ascertain that these old feelings are really relinquished.

The *smile test* is positive. Now the *smile test* is used by Jane to discover any other source of unconscious tension.

PT I'm sixteen.

DR Sixteen year old Jane, what is happening there?

PT I ran away from home.

DR Are you scared?

PT Uhum.

DR Why did you run away from home?

PT Because I hate it there.

DR So it really is scary there, isn't it?

PT Uhum.

DR Where do you go to?

PT Up north.

DR Do you have somewhere to go up there?

PT My cousins.

DR Do you feel better there?

PT I think so, yes.

DR It feels better there, okay. Is there anything else to tell us? If there is, the yes finger will lift. *No.* Okay. We've got sixteen year old Jane who is still feeling uncomfortable. I think that she is feeling scared still and does not know quite what is hap-

She is now able to verbalise very readily in hypnosis.

In this critical experience, fear is very prominent and again is presumed to result from fear of the father.

This fear is the only repressed tension that the sixteen year old ego state feels that it is retaining.

The therapist now suggests that she may also be experiencing some guilt feelings.

pening. She may even feel a bit guilty about leaving home. Will you please use all of your twenty-five years of wisdom now, with your understanding, and when you have done that, raise your yes finger. *Yes.* Okay, sixteen year old Jane, now that you have heard that, do you still need to keep those uncomfortable feelings any longer? *No.* Okay, twenty-five year old Jane, we've got sixteen year old Jane saying that she feels that she doesn't need to keep those uncomfortable feelings any longer; so we have got to find a way for her to let them go. When you have found a way for her to let them go, raise the yes finger. . . *Yes.* There you are, sixteen year old Jane, let those uncomfortable feelings go. It's finished with, over and done with, and past. You don't need them any more and, when they've all gone, raise the yes finger. *Yes.* Now, if they really have gone, that should be really comfortable inside. If it is really comfortable inside, raise the yes finger. . . *Yes.* Got a smile for me, sixteen year old Jane? *Smiles.* Yeah, good. That's nice, isn't it? It's about time. Sixteen year old Jane is smiling for the first time in nine years and that feels good.

Now, let us have a look and see if there are any other Janes older than sixteen who are still uncomfortable. If there are, raise the yes finger; if there aren't, raise the no finger. *No.* Have we got all of the Janes smiling? Sixteen, seventeen, eighteen, nineteen, twenty, are they all smiling?

Again, the Adult's help is successfully enlisted.

Following this reassessment, there is seen no further need to remain afraid.

Again, there is a need to find a means of relinquishing a fear that had appeared to be necessary for the previous nine years.

Although no enquiry need be made into the means of relinquishing the fear, the therapist adds some possible reasons for doing so.

A positive *smile test* is once again elicited and there is a recognition of the sixteen year old's release from nine years of distress.

The search for all of the relevant tensions continues.

The first indication is that no other tensions remain to be dealt with. The therapist demands a more careful search, but this fails

PT   Uhum.

DR   Twenty, twenty-one, twenty-two, twenty-three, twenty-four, twenty-five; are they all smiling? It's about time, isn't it, eh?

PT   Uhum.

DR   Now, if they are really all smiling, notice what happens now. You can now get into the car. Can you feel yourself get into the car?

PT   Uhum.

DR   Start it up and drive and keep smiling. Have you got the smile?

PT   Uhum.

DR   Feels good?

PT   Uhum.

DR   Driving okay?

PT   Uhum.

DR   Now that you are feeling more comfortable, you can do all kinds of things, can't you?

PT   Uhum.

DR   Okay, let's go to work and see how it feels there. Walk into work and tell me how it feels.

PT   Uncomfortable.

to reveal any further problem, and the patient declares herself tension free.

The time has come to put the therapy to the test.

So far so good.

Another test appears to be warranted, since her work had been located as an area of anxiety. All is not well: work is still a source of tension.

DR Okay. Look and see why that is. Something there is uncomfortable. You've driven to work all right, and now when you're at work, you're not comfortable. Why is that?

PT I don't know.

DR Okay. Let's ask the deep part of your mind to find out what it is. You won't know consciously, but when the deep part of your mind finds out what it is, the yes finger will lift. There is something uncomfortable about going to work. *Long pause.* Something deep inside that is uncomfortable, and when that deep part of your mind has found that, the yes finger will lift. . . *Yes finger lifts.* There we are. I am going to ask the deep part of your mind, can Jane up here know what that is — can she know what that experience is?

The reason for the persistent tension is not immediately apparent, so the ideomotor responses are enlisted to search deeply into the memory to discover its probable cause.

PT Uhum.

DR Oh, you've got it now. Okay. Can you tell me what it is?

PT I think it's — I don't know — cutting men's hair.

The patient appears to have some doubt as to the validity of the information received from deeper levels of consciousness.

DR Something to do with men's hair, is it?

PT Yes.

DR That's what scares you, is it?

PT I think so.

This doubt continues, so further

278   Analytical Hypnotherapy

DR Let's ask the deep part of your mind. If it is cutting men's hair that's scary, the yes finger will lift. *Yes.* Okay, let's go back in your mind to where that scared feeling comes from. Go right back in your deep inner mind until you are where that feeling comes from, and when you know where it is, the yes finger will lift. *Yes.* How old are you right there?

confirmation from ideomotor responses is sought.

PT I'm ten.

DR Ten year old Jane, what is happening there?

PT Getting raped. Well, almost.

DR What is it about that event that is making you scared of hair?

PT I don't know.

DR Is it close to you, the hair, is that what it is?

PT It may be.

She goes back to the first critical experience which had apparently been dealt with. There still persist some tensions and there appears to be a very strong association of hair with the father's sexual attack upon her, although the patient does not freely admit this.

DR Just feel and see what it is. There is something about that experience which still bothers you. It is preventing you from feeling okay about cutting men's hair. When you know what it is, raise the yes finger. It has to do with being raped — that scared feeling. It comes when you touch men's hair. As you go over being ten years old, what is it that is scaring you when you see men's hair? Something goes through your

The therapist plays back to the patient a summary of what he has learned in the hope that she will be able to discover the true nature of the fearful association with men's hair.

mind when you see men's hair. Something awfully scary. *Long pause.* Okay, let's ask the deep part of your mind to go through what it is that is going through your mind when you see men's hair. When that has been done, the yes finger will lift... *Yes.* I am going to ask the deep part of your mind to let us know what that is.

Since no verbal response is forthcoming, the ideomotor responses are invoked to locate more clearly the source of the fear.

PT   I don't know.

DR   You can't let anyone know, eh? You have to keep it to yourself? If you have to keep it to yourself, the yes finger will lift.

The therapist is beginning to believe that the unconscious information is privileged and must remain secret.

PT   No.

DR   Okay, can you tell us what it is, then?

It becomes more conscious, although the patient is unable to verbalise it at first.

PT   I don't know how to say it.

DR   Okay, how would you say it?

PT   I don't want them looking at me.

I don't want them looking at me betrays her intense fear of men. The therapist defines this fear for her.

DR   Is that what is going through your mind? Yeah, but there is something more than that, isn't there? Are you afraid that when they look at you, they will want to rape you? Is that what you feel?

PT   It may be.

DR   Ten year old Jane, if that really is what is making you feel so bad, the yes finger will lift. *Yes.* Okay, twenty-five year old Jane, will you talk to ten year old Jane about that, because she really is still scared. When you have done that and have given her all the comfort that you can, please raise the yes finger. *Yes.* Now, ten year old Jane, now that you've heard that, do you still need to feel scared about cutting men's hair?. . . *No.* Okay. Will you now, please, twenty-five year old Jane, find a way for ten year old Jane to let go of that bad feeling right now? When you have found a way for her to do that, the yes finger will lift. . . *Yes.* There you are, ten year old Jane; let go of that feeling and when you have done that, raise the yes finger. *Yes.* Okay, ten year old Jane, let us go with twenty-five year old Jane into work and see if it feels okay and comfortable. If it is okay and comfortable, give me a smile. If it is not okay, the no finger will lift. *Smiles.* Okay, you can do it, can't you?

PT   Uhum.

DR   There's no need to be afraid of that any more, is there? You now know that there is nothing more there than men's hair, and there's nothing there to be afraid of. The past is finished with and done with.

PT   Yes.

DR   Now, let us see. . . is every part of Jane feeling comfortable? If so,

With this new information, the Adult can have a far greater understanding of ten year old Jane's fears and will therefore be better able to assist her to deal with them.

This is the final check.

the yes finger will lift; if not, the no
finger will lift. *Yes*.

The remainder of this session was spent in confirming that Jane had freed herself of unconscious tension and in giving her strong ego strengthening suggestions. Direct suggestions that she could now relax much more and could drive without anxiety were repeated, and appeared to be very well accepted.

The following week Jane was seen again, and reported that things had gone extremely well for about three days; she then had a minor recurrence of anxiety with a feeling of tension while driving, and some frequency of micturition. However, she had been sleeping much better and was generally much more relaxed. In the next session, she discovered other experiences which had been the source of intense fear of her father and dealt with each of them as before. Moreover, she noted her father's intense jealousy of her mother, whom he constantly accused of running around with other men. She then focused on her current relationship with her boyfriend, and was able to admit that it had not been as good as she liked to think. In fact, she left him on one occasion because he constantly criticised her. While away from him, she had had an affair with another man. She admitted that this had made her feel extremely guilty because in spite of his faults, she felt that she loved her boyfriend.

The other important piece of information that she was able later to divulge was that she had never had intercourse with her husband during their short marriage. Her current boyfriend was the only person with whom she had had sex prior to the temporary breakdown of their relationship. We also learned that her father had sexually molested her younger sisters, and that some of her guilt at sixteen was due to her feeling that she had abandoned them to their fate when she left home. Each of these sources of guilt and fear was dealt with in subsequent sessions. Her anxiety symptoms had completely gone by the fourth session and no further therapy was deemed to be necessary. Six months later, she was still symptom free. In attempting to understand the psychodynamics of this case, it is reasonable to assume that her fear was retained to protect her from father figures who would rape and beat her for having dared to have intercourse. When, through therapy, she realised that this was not the case, she could let go of this protective fear.

Obesity
The second most common disorder which the hypnotherapist is called

upon to treat is perhaps obesity. A susceptible individual who can be made to exhibit an aversion to something that he previously liked illustrates a posthypnotic effect that has been well publicised on stage and in fiction. (e.g., *A Clockwork Orange*). This aspect of hypnosis has been dramatised to such an extent that the general public believes that hypnosis can terminate an unwanted habit, such as overeating, simply by administration of an appropriate hypnotic suggestion. In fact, there are many excellent examples of the very powerful effect that posthypnotic suggestion can have on weight reduction. Unfortunately, few of these cases ever reach their target weight, and of those who do, even fewer are able to maintain it permanently. Because of this high failure rate, there are many hypnotherapists who have given up treatment of obesity by hypnosis.

This low success rate is due to the failure to consider adequately the complex psychodynamics of the obese person, for whom there may be compelling reasons to overeat or to remain fat. In any case, these are essentially protective reasons which, enable them to deal with uncomfortable feelings. Generally, overeaters have learned that food is associated with comfort and approval, and these associations are too strong to deny when life becomes difficult and painful. Food is then used in the expectation that it will relieve this discomfort. Most overeaters are not allowed to express their normal feelings, and have an ongoing unconscious Parent/Child conflict resulting in the repression of normal Child feelings such as anger, hurt and fear. Expressing these feelings by overeating leads to a sense of release from these uncomfortable feelings and temporarily provides comfort at a conscious level, thus reinforcing the habit. Those who must remain fat unconsciously consider it hazardous to become slim: they will be more attractive and therefore a prey to their sexual feelings or a possible sexual attack. To some, becoming slim will mean losing many secondary gains which have enabled them to function; they doubt their ability to cope without these benefits.

In all cases, there exists one or more unconscious ego state whose task it is to keep the individual overeating, with the avowed objective of keeping him or her safe. Successful therapy for obesity depends upon maintaining internal security by other ways that are acceptable to that ego state. In a high proportion of cases, no such alternative can be found; but if new ways of functioning are acceptable, the loss of weight can be dramatic and permanent.

One of the major intrapsychic problems of the obese patient, which has received much attention, is the disturbance of the body image.

Bruch (1973), and Stunkard and Mendelson (1967) have all noted body image disturbances in patients whose obesity began in youth. Even following effective weight reduction these feelings of obesity remain, thus rendering it difficult for weight loss to be maintained. It can be postulated that this obese body image is a function of the ego state responsible for the obesity and perhaps identical with it. Only when this ego state is convinced that overeating and obesity are no longer in the best interests of the individual will this body image be relinquished. Steiner (1974) gave a useful thumbnail portrait of the fat woman: He suggested that she has a life course in which she is encouraged to eat carbohydrates in quantity. She is given food as a reward and told to 'eat everything up'. She has trouble in expressing anger and difficulty in saying 'no'. She has learned to swallow almost anything. Her fat keeps men away and serves as a 'wooden leg' which gives her an excuse to remain uninvolved. Not surprisingly, she is convinced that she is not okay.

Every analytical hypnotherapist has recognised many psychodynamic factors underlying obesity. They are as follows:

There is an *unconscious fear of thinness,* for one of many possible reasons. To be thin may mean exposure of a weak, frightened and anxious, small ego. Such an exposure would force him or her to face sensitive, painful problems which he or she would rather avoid. To be thin also represents change, which in itself can be frightening to the insecure obese patient. Therefore, therapy must include much ego strengthening in addition to consideration of previously avoided issues.

Anger is expressed only with great difficulty by the obese patient who believes that he must never say *no* but rather must always try to please. Not only must he or she not express this anger, but must also feel guilty for feeling the anger; food is then used to repress both the guilt and the anger. Therapy must promote acceptance of the Child's right to these normal feelings of anger and must also seek to eliminate this guilt. Underlying this is the necessity to free the patient from the compelling need for approval.

There is often a persistently *operative parental injunction* (presumably maintained by the Parent): *Do not leave any food behind. Eat it all up. It will make you big and strong. Eat up like a good girl. . .* etc. These injunctions need to be removed by a direct assault upon the Parent which must be made to understand that these directives are no longer necessary.

Unconsciously, fat may be seen as a *punishment* for previous wrong doing and as a defence against future wrong doing, particularly when it prevents sexual involvement. Therapy must include a reappraisal of the previous wrong doing, self forgiveness if this is still deemed to be necessary, and more mature methods of self defence if these are relevant following reappraisal by the Adult.

There is often a family *preoccupation with food* and being fat. The obese may feel family pressure to remain fat when attempting to lose weight for becoming slim might lead to the loss of his membership card to the family. Therapy needs to promote a strong sense of self through ego strengthening which will enable the individual to survive these threats of *ostracism*.

Obesity Profile
Certain psychological characteristics are common to the obese;
1   They have a preoccupation with food and weight. The events of the day are punctuated by food, indeed they tend to measure events, time, parties etc., in terms of food. They always have superb food memories.
2   The obese person has difficulty in knowing when he or she has eaten enough and finds it impossible to eat only small amounts. There is always room for a little more. He or she has great difficulty in refusing food of any kind.
3   The strong oral orientation leads to constant mouth hunger. The obese person will eat anything, frequently smoke heavily, and often indulges in nailbiting.
4   The obese patient is essentially a *food addict* for whom food deprivation means emotional deprivation and great distress. For him or her, eating is now and thinness is many light years away. This attitude is frequently associated with a strong feeling of hopelessness which makes it difficult to envision a state of thinness.
5   An underlying depression due to *self rejection* is common and is frequently concealed by compulsive eating.

Therapy
Only rarely does an obese patient present to the analytical hypnotherapist who has not, at some time, effectively lost weight. Many are very experienced and knowledgeable dieters who continue to search in vain for *the* diet which will finally resolve their problems of overweight. Although the analytical hypnotherapist should be acquainted with modern weight reduction programmes, it would be a mistake for him to share the obese patient's preoccupation with them

since the patient rarely needs any instruction in dieting. Rather, he should concern himself with enabling the patient to discover why he or she cannot stick to an effective programme or, if he or she has done so, why this programme is followed by a return to the previous pattern of overeating and obesity.

Early in therapy, it should be made clear to the obese patient that hypnosis is not magic: it will not automatically eradicate the compulsion to overeat by the mere administration of a posthypnotic suggestion. The analytical hypnotherapist will encounter many obese patients who are not prepared to deal with their underlying problems; they soon opt out of therapy when they discover that it is unlikely to be as comfortable and simple as they had supposed. For many obese, the resolution of unconscious conflicts can be a long and arduous battle with an unrelenting Parent ego state which will brook no interference in its autocratic handling of internal affairs.

Direct suggestion is only of temporary value in treating the obese until the need to overeat and remain fat has been dealt with and eliminated. Therefore, this technique is best left until analysis has been progressing favourably and is nearing completion. Suggestions should be formulated to promote the following: the establishment of new eating habits so that nutritious but less fattening foods can be enjoyed; an increased sensitivity of the stomach to normal quantities of food; and finally belief that greater health and fitness are possible through weight loss.

As the patient loses weight, new conflicts tend to arise. The analytical hypnotherapist must maintain a constant vigil with his patient to help him or her to discover those resources necessary to deal with these conflicts. In the case to be described the psychodynamics appear to be clear during the initial interview, but long term supervision is required to ensure that the gains made are maintained. Barbara was a twenty-seven year old woman who, at 250 lbs, was more than 100 lbs overweight when she first presented herself for therapy. She previously spent a year in psychotherapy tackling this problem of overweight and has so far discovered only that she was using fat as a sexual barrier. She found that every time she began to lose weight, she became extremely irritable, and that only putting the weight back on would alleviate this. Three years prior to attending analytical hypnotherapy, she had been successful in losing weight and had reduced to about 160 lbs and felt very good about this. She described this as a very happy period of her life because, prior to that time she had always been overweight; to be slim was sheer joy for her. She was able to go to parties and join in the fun that she had felt previously was denied to her. Something then happened: for some reason, she became scared of being slim and rapidly put on weight again.

Barbara scored grade 4 on both HIP and ACE and clearly was a good hypnotic subject. It should be noted, however, that this great ability to dissociate from consciousness can indicate a well concealed ego state, so that in obesity, good hypnotisability is not necessarily commensurate with good therapeutic results. The following excerpt commences after hypnosis has been established and ideomotor head signals are deemed to be satisfactory. Barbara's birth experience is described as positive. She has located the first relevant experience at the age of eleven years, and has indicated that it is a sexual experience which makes her feel ashamed, hurt, angry and scared. She indicates that it is okay for her to talk about it with the therapist.

PT My brother Terry is making fun of me and my first brassiere. I've just got it.

Strong feelings of shame, rejection, and sadness are very evident in this first critical experience.

DR Oh, he's making fun of that is he?

PT Yeah.

DR Why should he make fun of that?

PT I don't know.

DR Does it make you feel that you do not want to be a girl when he does that to you?

The therapist is looking for some evidence of the rejection of femininity so common in the obese female.

PT Uhum. And he snaps it at the back too.

DR Does he?

PT Uhum.

DR Oh, dear, that's really awful

The therapist expresses his under-

isn't it? Does mum know about this?

standing of Barbara's great discomfort. Even mother, another female, appears to condone this rejection of femininity by allying herself with the mounting tide of ridicule.

PT   We're all having dinner.

DR   And what does she say?

PT   She just laughed and told him not to do it.

DR   But you feel awful don't you?

PT   Uhum. But they're all laughing.

DR   They all are. You can't do anything about it if they are all laughing. You just have to bottle up everything inside eh?

The therapist recognises the helpless, trapped feeling that is present.

PT   Uhum.

DR   Are you hurt — are you crying inside?

This sadness is not being expressed but is assumed by the therapist to be there. He also assumes that feelings of shame (guilt) keep these feelings repressed.

PT   Uhum.

DR   No one can see how you are hurting. Why don't you let them see how it hurts? Are you ashamed to let them know how much it hurts inside? Do you think that they wouldn't understand?

PT   My dad doesn't like to see us cry.

This assumption is now confirmed: dad does not allow the expression of sad feelings. He ridicules them.

DR   So he would not let you cry eh? So you can't even let yourself cry, is that right?

PT   He'll just make fun of me anyways.

DR   So you can't cry. You can't feel anything can you? You can't hurt, you can't cry, you can't do anything. I see. That's awful isn't it? You must be feeling awful there.

The therapist exhibits further understanding of her need to keep uncomfortable feelings repressed.

Twenty-seven year old Barbara, did you hear that?

The Adult must now be directly involved. The therapist employs his own Adult to encourage the patient's Adult to seek a solution to the problem.

PT   Uhum.

DR   She feels as if she has nobody to turn to. I want you please to help her. Give her all your understanding, all your wisdom. When you have done that, let me know by nodding your head. . . *Nods.*

Part of the understanding may well be that she had to deal with her uncomfortable feelings at the dinner table. Eating was the only readily available source of comfort.

Eleven year old Barbara, now you've heard that, do you still need to go on feeling so awful?. . . *Shakes head.* Twenty-seven year old Barbara, eleven year old Barbara has decided that she doesn't need to go on feeling so bad any more. She's been feeling like this for almost seventeen years.
   Twenty-seven year old Barbara, will you find a way for her to let go of that awful feeling that she has got deep inside? When you have found a way for her to do that, nod your head to let me know. . . *Nods.* Eleven year old Barbara, there's a way to let go of those old, unnecessary, uncomfortable feelings. Will you use it right now? *Head shakes.* You won't? Do you want to hang on to those uncomfortable feelings any longer? *Head shakes.* Well, why not use that way right now to let them

We do not need to know how uncomfortable feelings are relinquished. It is enough to know that there is a way for release from tension for the uncomfortable ego state.

However, Barbara does not feel that she can use this way at first. She is not certain that she can trust the Adult to take good care of her; eventually, she decides that she

all go? Will you? What do you think? Twenty-seven year old Barbara will take care of things. *Nods.* Okay, take a nice deep breath and let go of all those uncomfortable feelings. It's finished with, done with, past and gone. It's all in the past. It can't hurt you any more. Eleven year old Barbara, have you got a smile for me? *Smiles.* You have? It's finished now? Do you feel as good as anyone else? *Nods.* Good. Okay. We've helped eleven year old Barbara and she feels good.

Now, look before eleven, to see if there is any Barbara younger than eleven who is still feeling uncomfortable. If there is, nod your head for 'yes'. If there isn't, shake your head for 'no'. . . *Shakes head after a long interval.* No, Okay. Now, let's look after eleven. There must be some more Barbaras after eleven who are feeling uncomfortable, particularly to do with her body. Have you got another Barbara older than eleven who is feeling uncomfortable?. . . *Nods.* How old are you there?

PT Sixteen.

DR Sixteen year old Barbara, what's happening?

PT Everybody's going out. Everybody's going to the dance at the school. I'm not going.

DR Why not?

can risk being without the protection of uncomfortable emotions.

A good *smile test.*
Some ego strengthening seems to be appropriate right here.

It is good practice to scrutinize the memories prior to the first critical experience located, since a seemingly insignificant but critical experience may have been overlooked.

Barbara is now immediately able to verbalise and so ideomotor questioning is not necessary at this point. The feeling of ostracism is extremely strong.

PT I've got nobody to go with.   Nobody loves a fat girl!

DR Oh, dear.

PT I'm too fat. Nobody wants to
take me. I just stay home. I'm having   The next best thing to going to the
a big cake — chocolate cake, my   dance is to eat one's favourite
favourite.   chocolate cake — but even this is a
    very poor substitute.

DR Aha. Is that what you have. Do
you eat it? Does that feel good?

PT No.

DR But it's your favourite.

PT I know, but everybody's going
to the dance and I want to go. . .
Sadly.

DR Do you? Really badly?. . . So   The therapist forces her to con-
what are you going to do? All you   sider the alternatives. She has
can do is eat. Are you going to   none. All she can do is eat.
eat? Do you eat it all up? *Nods.*
Does that feel any better? *Shakes.*
No, it doesn't, does it? What do you
really want to do?

PT I want to go.

DR Yeah, but how would you go?   Again the therapist forces her to
How could you go? How would   consider what she must do in
anybody invite you? You're big and   order to become acceptable to her
fat. They don't like fat girls do they,   peers. This immediately highlights
those boys? *Shakes.* So what would   her conflicts.
you have to do to be able to go to the
dance?

PT I have to lose the weight.

DR Of course, you would have to

lose the weight, wouldn't you. But you can't, can you?

PT   Everybody tells me to.

DR   But you can't. . . because you really want those chocolate cakes and they're much more important. Eleven year old Barbara, tell sixteen year old Barbara why she can't lose weight. You tell her, because you know why. . . Have you told her? *Nods* Okay. Now you know, sixteen year old Barbara, why you could not lose weight. Okay.
Twenty-seven year old Barbara, did you hear all that?. . . *Nods*. Could you talk to sixteen year old Barbara because she is really feeling very miserable. We understand a lot of things that she doesn't understand. Give her all the wisdom and understanding that you have and, when you've done that, nod your head. . . *Nods*. Okay, now sixteen year old Barbara, with that understanding and wisdom do you still need to keep that hurt any longer?. . . *Shakes*. Are you sure? You don't need that any more do you – all that hurt that you have been keeping – for more than ten years, isn't it? *Shakes*. All that shamed feeling that you have been keeping feeling just like you are a nobody, right? *Nods*. Twenty-seven year old Barbara we've got sixteen year old Barbara – she wants to get rid of all the uncomfortable feeling that she has been keeping as a kind of protection against further discomfort. I want

Everyone tells her to lose weight but no one tells her how to feel comfortable inside. She is unconsciously aware of all the repressed hurt that is eased only by eating her favourite chocolate cake. This is the only way in which she knows how to feel important.

Eleven year old Barbara knows about this and also about how fat can hide unacceptable breasts, and other signs of attractive (but frightening) femininity.

The Adult can understand all of this and is able to give excellent advice.

Barbara now decides that she no longer needs any of these feelings of rejection.

The therapist recognises that uncomfortable feelings are often retained to warn of other experiences which might prove damaging.

you to find a way for her to let go of all of it. Use all the wisdom and understanding that you have and when you have found a way for her to let go of all that uncomfortable feeling, nod your head for yes. . . *Nods after a very long interval of deep thought.* Now there's a way for you now. Use that sixteen year old Barbara and let go of the uncomfortable feeling. Let's have it completely gone. You don't need it any longer. When it has all gone, and you are sure that it has all gone, nod your head. . . *Nods.* It's gone? Got a smile for me?. . . *Smiles.* Now we have got sixteen year old Barbara smiling have we? *Nods.* Eleven year old Barbara smiling? *Nods.* That's a big step, isn't it? We've gone a long way from where we were.

In order to give Barbara further encouragement the therapist reviews their progress so far.

Now look and find any other Barbaras that are feeling uncomfortable today. If we can get them all comfortable, we can do marvellous things. Any other Barbaras uncomfortable? *Nods.* How old are you there?

A further search for uncomfortable ego states is initiated.
The goal of inner comfort is stated in a positive way.

PT   Nineteen.

DR   Nineteen year old Barbara, what's happening there?

PT   Twenty.

On second thoughts, she realises she was a little older.

DR   Okay, twenty then, what's happening there?

PT It's the same thing happening over.

Another similar experience reinforces her sense of isolation.

DR Yeah.

PT It's my last year at school. It will be graduation night. I don't want to even go.

She is so self-conscious and so self-rejecting now that she is unable to face her world.

DR I bet. It will be so humiliating won't it?

PT Uhum.

DR You will stick out like a sore thumb eh?

The therapist acknowledges her likely feeling of conspicuousness and shame.

PT Uhum.

DR You don't want that, do you?

PT No.

DR Do you go?

PT Yes.

DR You do? How do you manage, then?

PT I just went and got my diploma and went right home.

DR I bet. You made an excuse of some kind, eh? *Nods.* What did you say?

PT I was sick.

DR Ah. I don't suppose you were

really sick. You were just sick of the whole idea of staying, right?

PT   Uhum.

DR   Okay, twenty-seven year old Barbara, did you hear that? Twenty year old Barbara is so miserable that she couldn't even stay after she had taken her diploma. She couldn't join in the fun with the other people after graduation. She must be feeling awful. Do you know how she is feeling? *Nods.* Okay. Now, with that wisdom and understanding twenty year old Barbara, do you still need to keep that uncomfortable feeling? *Head shakes.* Okay. We have got to find a way to let go of that using all the wisdom and understanding that you have to find a way to let go of the uncomfortable feelings that you have been keeping for the past seven years.

The therapist sums up how twenty year old Barbara feels so that the Adult can be aware of, and deal with, all of these feelings.

Barbara decides that she really does not need to be ashamed of herself any longer.

When you have found a way to do that nod your head. *Nods.* Use that way right now, please. Let go of that feeling. It is finished with and done with. It's no good keeping it any more. When you have done that, nod your head. . . *Nods.* How's that feel? Feels good?

Having already considered the similar problem with sixteen year old Barbara, a solution is readily located and applied.

PT   Uhum.

DR   Okay, now we've got twenty year old Barbara feeling good, we've got sixteen year old Barbara feeling good, eleven year old Barbara feeling good. Let's have a look, are there any other Barbaras that we need to help? *Long pause.* . . Are there any? Are there any other Barbaras not feeling good?

PT   When I'm twenty-five.

DR   What's happening there? Be twenty-five and tell us what is happening.

PT   I am going with some friends. We're drinking and dancing.

DR   Feels good?

PT   Uhum.

DR   What is your weight there?

PT   I'm on Counterweight and I am down.

DR   Down are you? Feel good? Feel happy?

PT   Yes. I have fun and I'm alive.

DR   That's super. So what goes wrong there?

PT   Having a good time.

DR   And what goes wrong?

PT   We go to leave. . . This guy gets in the car that I don't even know. I know who he is, I just don't know him.

DR   What does he do?

This is the time when Barbara has lost considerable weight. She is now able to join in the fun which had previously been denied her when fat.

It feels okay to have a good time but something is evidently amiss.

PT He says lets go for a drive.

DR What happens? (patient looks extremely uncomfortable) It looks pretty awful. . . Does he maul you about?

PT He's making fun of me.

DR What does he say?

PT He calls me a frustrated virgin.

DR And how does that feel?

PT So I try to banter with him — back and forth.

DR Uhum. How do you get on? Are you winning or losing?

PT I'm losing.

DR Are you?

PT Yes.

DR Feel scared?

PT Yes, a bit.

DR What happens next?

PT I'm kind of dumb because I've had lots to drink (speech becomes slurred at this point).

DR Anything else happen?

PT So we battle around for awhile. Then we make love.

This is a difficult experience for Barbara to deal with. She is clearly very embarrassed. This is a situation for which she is unprepared and does not feel competent to deal with.

She handles it in the best way that she knows how but is aware that her defences are inadequate and are beginning to crumble.

It is interesting to note that, as she regressed to this episode, her speech became slurred as she re-lived her general powerlessness due to alcohol.

This is what is troubling her.

DR You make love, eh?

PT Yes.

DR Is it good?

PT No, it's awful. I don't like him.

DR You don't like him.

PT I don't like him at all.　　She is angry with herself.

DR Do you feel as if you wish you hadn't.

PT Yes. Because he doesn't mean anything to me.

DR Are you angry with yourself for making love to him?

PT Yes.

DR Do you decide then that you are never going to be slim again?

The therapist recalls that she had quickly regained her weight at this time. He rightly assumes that the decision to be fat once again was made at this time. Being thin is too dangerous. Fat protects her and also punishes her for her sexuality.

PT *After a long pause as if a new realisation is coming to her.* Yes.

DR Okay, okay. Is there anything else to tell us, twenty-five year old Barbara? (long pause during which she appears to be very distressed).

You are looking nauseated — as if you want to throw up. Am I right? Is that how you feel?

Barbara is evidently reviewing this experience in some detail and is very upset.

PT Yes.

DR I thought you did. You are really sick of everything aren't you?

PT Uhum.

DR Twenty-five year old Barbara is really sick with disgust with herself. She is ashamed and she's really miserable. Do you understand how she is feeling?

Therapy is now directed at revising the decision to stay fat by first relinquishing the uncomfortable feelings (of disgust and shame) which were relieved by eating.

PT Uhum.

DR Can you talk to her please. Give her all of your wisdom and understanding and comforting. When you've done that let me know. . . *Nods.*

Okay. Now you've heard that twenty-five year old Barbara, do you still need to keep to that decision to become and stay fat. . . *Shakes head.* No, okay. I want you to find a way to let go of that decision and all of the miserable awful, nauseated, sickening, disgusted, scared feeling that you have got there. Perhaps there is an angry or guilt feeling there. Is there a guilt feeling or shamed feeling?

PT Just disgusted.

DR You've kept that long enough now, haven't you? Do you need to keep that any longer?

Barbara has obviously been punishing herself and now is the time for self forgiveness. She is now able to protect herself without being fat and can allow herself to keep her feelings. She has punished herself long enough.

PT No.

DR Okay, lets find a way to let go of that and, when you have found a way to let go of that, nod your head because twenty-seven year old Barbara can take care of you now. I think that you have learned your lesson. *Nods.* Okay. Now let go of that feeling – let it all go . . . Has it gone? *Nods.* Smile for me? *Smiles.* Feel good?

PT   Uhum.

DR   As good as anybody else now?

PT   Yeah.

DR   Sure. Eleven year old Barbara, sixteen year old Barbara, twenty year old Barbara and twenty-seven year old Barbara, I want you to listen carefully to me. If you can really feel good about yourself right now, you can decide whether it is okay to lose weight. Is it okay? *Nods.* Does every part say that it is okay? Ask them all. *Nods.* All agreed? *Nods again.* Okay. Can we now work together to lose weight again *Nods.* and make sure that Barbara is taken care of without having to be fat? *Nods.* Okay.

I've got some ideas.

How about enjoying the thin foods? Will you do that? *Nods.* Enjoy them so much that there is no longer any desire to eat any of the sugary, starchy, fattening foods. Could you enjoy them so much that there will be no desire to eat between meals and no need to eat more than a

She can now accept ego strengthening suggestions well and this is a good prognostic sign. The time has come for direct suggestions for weight loss and weight control to be administered. First of all, permission is sought to lose weight from all of the unconscious ego states that have been involved in the problem.

There is a reference to the previous weight loss since this emphasizes that she does know how to do it.

She simply needs to feel safe at a reduced weight.

Few fat people really enjoy food because they usually eat too quickly. The enjoyment of food is associated with the idea of weight loss.

proper portion of the thin foods? Will you do that?

PT   Yes.

DR   Will you now listen to your stomach and when it says *satisfied,* stop eating, even if there is food still on the plate? *Nods.* Good.

This suggestion increases stomach sensitivity to food and is allied to a suggestion directed at removing any parental injunction to *clear your plate.*

What you could do to help yourself, is to put a picture of yourself, of what you would be if you went on eating and eating, on to those foods that make you fat. What picture have you got? Three hundred pounds, four hundred pounds? *Nods.* Scary, eh? You'd better put that picture on all of the fattening sugary, starchy foods that you can think of — candies, cakes, sweets, desserts, pop, bread, potatoes. Stick that big fat picture of Barbara at four hundred pounds on all of those foods. Have you done that? Now can you really feel what it would be like to eat those foods and get so fat? You are not going to touch them are you? *Shakes.* They would make you throw up wouldn't they? Okay. Now you are sure of that aren't you? *Nods.* Okay. Now get a nice thin picture of yourself at the weight you want to be. What weight is that?

Imagery is a powerful aid to motivation and is invoked to harness other unconscious resources in the dieting programme.

Some aversion is used here.

PT   130.

DR   Okay. Is that okay with every part of you — to be 130? Just check around inside. *Nods.* They all say it's okay. Right. Put a 130 lbs pic-

The slim Barbara will be sexually attractive and she must feel safe and able to cope with this.

ture of Barbara — a nice picture — on all the thin foods. What is she wearing?

PT A pink dress.

DR Good. Lovely. Looks good from the side?

PT Yes.

DR Is it okay for her to have nice breasts? *Nods.* Is it? Remember eleven year old Barbara was made to feel that breasts were something to ridicule and didn't feel good about having breasts did she?

Is it now okay for her to have nice breasts? *Nods.* It's okay. Has she got them in that picture? *Nods.* Okay. You have a nice picture of her.

Being fat makes her breasts inconspicuous. Becoming slim will make them apparent once again. Barbara needs to feel good about her body, especially her breasts, so that she will not fear ridicule.

PT Uhum.

DR Will you put that nice picture of Barbara on all the thin foods. . . *long pause and then nods.* Good. From now on that is what you will eat — thin foods. Because it is okay to be 130 lbs. It's not okay to be three hundred pounds or four hundred pounds. And you don't have to be scared about being slim because you can take care of things now. Right? *Nods.* You know a lot more about and you have learned your lesson and you now know how to take care of yourself. Right?. . . *Nods.* Good.

The therapist now summarizes Barbara's position.

Now what I want you to do is to believe me when I say that you are just as good and just as important as any other human being. Can you agree with that? *Long pause — then nods.* Yeah. It is about time that you believed that isn't it? Sixteen year old Barbara, eleven year old Barbara twenty year old Barbara, twenty-five year old Barbara, did you hear that? You're just as good and just as important as any one else. Did you hear that? Don't forget that! You take care of Barbara, will you? Look after her in a nice way. Get her to be nice and slim and feel good. Like her, protect her, take good care of her. Right? *Nods.* Okay.

Essential ego strengthening and assertiveness training suggestions are given here in a condensed form, but in a very forcible manner, with every ego state involved in the problem.

Barbara was seen again in therapy about two weeks later and reported that she had felt relaxed and very good after leaving the office. She was able to recall very little of the interview, but was aware that it had created some disturbing feelings. What struck her, however, was that, instead of eating less as she had hoped, she had begun 'eating like crazy'. Instead of losing weight as she had expected, she had begun to put weight on and was some two or three pounds heavier at the second interview. She also admitted that she felt apprehensive about returning for the follow up visit, not so much because of the disappointing result but because, in some inexplicable way, she felt threatened by therapy.

We have already commented upon Barbara's excellent hypnotic potential, as demonstrated during her first visit; yet, when reinduction of hypnosis was attempted, she showed strong evidence of resistance, saying that she did not feel that she could relax this time, that her eyes could not close and that the light was too bright. The therapist accepted all of this as clear evidence of resistance and commented that perhaps Barbara, or a part of her, did not want any further help from him; that perhaps she needed to stay fat and he could not force her to do anything that she did not want to do and that being fat was perhaps, what she really wanted. All resistance evaporated at this point and Barbara entered hypnosis readily. In hypnosis, after establishing the fact that she still wanted to lose weight and, after reviewing the events of the first meeting, it was indicated that none of these experiences was the source of a problem. The therapist then asked if that part still responsible for the persistence of overeating would communicate with him. This request was met with acceptance and the therapist was able to communicate with a distressed twenty-one year old Barbara who had not been located in the first meeting. This ego state arose at a time when Barbara had lost some weight and was out with a girl friend. She had been drinking heavily and then decided to go back to the girl friend's apartment with two men they had met. At the apartment they had all smoked marijuana. Barbara was surprised at the effect that this had on her; she began to laugh uncontrollably and found herself acquiescing to every request made of her. There was considerable sexual activity which, at a purely physical level, she enjoyed. However, there was a part of her that remained aghast at her behaviour, that felt powerless to control it and was scared of this evident loss of control. She decided right there and then that this must never happen again. However, at twenty-five, she had relented and allowed herself to lose weight; but, as we have already learned, she made a bad judgment. At our first meeting, this ego state had remained silent. It had determined not to allow hypnotherapy to be the means whereby Barbara might once again be exposed to these dangers that weight loss had previously presented.

There ensued a frank open discussion between this somewhat Parental ego state and the therapist. This state was reminded that the problems creating the need to take alcohol and drugs had been dealt with in the previous session. The therapist made it clear to the ego state that he agreed that it had the right to keep Barbara fat; but he wondered whether, in view of her new appreciation of the circumstances, it still felt that this was the only way to protect and maintain control over her body and its behaviour. After much consideration Barbara agreed that she would once again allow herself to lose weight. However, she stipulated that she would not allow the weight to decrease right down to the target weight since she felt that this would result in too great a loss of control; but she would accept a loss of about sixty pounds. This ego state also admitted that it had felt very threatened by therapy but now was much more at ease since the therapist had understood its point of view.

It told him that it had attempted to prevent Barbara from keeping her second appointment but the other parts of Barbara had been too strong.

A search for other ego states which might sabotage therapy was carried out but none was found at that time. General ego strengthening suggestions were repeated and accepted fully. Suggestions for weight loss were given in very general terms only, since it was felt that specific suggestions were unnecessary in view of the agreement already obtained from the ego state responsible for overeating.

At the following meeting a week or two later, Barbara delightedly reported that she was 'losing weight without even thinking about dieting'. At the time of writing, her progress remained satisfactory but constant vigilance for any evidence of loss of control which would lead to the reinstitution of the protective overeating pattern – was being maintained.

This case illustrates some interesting aspects of analytical hypnotherapy which deserve some comment. First of all, in spite of very careful work with a patient, it is not possible to ensure that all critical experiences are dealt with in a single session. Only the disappearance of symptoms will ultimately testify to this. Conversely, the persistence of symptoms always means that a critical experience has not been identified or has not been dealt with adequately. At each session a renewed search must be made for any such experience; any ego state arising from it must be communicated with and its problems dealt with. In Barbara's case, this was readily accomplished. In others, this search may be long and arduous. It has been the author's frequent experience that such hidden ego states which continue to sabotage therapy are often very young; birth experience and prenatal experiences are fertile sources of potent antagonistic ego states, usually Parental in nature, with a predominantly punitive and highly moralistic attitude.

Secondly, resistance in a second session must always be regarded as caused by a concealed ego state. It may effectively prevent any unconscious communication at this visit or it may prevent the patient from keeping the appointment through psychosomatic illness or by simply forgetting the date or time of the appointment. This kind of resistance can occur at any time during therapy when such an ego state feels that the therapist is likely to succeed in modifying what it regards as its essential function.

So long as the patient remains in therapy, such resistance is in itself a communication with the concealed ego state and should be used to make contact. Such questions as *Does the part that does not want me to help. . .?* are asked, and any answer to such questions indicates good communication with that part. If the therapist demonstrates an understanding of and a respect for its essential function as protector and law enforcer, satisfactory negotiations can take place. These are frequently delicate in nature; rapport can be fragile and requires the therapist's greatest skill to maintain. This skill can be acquired only through experience but the analytical hypnotherapist will certainly gain a great deal of this when treating the obese patient who often has a well concealed ego state responsible for the overeating pattern.

Migraine
This author has no doubt that analytical hypnotherapy is the treatment of choice for migraine; indeed even direct suggestion in hypnosis and the use of self hypnosis are still more effective than traditional methods. Harding (1967) demonstrated that of a series of migraine cases, 38% responded to direct suggestion with total relief over an eight year period; a further 32% exhibited partial relief over this same period. In these latter cases, there was a reduction in the use of medications, and in the frequency and severity of the headaches, and overall an increase in wellbeing. Analytical hypnotherapy offers the greatest chance of permanent cure since, when successful, the underlying conflict responsible for the migraine is permanently removed.

Glotman (1936) offered a good description of the mechanism of migraine: vascular in origin, it results when the intracranial blood vessels dilate after a period of vasoconstriction. The dilatation of the blood vessels irritates surrounding sensory nerves and creates the characteristic throbbing pain of the migraine headache. Typically, one side of the head is affected and the symptoms of headache may be preceded by warning symptoms which are presumably due to the prior constriction of the affected blood vessels. Such constriction may result in blurred vision, flashes of light, blindness, numbness, weakness and paresis since portions of the cerebral cortex become temporarily functionless because of the diminution of the blood supply to the affected area.

Normally, therapy is directed at relieving the pain by the administration of different analgesics and by reducing the frequent accompanying nausea and vomiting by giving antiemetics. Prevention of the headaches has usually been accomplished by the administration of ergot products which act by constricting the arterioles and thereby preventing the painful dilatation of migraine. This usually depends on successfully administering the drug during the prodromal phase of vasoconstriction. Because these methods are only partially successful, there has been an attempt to identify precipitating factors; in some cases, these have been found to be so specific as to suggest that migraine is some form of allergy. General relaxation induced by tranquillizers has sometimes reduced the effect of recognised precipitating factors which when identified, are often found to be emotional. However, suggestion in hypnosis has frequently been found to be effective because by duplicating the effect of drugs, it produces a direct reduction in pain, a constriction of dilated and painful arteries, and a general relaxation eliminating tension in a blanket fashion. There seems no doubt that the primary vasoconstriction results from tension affecting the muscles surrounding the blood vessels, just as it can create the well known tension headaches caused by tensions in head muscles. However, unlike the obvious tension associated with tension headaches, migraines often occur when the patient appears to be tension-free. The causes of this migraine producing tension are therefore deeply unconscious, and only the techniques of analytical hypnotherapy are likely to locate them, since they usually originate in the distant past.

The usual psychodynamics discovered in analytical hypnotherapy of migraine are those of a trapped, angry Child forbidden to express its anger by a watchful, repressing and disapproving Parent. The Child is periodically unable to contain its anger and consequently it spills out into a *silent screaming in the head*. Because of their relative insignificance, the precipitating factors can easily go unrecognized at a conscious level, and yet they are the straws that break the camel's back. In other cases the precipitating factors may remind the Child of its repression and, because of their specificity in triggering these memories, they have some of the characteristics of an allergen. The techniques used to resolve the underlying Child/Parent conflict in treating migraine headaches do not differ from those already detailed. Any persistence of symptoms will indicate that this conflict remains unresolved.

In the following case, Elaine was forty-one when she came for therapy for migraine from which she had suffered for about twenty years. The attacks are preceded by a buzzing in the ears except for those occasions when she awakens with a full blown attack. Usually the attacks increase in severity during the day until she becomes nauseated and finally vomits. At this point she usually falls asleep and awakes late in the day, feeling better although weak and exhausted. She had been on every kind of medication for migraine, including injections for the pain, ergot preparations to prevent the attacks and tranquillizers to relax her. Elaine was a very tense person who revealed that, even when asleep, tension made her jaws clench so much that she had developed pains in the temporomandibular joints and suffered the typical temporomandibular joint syndrome. She felt that her tension was due to an unhappy childhood: her parents separated when she was twelve. Subsequently, her mother became sick with cancer and Elaine had to look after her young brothers and sisters. There was never very much money in the house and the thirteen year old Elaine had much to worry about during her adolescence.

Elaine realised that certainly there were no longer any worries in her present secure situation; and although she had no need for concern, the old habit of worrying persisted. She married, at seventeen, a ne'er do well who did not work, and while she had at times occasional headaches, they were no great problem. Nine years and three children later, she divorced him, much against her deeply held principles. Around the time of the final breakdown of her marriage, she felt the headaches begin in earnest; they began to assume a pattern which continued until the time of the first consultation. Some eight years after the divorce, she married her present husband with whom she has an excellent relationship and with whom there are no financial or other anxieties; still the headaches persisted because she was still unable to leave the old anxieties and worries behind. The following excerpt from this initial interview begins after Elaine has agreed that there must be a part of her that still needs to keep the headaches.

DR   So we've agreed that there is a part of you that's still keeping these headaches.

PT   Yeah, *laughing*. I'm sure. Much to my dismay. Uhum.

DR   First we'll try a little experiment with you. Just sit back in the chair. Are you comfortable there?

PT   Uhum.

DR   Then just close your eyes. Okay? Then I'll get you to ask a simple question.

The therapist decides that he will attempt to locate the part responsible for the symptoms and endeavour to reframe its terms of reference.

PT   I'm asking you or you're. . .?

DR   No. I'm getting you to ask your own question.

PT   Okay.

DR   And I'll tell you the question to ask. You go right deep inside, as if you are asking the parts inside. Ask the part of you that gives you the headaches if it will communicate with you. If it will, you will get a 'yes' feeling or you will hear a 'yes' or you will see a 'yes' or you will experience something. *Patient nods.*

DR   Did you feel a 'yes' already?

PT   When you said it. I didn't even ask it.

DR   You got a 'yes'?

PT   When you said it, I got a feeling of 'yes' that's all.

DR   Good. Okay. Ask that part there — the part that's giving you the feeling of 'yes', would it let you know what it's trying to do for you by giving you the headache. Ask it if it will let you know. . . It may say 'yes', it may say 'no'. What is it trying to do for you?

PT   *Shakes her head.*

DR   It says no? A definite no?

PT   I don't see anything yet.

This seeking of unconscious information constitutes the entire induction procedure. The phrase, *go deep inside* is the only direction necessary.

The response to a request for communication with an unconscious ego state may not always be such a clear yes or no as in this case. The immediate response suggests good unconscious communication and cooperation is forthcoming, which indeed, proves to be the case.

Here the therapist is seeking to discover the intent of the headache-producing ego state.

There is no immediate response so

DR   Okay. Just ask the question: the therapist gives further encour-
Will that part of me that gives me agement.
the headache let me know what it's
trying to do for me?

PT   *Nods.*

DR   Okay. Got a yes straight away?   The ego state is prepared to com-
                                      municate further.

PT   I think so.

DR   Okay. Ask that part to let you   The therapist endeavours to re-
know what it is that it is trying to do   move the fear from the uncon-
for you. When you know what it is   scious ego state that it might be
and it comes to you, just nod your   forced to divulge privileged in-
head. Don't tell me what it is, but   formation.
when you know what it is − what
it's trying to do for you, just nod
your head. You don't even have to
tell me. Just the minute you get it. . .

PT   Okay.

DR   You've got it? Okay. Now ask   Permission to divulge the reasons
if you can tell me what it is.   for its actions is sought and given.

PT   Yeah? It's okay.

DR   Okay. What is it trying to do
for you?

PT   Well, I think it is trying to make
me feel guilty.

DR   Make you feel guilty?   *Making her feel guilty* indicates
                             the active functioning of a Paren-
PT   Uhum.   tal element in the ego state com-
             plex.

DR   Okay.

PT   That's the thing that came to mind.

DR   Okay. That's good. Ask whether, by making you feel guilty, it is protecting you in some way.

Here the therapist is seeking the protective element in the Parent's functioning.

PT   Uhum.

DR   It is? Is it protecting you from doing something else even worse by making you feel guilty?

PT   I don't understand that.

Consciously this is not understood. The therapist directs Elaine to put the question to the unconscious ego state, which readily understands it.

DR   Well, ask the question, are you trying to protect me from doing something worse by keeping me feeling guilty?

PT   No.

DR   No. Is it punishing you in some way?

The Parent ego state sometimes interprets its protective role as an essentially punitive one.

PT   Yes.

DR   It is punishing you in some way. Okay. Would you please ask that part if it will tell you just how old it is? You'll get a 'yes' or a 'no.

PT   It feels old. It's old.

This *old* feeling is probably due to identification with the real parent. But the therapist needs to discover the time of the formation of the ego state complex.

DR   It's old, eh? But ask if the actual part inside you is a young part of you.

PT   I'm not getting anything.

DR   Just ask a specific question.

Ask that part that's giving you the headaches if she's ten years of age or younger.

PT   No.

DR   Ask her if she is twenty years of age or younger. What did you get, 'yes' or 'no'?

Answers are sometimes slow in emerging possibly indicating some uncertainty as to how to give the correct answer.

PT   No. I didn't get anything.

DR   Ask again. Are you, the part of me that is trying to make me feel guilty, twenty years of age or younger?

PT   *Nods.*

DR   What do you get?

PT   I get twenty-five but. . .

Although twenty-five comes to mind, consciously she is reluctant to accept this.

DR   You're twenty-five. Okay. . .

PT   But. . .

DR   Don't argue with it. Just say, 'well are you twenty-five?'

PT   That just popped into my head.

Unconscious communication frequently *just pops* into the head.

DR   Well just ask her, are you *twenty-five?* What do you get?

PT   Yeah *nodding vigorously.*

It is confirmed as a true unconscious communication.

DR   Pretty positive yes?

PT   Pretty positive.

DR   Ask that twenty-five year old part of you if she is scared.

The therapist now seeks to define persistent emotional attributes and finds that all of the primary emotions are represented unconsciously.

PT   I think she is scared.

DR   Ask her if she is also hurting.

PT   Uhum.

DR   Ask her if she's resentful or angry.

PT   That too.

DR   Ask her if she is feeling guilty.

PT   Uhum.

DR   And ask her if she will now let you feel all of those feelings.

He now asks her to bring the emotions up to a more conscious level — but they are already there.

PT   Oh, I feel them all.

DR   You feel them all. Okay. When you have felt them all, will you please ask her to tell you what's happening right there. You're twenty-five years of age. Just feel yourself twenty-five. Be right there. See what's happening there. At twenty-five years of age, what's happening?

To render these feelings more understandable, the experiences responsible for them must be invoked.

PT   A whole lot of mixed up feelings are there.

Confusion.

DR   Okay, be right there and see what it is that's really happening. Something is really happening right there that's bothering you an awful lot. What is that?

The therapist attempts to create some order from the confused memories which crowd in. He hopes to locate the essential source of the discomfort. Further

PT It's the divorce.

DR It's the divorce, eh? and how are you feeling as you're going through the divorce? What is the feeling you've got?

PT Um — Scared, alone.

DR Alone and scared.

PT I guess that's basically taking me back to when I was twelve, but I didn't feel guilty when I was twelve.

DR Okay. Slip back to being twelve now. Are you twelve?

PT Yeah.

DR Twelve year old — twelve year old Elaine.

PT Uhum.

DR What's happening right there? Look around and see what's happening. You're right there.

PT I don't know where my dad is and my mum is sick and. . .

DR Which means. . .?

PT Nothing. . . I. . .

DR Look around the room and tell me what you are doing.

PT Hmm. Gee, I'm sitting on the

definition of the experience is necessary.

As she defines these feelings, she recognises their connection to an earlier time which appears similar, except that she was not aware of any guilt feelings at that time.

Regression is surprisingly easy and the twelve year old ego state is very ready and willing to communicate. Persuading the ego state to look around, *right there* readily establishes the regression. The scared and lonely feeling is obvious but she does not comment upon this.

Elaine is surprised at the vividness

chesterfield and I'm waiting for my dad to come home. . .

DR Uhum.

PT And – er – wanting my parents to get back together.

DR Uhum. . . Are you scared?

PT Oh, yeah.

DR Is dad anywhere about?

PT No.

DR Twelve year old Elaine, is there anything else that you can tell me? If there is your head will nod for 'yes', or it will shake for 'no'.

PT *Shaking head.*

DR Okay. Forty-one year old Elaine, did you hear all of that?

PT Uhum.

DR There's twelve year old Elaine, can you see her sitting on the chesterfield.

PT Yes.

DR Would you just sit by the side of her please? Put your arm around her shoulders. Can you do that? If you can, just nod your head. Do you want to?

PT Yes.

of her recollection. Dad will not come home and she is naturally afraid she will never be secure. He does not come – he never comes and Elaine must remain alone. Perhaps she is angry with him for leaving her alone.

She has been unjustly treated but she must not express her anger. The Parent will see to that.

It is time for the Adult's help and intervention.

The Adult has been watching events with interest and is encouraged to do something to reassure and comfort the young Elaine with its more mature strength.

DR Okay. She's scared and she's lonely. I want you to take hold of her hand there, that's all you have to do. Just see yourself doing that and will you tell her all the good things that you know that she doesn't yet know. When you have done that, just nod your head... *Nods.* Twelve year old Elaine, now you've heard that, do you still need to go on feeling scared?

Putting an arm around her and holding her hand are symbolic of comfort, security and love. She is also asked to put her Adult wisdom at the disposal of the twelve year old Elaine. With this wisdom and support, the old uncomfortable feelings are clearly no longer relevant or necessary.

PT No, not really.

DR Do you need to go on feeling guilty?

PT No.

DR Need to go on feeling hurt?

PT Shouldn't.

DR Need to go on feeling angry?

Even the angry feelings can go.

PT No.

DR Forty-one year old Elaine, you've heard that. Twelve year old Elaine has listened to you and she says, 'no, I don't need to go on feeling like that any more'.

This is played back to the Adult who now understands.

PT No.

DR Now you have got to find a way for her to let go of those uncomfortable feelings. So, using all of your wisdom and understanding, I want you to find a way for her to let go of all those uncomfortable feel-

The Adult must now use its resources to find means of ridding twelve year old Elaine of uncomfortable feelings that have persisted, unchanged, for almost thirty years.

ings. When you have found a way, just nod your head. . . *Nods.* Twelve year old Elaine, there's a way for you now. Let go of all those uncomfortable feelings. Just let them all go.

This way is accepted and is readily used.

PT *After an interval.* Okay.

DR Just let them go and when you know they've gone just nod your head. . . *Nods.* Twelve year old Elaine, if you've really let those uncomfortable feelings go you can get up from the chesterfield and you can really be quite close to forty-one year old Elaine and you can give me a smile.

Twelve year old Elaine is okay at last but the therapist is not yet entirely convinced. He gives her further encouragement to let them go.

The *smile test* again.

PT *Laughing.* Mm — I can do it!

DR Isn't that great? Okay. Now twelve year old Elaine, I've got a job for you to do.

It is very positive! Greatly encouraged, the therapist feels that he can use twelve year old Elaine's new found knowledge to help twenty-five year old Elaine who is feeling guilty.

PT Uhum.

DR I want you, please, to come forward in time from twelve years of age. Come up to twenty-five year old Elaine. Twenty-five year old Elaine is having a real problem there and needs our help. Will you please, now that you understand things from both sides, help twenty-five year old Elaine? She's really got a problem. When you have done that, nod your head for 'yes'. . . *Nods.* Twenty-five year old Elaine, with that understanding and help from twelve year old Elaine and forty-one

In conjunction with the Adult, the

year old Elaine, do you still need to keep that scared feeling?

PT   No, not. . . no.

DR   What do you think?

PT   No, I really don't.

DR   Good. How about that sad feeling you've got, do you need to keep that?

PT   No, I'd like to get rid of that.

DR   How about that guilty feeling, need to keep that?

PT   Not really. No.

DR   Okay. Forty-one year old Elaine, I think that twenty-five year old Elaine is ready now to let go of all those uncomfortable feelings. She understands why she has them but she now says, *hey, I don't need them any more.*

So I'm going to ask you now, using all of your wisdom and understanding, to find a way for her to let them go and when you have found a way, just nod your head.

PT   Okay. *Nodding.*

DR   Twenty-five year old Elaine, there's a way. Just let them go. Just let them fade right away. You don't need those scared feelings, those guilty feelings, those angry feelings,

twelve year old enables twenty-five year old Elaine to deal with the scared feelings resulting from the guilt.

Some indecision is at first apparent but on second thoughts there is clearly no real need to retain old anxiety, sadness or guilt.

Again, a way has to be discovered to relinquish old uncomfortable feelings which had been retained for the previous sixteen years.

She is now ready to relinquish them.

A way is readily located so that she is encouraged to relinquish all the old, uncomfortable feelings, particularly those of anger and of

any of those uncomfortable feelings, any more. When you have let them go, you'll know that you've let them go. You'll feel so good you will just have to nod your head to let me know.

PT   I really do feel good.

DR   Okay. If you feel that good, you can give me a big smile and say. .

PT   Oh, I do!

DR   Good. Now, twenty-five year old Elaine who feels so good, I want you to join up with forty-one year old Elaine and with twelve year old Elaine to feel good. As you feel good, will you look around inside and see if there are any other Elaines who are not feeling good.

PT   *Shaking her head.* No.

DR   Okay. I'm going to ask you then . . . would it be all right for you now to let go of all those headaches?

PT   Oh, yeah.

DR   Okay. I'm going to ask you to go forward in time to the next time when you would normally have a headache, to see yourself there, to see yourself dealing with whatever the situation is. *Nods.* Good. Feeling really good? Feeling so good there's no need to have them?

guilt, since these are presumably responsible for the headaches.

The patient is surprised at how good she feels now that she has relinquished her discomfort.

All of the ego states are now required to integrate and harmonise in a common good feeling. The therapist makes sure that no part of the personality is left out.

It is now time to check whether the symptoms are any longer necessary.

Projective imagery is a good means of evaluating progress.

It is positive which confirms success.

PT   Nothing.

DR   Okay. We'll pick another one like that. A really difficult situation – one that has always been guaranteed to give a headache and see yourself instead, really enjoying it. *Nods.* No headache at all? Feels so good doesn't it?

Another more difficult and complex projective imagery test is asked for.

PT   Okay.

It also is positive. The therapist makes a third test because success has been so rapid.

DR   Good. Can you find another difficult one which would really have given you a headache in the old days?

PT   Yeah.

DR   Okay, find that one and be right there with smiling twenty-five year old Elaine and smiling twelve year old Elaine both absolutely free of guilt and feeling so good. Now as you do that notice some important things. As you have been doing that you've been feeling 'Yippee, I'm okay. I'm just as good as anybody else'. You've been feeling that you don't need to feel bad about that anymore.

Again the *smile test* is positive.

The therapist has assumed that Elaine must be feeling strong and has been telling herself good things because permission to relinquish the symptoms has been granted so readily.

PT   That's true.

Elaine confirms his assumption.

DR   Just as good as anyone else. You no longer need to put yourself down. No longer need to allow anyone to put you down. I'm going to ask you to make some promises. Number one – promise that you are going to, from now on, really re-

Assertiveness training promotes self support and self protection.

spect Elaine: like her, and don't put her down.

PT I guess that's what I want.

DR And love her. You can do that can't you?

PT I guess so.

DR I want to see you doing that. Loving Elaine.

PT Would you say that again?

DR Would you please love Elaine? Can you do that?

PT It's dumb.

DR Oh, come on.

PT It's hard to do.

DR She's as good as anybody. And you know how to love.

PT Oh yes, I do.

DR How about loving Elaine? She's as good as anybody you've loved and she has needed your love more than anything else, hasn't she?

PT Uhum.

DR Okay, how about giving — you've been giving your love to everyone else — to Elaine. *Nods.* Is that a promise?

Loving Elaine is the ultimate objective of therapy but Elaine at first is not sure that she should do this.

It's dumb is a Parental judgement which is a reflection of her assessment of the popular attitude to loving oneself. Her Parent makes a token last ditch stand against this departure from convention but ultimately gives way to Adult reasoning.

PT   Yes. *Laughing.*

DR   Okay. You feel close to her now?

PT   Yes.

DR   Does she feel calm?

The resulting serenity is something that Elaine had never previously experienced.

PT   Much calmer than she has ever been I guess. Yes.

DR   Okay.

Elaine was seen a week after the first interview and reported that several striking changes had already taken place. She had lost the constant feeling of discomfort in her head and had felt considerably more relaxed. She said that she found herself looking at things differently and was not feeling so put upon. Previously, if someone had said no to her, she had taken it as a rejection but now she found that she could accept it at face value. She reported feeling more positive about things and did not need to feel totally responsible if things did not go well. She gave some examples of how she had been very self assertive in a pleasant but positive manner. She had been agreeably surprised by this change in her behaviour which demonstrated to her that she could become self protective without creating any problems.

Elaine described her feelings following the first interview as if a dam opened up releasing a flood of new ideas. She found that she could allow herself to enjoy things without her old feelings of guilt welling up and leading to a headache. She now understood why she got headaches when things were apparently going very well. She discovered that she was now able to discuss her fatigue with her husband. She had never been able to do this previously and subsequently experienced a degree of closeness with him that she had not dreamed possible.

She admitted that she still had some problem with total self acceptance but was aware that she was feeling much warmer feelings towards herself. She felt that she now understood what 'I'm O.K., you're O.K.' really meant. She described her week as a kind of high from which she was only gradually coming down to a more normal level. However, she was convinced that she would never drop down to the level at which she would suffer headaches, and if she did, she would know the reason why.

Because this patient had to leave the country shortly after this second interview, she was not seen again in therapy. However, some eighteen months later a fortuitous contact was made. She reported that she had never looked back from the time of receiving therapy and was feeling much happier than she had felt before. She still had the occasional headache but it was never severe enough to require medication. These would occur whenever she had not been as open or as self protective as she had resolved to be. She said that she did not need any further therapy but would return if she ever did feel that need.

In reviewing this case, specific features of the therapy can be commented upon. The decision to seek direct communication with unconscious ego states responsible for symptoms, without any prior formal induction or establishment of ideomotor responses, was made on the basis of the patient's evident eagerness to cooperate. This is the hallmark of the good hypnotic subject. This unreserved cooperation immediately indicates that there is no likelihood of unconscious interference with communication. This proved to be the case with Elaine. Had this not been so, a more formal approach could easily have been substituted.

This case was somewhat unusual in that only two critical experiences held the psychodynamics for so much distress; however, it is more than likely that many similar experiences reinforced Elaine's pathological responses.

This rapid response to therapy, though not common, should not be thought of as extraordinary. There have been, in the author's experience, many equally complex and distressing cases of patients with long standing symptoms who following a single session of analytical hypnotherapy have not returned simply because, as they put it, *there isn't any need for further treatment*. In Elaine's case, no further analysis was necessary at the second session, and hypnotherapy was used only to reinforce the direct suggestions already given.

It seems clear that, at age twelve, Elaine had decided to repress her mounting resentment at the increased responsibilities thrust upon her by her parents and decided to accept this as her lot. However, the unconscious anger did not disappear and was controlled only by her strong feelings of guilt. At age twenty-five, to have been let down by her husband (another father figure) must have created enormous feelings of rage, which only strong feelings of guilt about leaving the marriage could contain although not suppress, beyond allowing the expression of the frequent migraine headaches. Only by dealing first with the guilt and then the anger could she be freed from the consequences of this concealed resentment. Presumably the old mechanism of migraine has been difficult to dismantle and goes into operation whenever she fails to express feelings of resentment in an appropriate and satisfactory manner. However, since she now is aware of this, she well knows how to avoid further attacks.

Those patients with migraine who fail to respond to analytical approaches should be taught self hypnotic techniques for the relief of pain. Either the development of glove anaesthesia, or a warm hand in hypnosis, appear to be effective agents applied at the source of pain for relief during an attack. Ansel (1977) has described a simple excercise which increases the blood flow to the hand in the treatment of migraine. Rotating the arm in a rapid circular motion uses centrifugal force, which appears to be of value in creating a warm hand in subjects with low hypnotisability.

Ego strengthening suggestions given by the therapist and repeated in self hypnosis combined with assertiveness training suggestions, will encourage the migraine patient to alter his or her life style sufficiently to avoid those factors which can precipitate headaches.

Some Further Illustrative Case Histories

There are numerous symptom complexes which come to the analytical hypnotherapist's attention, all of which can find a place in the theoretical model of the Child/Parent conflict. These can be readily placed in one of three main groups: the emotional disorders, the habit disorders, and the psychosomatic disorders. To some extent, these groups are not very distinct from one another, so that a psychosomatic disorder may be accompanied by elements of an emotional disorder; and so may a habit disorder, as we have seen with overeating. In order to illustrate how different symptom complexes may present and how the analytical approach can effectively promote change, this chapter will offer some interesting case histories.

Drug and Other Addiction Disorders

Every hypnotherapist has been approached by a person wishing to break a recurrent pattern of behaviour which he believes if continued is likely to prove damaging. Chief of these is the compulsively persisting habit of consuming a particular drug, a habit which defies all efforts to break. All of our functioning depends upon the formation of habit patterns which are complex responses to various appropriate stimuli. Such activities as walking, talking, driving etc., depend heavily upon established habit patterns for effective execution. The acquisition of any new skill is dependent upon effectively establishing new habit patterns. These habits are welcomed because they remain subservient to their obvious needs and beneficial functions. Since the needs they serve are completely conscious, they can be started or discontinued at will. On the other hand, in the habit disorders, patterns of behaviour continue in spite of a conscious decision and desire that they should cease, simply because these habits are maintained to serve a need, but that need is unconscious and therefore below the level of awareness. The individual is aware only of a feeling of compulsion to carry out the unwanted behaviour, or perhaps he carries out the behaviour without any conscious awareness whatsoever. The drug addiction or any other compulsive behaviour will continue until the unconscious need disappears or finds other more acceptable means of fulfillment. This is true of all cases of drug addiction and compulsive behaviour. All successful therapies of habit disorders operate on this premise although not as directly as the analytical approach.

Drugs of addiction become so because of their anaesthetic proper-ties: in some way or another, these drugs are able to relieve discomfort. Whether the addictive drug be nicotine, alcohol, marijuana, valium, heroin or any one of dozens of others, the mechanism is the same. All addictive drugs, e.g. analgesics, tranquilizers, and the illicit drugs share this anaesthetic property of reducing sensation, thereby relieving pain and distress. All those who become drug addicted are suffering unconscious pain, fear, or anger of varying intensity, which is not permitted normal expression. The Parent/Child conflict is strongly operative, and the discomfort resulting from this conflict often reaches such intolerable levels that only the consumption of one of these drugs can provide some temporary relief. Much of this discomfort is not at a conscious level, but such that is conscious, is interpreted simply as a craving for the drug. Taking the drug usually affords some relief from the craving. This relief is consciously interpreted as enjoyment, and such relief and enjoyment provide reinforcement for the habit.

Many helpful therapies have been described for the addict. One such therapy is the substitution of one drug for a less potent one. Supportive treatment and ego strengthening therapies combined with programmed withdrawal of the offending drugs, are all excellent behavioural approaches; even aversion therapy has its place. How-ever, this author believes that so long as unconscious pain persists or no satisfactory alternative means of dealing with it has been disco-vered, the risk of returning to addiction remains very high. The only true avenue for certain cure is to go directly to the underlying need which the drug meets, i.e. the removal of unconscious distress.

In analysis, the cause for the addiction is often found to be severe unconscious pain usually resulting from parental rejection. Because angry feelings are also likely to be repressed, depression is common. Psychosomatic symptoms also go hand in hand with drug addiction since the drug does not always effectively repress the unconscious tensions. The Parent often permits the use of the drug as a means of repressing feeling because it is the method that the real parent has used. So it is that the history of drug addiction so often has a familial element, the Parent choosing the repressing agent that the real parent used. Sometimes, the use of the drug temporarily reduces the Parent/Child conflict, by removing some of the Parent's influence on the Child's repressed agressive and angry feelings which are then freed to gain irrational expression.

Excessive Smoking
In Western culture, tobacco smoking has been a permissable habit until very recently when there emerged a mounting opposition to it. Many smokers are seeking help in relinquishing what has become for them an unpleasant and unwelcome habit. In increasing numbers, they have turned to the hypnotherapist for help in terminating a habit which they appear to be powerless to do on their own. There is no doubt that a proportion of smokers will respond favourably to suggestion given to stop smoking in hypnosis. Hypnotherapeutic results have ranged from a 10% to 80% cure rate. Pederson et al (1975, 1979), found that hypnosis alone was no more effective than non treatment, but that hypnosis, when combined with counselling, produced a six month abstinence rate of 53%. Watkins (1976), whose method included five sessions of hypnosis with much counselling, produced a cure rate of 67% but found that the failure rate was highest among those who used smoking to help them control their anger. To the analytical hypnotherapist, it seems probable that those smokers who respond to direct suggestion to quit are probably ready to give up smoking. Either they have discovered ways of dealing with the underlying tension, or the relaxation of hypnosis gives them an alternative method of relinquishing tension. In either case it seems that the part of the individual responsible for maintaining the smoking habit is sometimes able to discover effective substitutes for smoking. The fact remains that, even with the most intensive therapy using hypnosis, only 67% give up their habit. The same is probably true for other drug addictions treated by using hypnosis.

In the following case the response to therapy was dramatic and yet logical in the context of analysis. Marion was a fifty-four year old widow who had been smoking two packs of cigarettes each day for 35 years. She had been feeling increasingly depressed during the previous year or so and during periods of depression might even have increased her smoking. Marion had ten children; but the youngest had left home, leaving her alone, although she was visited frequently by her children and grandchildren. Her husband had been killed in a car accident some six years before but she felt that she had managed to cope with that loss very well. He had had a heart attack six months prior to his death which had forced her to deal with the possibility of his death. Although she was highly motivated to stop smoking she found that when she did so for three days, she became very anxious and ate to excess. She slept poorly, because of her high level of tension, and partly because she became breathless if she rolled off her pillows during the night. She had extreme difficulty in breathing when lying flat and had been told by her physician that this would not improve until she stopped smoking. She also complained of an awful taste in her mouth and no longer enjoyed smoking because of it; yet she felt powerless to give up the habit. She also asked if she could be helped to lose some weight since she was twenty pounds overweight and attributed this to her tendency to overeat.

She proved to be an excellent hypnotic subject and ideomotor head signals proved satisfactory, as they frequently do in good subjects. She reviewed her birth experience and found it to be positive and was then asked to go to the first experience relevant to her current depression and excessive smoking. She indicated that the experience occurred when she was one year old. She was able to talk about the experience and it was established that it was both a frightening and hurtful one. Therapy commences at this point.

DR One year of age. What's happening?

PT I walk back and it's at my uncle's.

DR You're at your uncle's, are you? And what's happening there?

PT And he put down a pot of hot pig feed.

DR Yeah?

PT And I backed into it. And screwed up my back!

DR Screwed up your back? What

The therapist's use of the present tense: *What's happening?* emphasizes the regression. The patient reviews the salient points and gradually completes the picture of a very traumatic and painful experience.

Identification of the uncomforta-

are you feeling? What's the feeling that you have?

PT   Pain.

DR   Are you screaming with pain? Is it an awful pain?

PT   Uhum.

DR   What's happening next?

PT   My mother pulled my dress off.

DR   Is there a smell? Do you smell the burning?

The therapist is uncertain whether the dress had caught fire or not.

PT   Uhum.

DR   And what happens next?

PT   I have to sleep on my stomach.

This indicates the extent of one year old Marion's pain and disability.

DR   Oh, that's awful, isn't it? Are you crying?

PT   Yeah.

DR   It is awful isn't it? Are you scared?

Again the element of fear needs to be clearly defined.

PT   Uhum.

DR   Okay. Is there anything else we need to know about that in order to understand? If there is, your head will nod for 'yes'. If there isn't, your head will shake for 'no'. . . *Head shakes slowly and deliberately.* No. Okay. Fifty-four year old Marion, there is one year old Marion there.

All that the Adult *needs to know in order to understand* has now been disclosed.

The Adult is now presented with the problem in detail.

ble feelings which are presumably persisting at an unconscious level is important in forming an understanding of the experience.

She is still feeling scared and she's feeling very sad. She's in so much pain. Tell her that she's going to get better and that she's going to be all right. When you've told her that the pain's going to completely go and that she does not need to go on being scared, when you've told her all that you might, give her a cuddle to make sure that she feels okay. When you've done that, nod your head. . . *Nods.* Good. One year old Marion, now you've heard that, do you still need to go on being scared or being sad?. . . *Head shakes.* One year old Marion, listen and I am going to ask fifty-four year old Marion now to find a way for you to let go of all of that scared, sad feeling and, when she's found one, your head will nod for 'yes'. . . *Nods.* There you are, one year old Marion, there's a way now for you to let go of all that scared, sad feeling. All the pain goes away. All the scared feeling goes away. When it has all gone, nod your head .. . *Nods.* Now give me a smile.. . *Smiles.* Feels good?

PT   Uhum.

DR   Nice. Okay.
Now, one year old Marion, you're feeling really good now. That feels better than you've felt for fifty-three years. Isn't that nice? Okay, now I'm going to ask you to grow up from being one year old. Come up to the next time something happened which made you feel scared or feel uncomfortable and when you're

The Child ego state is in pain, which, it fears, will go on for ever. Marion is lonely as well as afraid since she has retained these painful memories of isolation at the one year of age level. However, she agrees that she need no longer retain them and can free herself from this distress.

She is now free of all the old pain and fear that she had retained.

A search for other sources of discomfort is initiated.

there your head will automatically nod for 'yes'. . . Go through all the years as you come up from being one. . . two, three, four. . . up to the next experience where something happens where you're not feeling okay. When you're there, nod your head for 'yes'. . . *Nods after a long interval.* How old are you there?

PT   I can't remember.

There is considerable difficulty in locating this experience.

DR   Does everything feel okay?

PT   Uhum. *There is some uncertainty in the tone of voice.*

The discomfort is located but is not definable without further encouragement from the therapist.

DR   Does everything feel okay? Does Marion feel good?

PT   Uhum. *Uncertainly.*

DR   All the Marions feel good right up to fifty four?

PT   No. I guess not – when my mum died.

Marion identifies the sad feeling but has some difficulty in locating it.

DR   How old are you there?

PT   I was married.

DR   Yes? How old are you? Be right there – tell me how old you are.

PT   In my thirties.

DR   In your thirties, eh? She dies. What are you feeling right there? Feeling scared?

The therapist seeks to define the experience emotionally and the patient can only locate sadness.

PT   No, just sad.

DR   Just sad. Okay. How old would you be there? Just make a guess.

PT   Thirty-six.

DR   About that, eh? Thirty-six year old Marion, are you still feeling sad?

PT   No.

DR   Have you let go of all of that old sadness now?

PT   Uhum.

DR   Are you smiling now?

PT   Uhum.

DR   That's good because mum wouldn't want you to be sad any longer, would she?

It is often a good plan to suggest that the real parent would not want the patient to retain old discomforts. This is more likely to secure attention and greater cooperation from the Parent which sometimes prevents, by its guilt-laden punitive manner, the release of old sad feelings.

PT   No.

DR   Okay. Are all the Marions up to thirty-six feeling okay?

PT   Uhum.

DR   All smiling?

PT   Uhum.

DR   Good. Let's come up now from thirty-six to see if there are any other Marions who are not feeling okay. *Uncertain puzzled movement of the*   Again, during the search for other *head.* Is there? All smiling? All feeling good?

PT   No.

DR   There's a not-good feeling somewhere isn't there? How old are you there?

PT   *Tearfully.* Forty-seven.

DR   Forty-seven year old Marion, what's happening there? You look very sad, awful sad. . . *Long pause.* When you are ready to tell me what's happening that's making you so sad, you can let me know. Right now, just feel all of the feelings that you have, every one of them. . . Feels awful, doesn't it?. . . Feel every bit of it, Marion, don't hold any of it back *she is extremely distressed at this point* feel every bit of it. . . feel every little bit of it. . . What's happening there, Marion?

PT   *Sobbingly makes an inaudible reply.*

DR   Um?. . . Forty-seven year old Marion, are you feeling scared?

PT   *Sighs deeply but makes no audible reply — she is still too distressed to speak coherently.*

DR   I know you're feeling sad, are you feeling scared too? Are you? *Nods.* Feeling angry as well?

PT   Yeah. *With much feeling.*

critical experiences, evidence of great sadness emerges.

The therapist's sympathetic comments upon Marion's evident sadness encourages her to discover more about it.

Further encouragement makes her aware of all her feelings and removes her previous repression of them.

The distress is great and it is some time before Marion has experienced all the feelings that have been unconsciously repressed.

She is surprised at the extent of the

DR   Yes. Surprised at how angry you are feeling, are you? Really angry aren't you? Who are you angry with?

PT   *Sighs deeply.*

DR   Who are you angry with? With your husband for leaving you all alone?

PT   No, with a guy.

DR   With a guy for killing your husband? Are you as angry as hell with him?

PT   At my friend.

DR   At your friend. Why? Because she should not have taken him?

PT   I'm not mad at her. I'm. . .

DR   Which friend are you mad at then?

PT   He was no good. *Sobbing.* The guy that killed. . .

DR   Killed him? Is he a friend.

PT   No.

DR   Okay. Feel guilty at all?

PT   No. *Calmer.*

DR   Marion, is there anything more to tell me, forty-seven year old Marion?

anger that she had so successfully concealed from herself.

The intense anger following a bereavement is often directed at the deceased who has left the individual to fend for herself. Marion readily identifies her anger, although there is a temporary confusion as to whom it is being directed – her friend who had asked her husband for a drive, or the drunk who had caused the accident and was also killed.

She is now in touch with all of her previously hidden feelings.

PT   No.

DR   Fifty-four year old Marion, I've got forty-seven year old Marion still feeling awfully sad. She's feeling extremely angry and she's feeling a bit scared. I want you to talk to her. Tell her that it is now seven years later and she doesn't need to go on feeling bad about it any more. It's finished with, over and done with. There's nothing to be gained by keeping those old feelings. Tell her all the things that you need to tell her and, when you have done that, let me know. Give her all your loving, all your comforting, all your wisdom, all your understanding and, when you've done that just nod your head. . . *Nods.* Oh, you have done that eh? Good. Forty-seven year old Marion, now that you have heard that, do you still need to go on being sad? Do you still need to go on being angry? Do you still need to go on being scared? *Shakes head after each question.*

Since this is clearly such a traumatic experience, the therapist not only enlists the aid of the patient's Adult but uses his own Adult to suggest specific ways in which help might be given to the distressed Child ego state.

At last she decides she can relinquish these uncomfortable feelings.

DR   fifty-four year old Marion, forty-seven year old Marion has told me that she no longer needs to go on being scared or angry or afraid or sad. Will you please find a way for her to let go of that sadness and that anger? When you have found a way nod your head for 'yes' . . . *Nods.* Forty-seven year old Marion, okay, there's a way for you. Let go of those uncomfortable feelings. Just let them go. Finished with; done with now; had them for long

Once again, there is no need to enquire into the means she discovered of relinquishing feelings that have been revealed and found to be unnecessary.

enough. Let them go. When you've let them go, nod your head to let me know that you have done that. . . *Nods.* Forty-seven year old Marion should now be feeling very calm inside. Are you feeling calm inside? *Nods.* Got a smile for me? *Smiles.* Good. That's good. Keep that smile, will you forty-seven year old Marion?

A positive *smile test.*

PT   Yes.

DR   Okay.

PT   Yeah.

DR   Notice how good that feels. You're just as good as anybody else, aren't you?

PT   Yes.

DR   Now I'm going to ask you to look and see if there's any other Marion who's feeling uncomfortable. If there is, your head will nod, 'yes'. If there isn't any your head will shake for 'no'. *Head shakes.* Okay. Is every Marion inside feeling very good now?

A further search for any other uncomfortable unconscious ego states must be instituted but none are discovered.

PT   Yes.

DR   Is every Marion smiling?

PT   Yeah.

DR   I want every Marion to listen very carefully to me. Listen to me very, very carefully. Every Marion, I

Every effort is made to secure the optimum unconscious attention from all of the previously uncom-

want you to listen to me. We want you, please, to stop Marion from smoking. Will you do that?

PT   Yes.

DR   Okay. I want you to tell her that, when she stops smoking, she will feel so good. She'll feel so relaxed and so calm she can now really be without cigarettes. Good breathing. Her breathing is so good that she will be able to sleep well at night because the breathing is so good. She will not have that awful taste in the mouth any more. Isn't that a good feeling? *Nods.* Let's go back to where Marion never smoked at all. Let's go back to where she was a non smoker. How old are you there?

PT   Not really sure.

DR   Sixteen? Seventeen?

PT   Uhum.

DR   Breathing's good?. . . Sixteen/ seventeen, is your breathing good?

PT   Uhum.

DR   Taste in your mouth good?

PT   Uhum.

DR   Okay. Sixteen/seventeen year old Marion, I want you to give that nice good breathing feeling to fifty-four year old Marion right now be-

fortable ego states which might have welcomed the relief from discomfort affording by smoking.

A strong direct suggestion for relaxation, which she previously sought through smoking. These suggestions are coupled with other strong direct suggestions for relief of the unpleasant side effects of smoking. A recall of the non-smoking memories emphasises these ideas and are reviewed.

This is a direct suggestion to the former non smoking ego states to help those which have been responsible for the smoking and now wish to quit.

338   Analytical Hypnotherapy

cause she is going to be a non smoker just like you. I want you to give her that nice taste in the mouth so that she can have the nice non smoking taste. Have you done that?

PT   Yeah.

DR   Yes, you've done it. Feels good, doesn't it?

PT   Uhum.

DR   I'm now going to ask you to find the most awful taste and awful smell that you can find. You've got one?

Some aversion conditioning suggestions are offered, which are always of value if accepted.

PT   It makes your lips and your tongue taste awful.

DR   Yeah. Is that the most awful taste and smell you can find? One that really almost makes you want to throw up?

Marion already associates the nausea with smoking and it is therefore most appropriate, even though it had previously been ineffective in removing the need to smoke.

PT   When you wake up in the morning.

DR   That's the same taste? *Nods.* Makes you want to throw up?

PT   Yes.

DR   Okay. I want you to make that ten times stronger. When you've got it ten times stronger, nod your head. *Nods.* Okay, I want you to have that taste in your mouth anytime you're tempted to smoke a cigarette. Every time you're tempted to smoke a

Association of the nausea with all of the most likely times when the urge to smoke may arise is a well

cigarette that taste will come in you mouth so strong you just won't even touch it. *Makes a face.* You've got it. Okay. I'm going to ask you now to imagine that somebody is offering you a cigarette and, as they offer you one, you get that taste so strong that you just could not possibly touch it . . . Even stronger. You say, 'no thanks, I can't touch it. I don't want to smoke'. *Nods.* Okay. Done it?

PT Uhum.

DR Now, I want you to see yourself having a cup of coffee and, as you have the cup of coffee, you think about the cigarette you used to have and as you think about it that taste comes in your mouth so strong that you just can't touch it. You couldn't even bother to touch a cigarette. When you've done that, nod your head. *Nods.* Now, what other times are there when you used to smoke, Marion?

PT Watching TV

DR Okay, watching TV while watching TV, you might even see someone on the TV screen having a cigarette; as you see that person, suddenly the awful taste comes into your mouth and you just can't touch a cigarette. You just cannot touch it. So strong is that feeling you just wouldn't even want to. Got it? *Nods.* Now one more situation. There is somebody there who you can see smoking. Who is that?

tried and often effective posthypnotic manoeuvre.

Projective imagery in hypnosis gives a good indication of whether this suggestion is acceptable.

Coffee is a very common trigger for smoking because of its frequent association with smoking. Any other triggers identified in the history taking can be similarly dealt with at this time.

The therapist embellishes the image that the patient has offered so that she remains protected against other less direct triggers in the environment.

Attempting to leave no stone unturned, the therapist seeks any other triggers that might exist and

PT It's my daughter.

DR Yes, she is smoking and as you can see her smoking you get that awful taste in your mouth. It's so strong, it's so strong. It's even stronger than before. It really is so strong that you just couldn't possibly touch that cigarette. You couldn't. You're just so pleased that you are not smoking. You are so pleased because you have that taste so strong that you couldn't smoke another cigarette. You feel so relaxed. You feel so calm. That's a really lovely feeling. I'm now going to ask you to have a very pleasant and wonderful dream, feeling so good, so happy and so pleased that you're not smoking and will never smoke again. . .

When you find any cigarettes at home, you are to throw them away immediately into the garbage. You simply do not want them around you. Any cigarettes that you find in the house, throw them into the garbage, burn them or destroy them. You don't want them anywhere near you. If you'll agree to do all of that, nod your head. *Nods.* Okay. Feel very good about that. When you do things like that you feel good. You just feel so relaxed that you want to smile. *Smiles.* It's a lovely feeling, isn't it? In fact today is going to be a very good day, a beautiful day at the end of which you will feel so good, so pleased with yourself, that you've done

similarly applies aversion suggestions.

Reinforcement with the good feelings of achievement is important and is associated with the relaxation and calm previously derived through cigarette smoking.

Again there is further emphasis on treating cigarettes as enemies rather than the friends that they had pretended to be.

something you've been wanting to do for such a long time. You've let go of all the uncomfortable desires that you had. You will not miss cigarettes at all. You won't feel them to be necessary anymore. You won't feel deprived at all. You'll find other things to do with your hands. You'll find other things you want to do. You'll feel no sense of loss, no sense of being without anything that you really want. That feeling will be completely gone because from now on you'll feel very good.

Some smokers find that smoking satisfies hand restlessness.

The feeling of deprivation when smoking is relinquished must be dealt with directly.

I believe that you're just as good and just as important as any other human being, living or dead, do you agree? *Nods.* Good. That's a good feeling and you really do care for Marion, don't you? *Nods.* You like her? *Nods.* So you are really going to take care of her and keep all of the thoughts I've given you, is that right? *Nods.* And not let her smoke anymore? *Nods.* Good.

The usual ego strengthening suggestions are given here in a shortened but potent form.

The session ended with some demonstrations of hypnoanaesthesia which emphasised the idea that, since Marion could so clearly modify feeling, she could equally well deal with all of her problematic feelings without resorting to smoking. Suggestions for sleeping well were also given. Prior to alerting from hypnosis she was advised that she need not let her conscious mind know anything of what had transpired; but that choice was hers.

A week after the first interview, Marion returned and reported that she had not had any desire to smoke at all. Several situations arose in which she fully expected to be tempted to smoke, but actually she felt no temptation at all. She remarked that she was feeling much calmer, that she had been sleeping well, and that she had no evidence of her previous breathing difficulty. She was delighted that her mouth and breath felt cleaner, although occasionally she had a bad taste in her mouth which occurred only when she thought about smoking. The only problem that she now felt existed was a tendency to eat too much. There appeared to be a total amnesia for all of the events that she had discussed during hypnosis.

Marion re-entered hypnosis very rapidly on a cue which had been established during the previous meeting; she was then able to review all of the experiences that she had dealt with earlier; and indicated that all of the tensions previously associated with these experiences were gone. When inquiry was made into the reason for the tendency to overeat, she explained that she needed something in her hands; food had replaced cigarettes in this regard only. In this session some of the previous suggestions were repeated in an abbreviated form, specific suggestions for eating wisely were given and strong ego strengthening suggestions were repeated. Marion was not seen again but a telephone conversation with her some nine months later established that she was still not smoking, was feeling very well and had none of her previous depression.

In reviewing this case and its very successful outcome, an important question is: if the painful experience at one year was relevant to her smoking, why was it not expressed in this way until the age of sixteen years later? It is probable that in those intervening years Marion suffered her unconscious distress in many other ways that were not revealed during the analysis. When she discovered that she felt more comfortable when smoking because of the analgesic effect, she then became hooked. When she did not smoke she would become uncomfortable again and either return to smoking or seek temporary solace in food.

Perhaps the most striking event in Marion's therapy was her discovery of the enormous amount of anger she felt toward the driver of the car that had collided with her husband's. She had had much difficulty in dealing with that anger because had he not responded to a request on that day to pick up a mutual friend, her husband would not have been killed. In therapy she determined that she was not really angry with her friend and consequently was able to get in touch with the true anger she felt and finally relinquish it. Presumably, her depression resulted from anger repressed by strong feelings of guilt, which could be expressed only against herself as depression.

Alcoholism

A second common form of drug addiction is alcoholism. Many programmes which have utilised hypnosis as an adjunct to therapy with the alcoholic have been described. Kroger (1942), Miller (1959) and Smith-Moorhouse (1969) are among those who have achieved some success using a conditioned reflex aversion treatment in which the individual in hypnosis is given a drink and an emetic so that association between drinking and vomiting is produced. Posthypnotic suggestions are given to reinforce the strong association between drinking and vomiting. Wolberg (1948) recommended an interesting technique utilising symptom substitution; the patient in hypnosis is informed that whenever he craves a drink, he will reach for an innocuous malted milk tablet which will give him all the relaxation and pleasure he desires. Although there have been few descriptions of the use of the hypnoanalytical approach to alcoholism, the psychodynamics in alcoholism are the same as with any other drug addiction: the relief of persistent unconscious distress.

The illustrative case that follows is that of a forty-four year old married woman who has two children, who found that she had been drinking more over the last ten years, and was now quietly drinking as much as half a bottle of vodka each day. She felt totally incapable of breaking the habit which she had begun to hate. Prior to meeting her husband (whom she had married some eleven years prior to therapy), her drinking was only occasional. His family drank consistently and urged her to drink as well. After she had a premature stillbirth in the first year of marriage she began to use alcohol more frequently until it had become a part of her functioning. she was unable to take on any new venture without first fortifying herself with a shot of vodka. Even letter writing required its support.

She complained that her drinking had caused her to lose interest in herself and her family. She knew that she was not doing as much for them as she could and, indeed, wanted to do. She had a constant feeling of shame about herself which served only to reinforce her drinking. She was not as assertive as she would like to be and kept many of her resentful feelings to herself; if her husband asked her what the matter was, she would give the standard reply of *nothing*. She came to hypnotherapy hoping that it would either increase her willpower to resist the temptation to drink, or make drinking so unpleasant that she would give it up.

It was explained to her that the traditional uses of hypnosis for modifying behaviour did not take into account the emotional need for drinking. She was informed that hypnosis could be used to discover the reasons why she needed to drink, and also whether these reasons were still valid ones that she needed to retain. She understood this but said that she was terrified of what she might say in hypnosis. She had to be assured that she would not divulge anything that she did not want to; this appeared to be reassuring. At any rate, the induction of hypnosis was readily accomplished and good finger signals attained. It was established that she had had a good birth experience and so she was directed to come to the first relevant critical experience. She accomplished this satisfactorily at an ideomotor level and, in response to questioning, indicated that it was a sad, scary shameful, sexual experience. The signals at this time became very slight and sometimes confusing and the information was a long time in forthcoming. It was evident that she was extremely reluctant to deal with this experience. However, she eventually agreed to talk about it and the following excerpt starts at this point.

DR   Would you please tell me what is happening right there — that experience? How old are you right there?. . . What's happening in that experience? *Patient commences to cry.* It sounds like a very sad experience to me. You look very sad. Can you tell me how old you are right there?

The therapist encourages the patient to stay with the experience despite the discomfort it produces.

PT   *Whispering.* Twenty-one.

DR   Twenty-one year old Colleen, what's happening? What's happening there?. . . *No reply.* You're twenty-one years of age. What's happening there, Colleen?. . . Can you tell me? Can you talk about it?

The whisper indicates that the experience is so uncomfortable that she really would rather not talk about it and certainly cannot speak of it in a normal voice.

PT   *Commences to sob and is unable to talk.*

DR   Is it scary?. . . Is it awfully sad? Makes you feel bad?. . . Are you angry? There's an awfully strong feeling there. Is that an angry feeling? *Yes finger is observed to be lift-*

Her distress is acute and it becomes increasingly difficult for her to communicate verbally. Consequently, she slips back to the deeper non verbal level of communication which was missed by the therapist at first.

ing; (it may have been lifting unob-
served before this in answer to the
previous questions because during
that time the therapist had been
closely observing her face.) It is, eh?
Okay. Would you like to be able to
talk to me about it? *Yes.* You would.
Okay. Think that you can do it
today?

PT   I'll try to.

She agrees to return to the verbal
level of communication but there
is still evidence of a continued internal struggle.

DR   It's pretty tough isn't it. This
experience of the twenty-one year
old, does Colleen know all about it?.
. . Does she? Just nod your head if
she does. *Nods.* She does know all
about it, eh? Does she know all of
the feelings of that experience
though? *Shakes her head.* Have you
kept the feelings from her? *Nods.* So
she doesn't know all the feelings
then does she? *Shakes her head.*
Twenty-one year old Colleen, can
you tell me what's happening there?
You don't have to tell her, just tell
me. She is now forty-three and
maybe she doesn't know all of those
things you have been keeping for
those twenty-two years. Can you
talk about it with me?. . . *Again
there is no answer and it seems that
Colleen has great difficulty in communicating her thoughts.*

As we can see, a critical experience
can be totally unconscious, or unconscious in parts only. In this
case the feelings had been concealed, although the events themselves had been consciously remembered.

Once again internal communication is fragile.

DR   Twenty-one year old Colleen
do you really want me to help? Nod
your head if you do. *Nods.* Okay. Is
there something telling you not to
tell me? *Shakes her head.* Okay, tell
me what is happening. Twenty-one

The question, *do you really want
me to help?* can be used at any
time to encourage communication
that has become weak.

year old Colleen, what is happening? Is it something that you are too ashamed to talk about? Is it something to do with having sex? *Nods.* Do you feel guilty about having sex at twenty-one?

PT *Sobbing.* It was terrible.

The therapist is correct in his assumption.

DR What was terrible? What was so terrible about it?

PT He forced me. *Sighs very sadly.*

DR He forced you? Who was that?

PT Whispering – *between sobs.* The boy I was going out with.

DR Did you enjoy it?

PT No. No!

DR Not at all?

PT No.

DR Not even a little bit?

PT No.

Some of the guilt associated with a sexual experience relates to the shameful enjoyment which unintentionally may occur as part of a normal sexual response.

DR Were you scared? *Nods.*

DR Did he hurt you. *Nods.* Okay. Are you still feeling bad about that? *Nods.* Is there anything else to tell us?

Fear and pain are probably persisting unconsciously from this experience.

PT I don't think so.

DR Forty-three year old Colleen,

did you hear that? If you did, just nod your head. *Nods.* Twenty-one year old Colleen has just told us that she is really feeling scared and hurt and angry and ashamed and guilty and just feeling awful about this episode that happened to her at twenty-one. Could you please help her? Give her all of your present day wisdom and understanding and comfort and compassion. When you have done that, just let me know by nodding your head for 'yes'. . . *Nods.*

It is necessary to stimulate feelings of compassion in order for the guilt feelings to be yielded by the Parent in exchange for forgiveness of the Child.

Twenty-one year old Colleen, now that you have heard that, do you still need to go on feeling so bad?

PT   No, I guess not.

This is successful.

There follows here the standard procedure for the relinquishment of these old feelings. The therapist establishes that this had been accomplished by seeking a positive 'smile test'. The search for other critical experiences continues.

DR   I want you to look now — come up from twenty-one — to see if there is any other Colleen older than twenty-one who is still feeling uncomfortable in any way at all. If there is, nod your head for 'yes'. If there isn't, shake your head for 'no'. *Nods.* How old are you there? *Once again Colleen looks very sad.* You are feeling pretty bad aren't you? How old are you there?

Another very painful experience has been located.

PT   Forty-two or three.

DR   You are forty-two, almost

forty-three, are you? What's happening there that makes you feel so bad?

PT I'm getting so mad.

DR Getting so mad – a lot of anger there, eh? Why is that?

PT No reason.

DR Okay, let us find out where that anger is coming from . Go right down deep and find out what part of Colleen is feeling so angry. When you have found her, nod your head for 'yes'. She is really angry about something. She's really angry, angry, angry. . . Have you found her?

PT No, I can't find it yet.

DR It's not twenty-one year old Colleen is it who is making you angry? *Shakes her head.*

DR Just go back to where the anger begins, to the very first time you feel it. When you are there, nod your head for 'yes'. . . *Nods.* I am going to ask the deep part of your mind to go to the very beginning of that anger and, when it is there, the 'yes' finger will lift to let me know. . . *Long delay without any finger movement.*

DR Let me ask – is there a hidden part of Colleen that is feeling the anger? If there is a hidden part of

All we are able to define is an unreasonable anger which suggests that the source is earlier than first thought. The regression proves to be difficult and Colleen is at first unable to employ the appropriate affect bridge to the causative experience.

The therapist ascertains that this anger is not relevant to the critical experiences so far dealt with.

He feels that ideomotor finger signals will pick up much earlier experiences present at a deeper level of memory. A long struggle ensues and the therapist suspects the presence of an ego state intent upon remaining concealed.

Colleen that is still feeling angry, that 'yes' finger will lift. If there is a hidden part there still feeling angry, the 'yes' finger will lift. . . *Yes*. Okay, hidden part of Colleen, you are feeling very angry, very angry indeed. Is you name Colleen? *Yes*. Are you a young part of Colleen? Are you younger than twenty?

The ideomotor signals locate it and is identified as having the same name as Colleen.

PT   *Yes finger lifting*. I don't know.

DR   The 'yes' finger is lifting. It thinks it is. If that anger seems to come from way back before twenty years of age, the 'yes' finger will lift again *Yes*. *At this point some time is spent attempting to establish the age of the hidden ego state without much success.* Are you five years of age? If you are, angry Colleen, the 'yes' finger will lift. *Yes*. Can you talk about what is happening right there, five year old Colleen, to make you so angry and making you so miserable? *Yes* All right Colleen, what is happening there? You're five years of age, what is happening?

At the verbal level there is no answer to the question but the nonverbal signal gives the correct direction for establishing the age of the relevant ego state.

When located at last, five year old Colleen is ready and willing to speak up. This suggests that a Parental part was attempting to silence her because of her unsavoury information about her mother.

PT   I was being scolded and punished.

DR   Who is doing that to you?

PT   Mummy.

DR   Why? What have you done?

PT   I didn't get to the bathroom in time.

DR What did you do – Did you
wet yourself?

PT Yes, on the stairs coming home
from school.

DR Oh, dear me.

PT It wasn't my fault. They
wouldn't let me go at school.

> The anger at the injustice suffered
> is no longer concealed.

DR They wouldn't let you go. Did
you wet yourself on the stairs at
school?

PT No, at home.

DR Aha – and mum didn't understand. Is that right?

> Mother's lack of understanding
> astounds the child.

PT Yes.

DR You feel awful bad don't you
but you're also very angry. She
should have understood, shouldn't
she?

PT It wasn't my fault.

DR It wasn't your fault, no. Okay,
it wasn't your fault that you wet
yourself. Okay, is there anything
else for us to know about that? If
there is raise the 'yes' finger. If there
isn't, raise the 'no' finger. *No.* Okay,
forty-three year old Colleen, did you
hear that? *Nods.* Five year old Colleen is feeling really, really angry,
isn't she? And you know that she
has a right to be angry, hasn't she?
Nods. It really wasn't her fault, was

> Mother should have known it was
> not her fault! This accounts for
> much unconscious hurt and anger
> which had to be repressed by the
> Parent until now.

> The Adult can now readily help.

it? *Nods.* Can you help her? *Nods.* Give her all your understanding and wisdom, put your arm around her and say, 'Hey, I do understand'. Will you do that? *Nods.* When you have done that let me know. . . *Nods.* Five year old Colleen, now that you've heard that do you still need to go on being angry? *Shakes her head.*

Imagining the placing of an arm around an unconscious ego state gives it a feeling of security, support and comfort.

Again, at this point the usual procedure for releasing unnecessary tensions is followed and ends with the *smile test* which indicates that it has been completed satisfactorily.

Is there any other Colleen feeling uncomfortable inside? *Shakes head.* Now we're going to ask you, five year old Colleen, and you twenty-one year old Colleen, will you help forty-three year old Colleen to say goodbye to alcohol? *Nods.* Okay. Now I am going to ask you to do something. The next time she goes to touch alcohol what will you do? How will you stop her? What's a good idea the next time she goes to get a drink?

All of the discovered tensions have now apparently been resolved and, if so, direct suggestions for dealing with the drinking habit should now be acceptable.

The exact nature of the suggestion is here requested and the patient provides it.

PT   Give her a ginger ale instead.

DR   Will you do that? Okay, everytime she goes to touch alcohol, give her a ginger ale instead. Is that a promise? *Nods.* I'm relying upon you to do that. Don't let her have that alcohol. Just let her be without it. She doesn't need it anymore does she? *Shakes head.* She had been getting that alcohol to stop that anger, hadn't she? That guilt feeling that twenty-one year old Colleen used to

Such a suggestion is more likely to be accepted than is one constructed by the therapist.

The assumption is now made that the anger against her mother, along with old guilt feelings, have gone. The craving for alcohol will also disappear and suggestions

have has now gone. So, anytime she goes to take a drink, just say, 'you don't need that anymore'. Will you try that? *Nods.* Could you make alcohol taste bad? Do you think that you could do that? *Nods.* What taste would you give it in case she tried it? *Makes a face.* Yes, what taste is that? Just like when you were young? *Nods.* You didn't like it then. Have you got that taste now? *Makes another grimace.* Okay just imagine that she is trying to have a drink — how is she feeling, nauseated? Wants to throw up, does she? *Colleen makes some swallowing motions as if she is attempting to control feelings of nausea.* Okay now, don't tell her that you are going to do that — just you do it, make her nauseated, make it taste awful, give her a ginger ale instead. Will you?

designed to rob it of all its previous attraction will be accepted.

She is reminded of the time when alcohol was objectionable to her and is asked to use that memory to remove any further attraction it might have.

If the suggestion for nausea is to prove effective, a strong response is important. Gagging, repeated swallowing, and facial grimaces are all good signs.

This session concluded with strong ego strengthening and assertiveness training suggestions. Another opportunity was taken to reinforce all the suggestions given to control the drinking; finally suggestions for amnesia were given so that she could remember or forget whatever she wished.

At the next meeting two weeks later, she reported that she had no desire to touch alcohol for the first week and on a social occasion, during the second week, had taken only one drink. She was very pleased about this and said that she wanted to be able to drink, but without compulsion. The former craving had completely gone, and she noted that she had become much more able to discuss with her husband problems that previously she thought she should not bother him with. She was agreeably surprised that he welcomed her sharing these problems with him. She said that she was much more at ease with herself and was able to feel more comfortable with groups of people and was able to communicate more easily with friends and acquaintances. Therapy was directed at seeking other unconscious sources of tension, but none were found. She was then asked to review all of the positive suggestions which had been given prior to terminating the session.

A month later, at the third meeting, Colleen was still taking only the occasional drink in a social situation. There had been one lapse when she had had a disagreement with her husband, had felt angry, and had taken a solitary drink. However, she had recognised what she was doing and resolved the problem by a heart to heart talk with him, which eliminated her tension. Apart from these improvements, she had lost fifteen pounds which pleased her enormously. All in all, she thought that she was now enjoying life. In a follow up communication six months later she reported that all was still well and that she did not feel any need for further therapy.

In reviewing this case, it would appear that Colleen at the age of five had developed a strong condemning Parent and thus was not allowed to express anger. She was a very docile child. At twenty-one, deprived of the defence of anger, she allowed herself to be seduced, which increased not only her repressed anger but also her sense of helplessness and rejection. Perhaps the premature stillbirth triggered the sexual guilt with Parental reminders about how bad she was. The increased pain and anger could be relieved only by a pain killer, and alcohol was available and effective. Adult reasoning ended this painful conflict and set her free to be normally self expressive and fully self protective.

Sexual Dysfunction

In the majority of those cases referred to the analytical hypnotherapists for treatment of sexual dysfunction, the frigidity or impotence is found to be due to an unconscious blocking of the normal sexual responses for protective or punitive reasons. The behavioural approaches of Masters and Johnson (1966) and Kaplan (1964) have been successful in treating sexual dysfunction. Both of these approaches depend upon strong Adult input against the Parent and it would seem that the Parent finally gives way when it is convinced that the need for protection or punishment has gone. In these approaches, however, the Parent/Child conflict is not directly resolved; instead it is repeatedly challenged in an atmosphere of optimism and security until it evidently becomes unnecessary. Wijesinghe (1977) and Chernenkoff (1969) have amply demonstrated the effective use of hypnosis, combined with free association, in the treatment of frigidity. Cheek (1976) described the successful use of ideomotor questioning in brief hypnotherapy to explore early life experiences and their causal effect on frigidity. The analytical approach, however, because it works inside the Parent/Child conflict, has an equal or greater chance of success in a much shorter period of time. Brevity of treatment is an important advantage since there are few who are able to afford the cost in time or money that the above mentioned behavioural techniques involve. Nevertheless, it must be admitted that cases of sexual dysfunction often resist the analytical approach because of a strong unrelenting Parent ego state.

The following case has some unusual aspects which make it of particular interest and illustrates how successful analysis does not necessarily equate with successful outcome. Brenda was nineteen years of age at the time of consultation when she gave a history of increasing painful intercourse over the previous two years. This had become so severe that she had not had intercourse with her husband for some six months. She had seen several sex therapists and gynaecologists who had not been able to discover the source of her problem. There was no sign of a local lesion although she had had a baby only six months or so prior to the first meeting. She had enjoyed normal sexual relationships with her husband and with other boy friends before marriage. She said that when her husband attempted penetration, she simply tightened and her vaginal area became very painful. She was able to touch the vaginal area and insert dilators without any discomfort but at the suggestion of intercourse she experienced pain.

To the therapist it seemed that a part of her was making a very clear statement: *I will not have intercourse with my husband.* It was therefore necessary to communicate with that part that had made this decision. To this end, ideomotor signals were established without any formal hypnotic induction. There appeared to be good communication and the part with the problem indicated that it welcomed help. The following excerpt begins at this point.

DR Now, that part of your mind that squeezes the vagina tightly and can't have intercourse, I want that part to listen to me very carefully and, when it is listening to me very carefully, the 'yes' finger will float up. . . *Yes.* Now, I am going to ask that part which has the 'yes' finger floating up, a very interesting question: Is that part, doing that, is that

The therapist makes a direct request for communication with the part responsible for the symptoms and is immediately successful.

The suspicion that this part is

part called Brenda? If she's not called Brenda the 'no' finger will lift; if she is called Brenda the 'yes' finger will lift. *No.* Okay that part that is not called Brenda and is making the vagina clamp down tight, could you please tell me your name? If you can, raise the 'yes' finger. *Yes.* What name comes to you now, Brenda? First thought that comes to mind.

PT   Dad.

DR   Pardon?

PT   My dad.

DR   Dad. Okay. I want to talk to Dad. If it is okay to talk to Dad, the 'yes' finger will lift. *Yes.* Okay. Now, Dad, are you protecting Brenda, taking care of her? Is that what you're doing? *Yes.* Okay. Can you tell me how old the Brenda is that you are taking care of? If you can tell me, raise the 'yes' finger. *Yes.* What comes into your mind? How old are you there?

PT   Fourteen.

DR   Fourteen. Fourteen year old Brenda. Listen to what Dad is saying and, when you can hear what he's saying, raise the 'yes' finger. *Yes.* What's he saying? Hear it. Repeat it to me.

PT   He's telling me I'm boy crazy. *Laughs.*

probably an alien ego state is soon confirmed since it does not answer to the patient's usual name.

Instead it identifies itself with the father and surprises the patient by the answer. It is obviously a Parent controlled ego state which will act like the father. (Hidden ego states frequently carry the Christian names of one of the parents and then exhibit very strong disciplinary attitudes to the Child).

The age determines when the ego state originated and the characteristics that it is likely to have. This one is highly condemnatory of her sexuality.

DR How do you feel as you hear that?

Within this ego complex is an extremely angry Child who feels unjustly judged.

PT Well I don't think I am.

DR Do you feel angry?

PT Yeah, I think I am.

This injustice is felt as a deep hurt and sadness.

DR Feel hurt?

PT More hurt than anything, I would say.

DR Are you crying inside?

PT Yeah.

DR Okay, now I am going to talk to Dad. Dad part, are you punishing Brenda? *No.* You're not punishing her. Okay. Nineteen year old Brenda, there's a Dad part of you really protecting you from the boys, is that right? If that's right, the 'yes' finger will lift. *Yes.* I want you to tell that Dad part that you are not fourteen anymore. You're grown up now. You're nineteen, you're married to a nice husband who really is very fond of you. When you have done that, raise your 'yes' finger. *Yes.* Now I want to talk to fourteen year old Brenda as well. Fourteen year old Brenda and Dad, do we still need to keep those uncomfortable, hurt and angry feelings and have to punish or protect Brenda by tightening up her vagina so that she cannot have intercourse? *No.* Okay. Now, nineteen year old Brenda, I'm going

Interestingly enough, the Parent ego state here is not punishing her but is protecting her in a belated fashion from sexual attack.

It needs to be informed that its protection is now irrelevant and out of date.

Here the therapist appears to be separating the fourteen year old ego state complex into its Parent and Child components and seeks an agreement from them to end their conflict.

to ask you to find a way for you to let go of all those uncomfortable feelings so that you can have intercourse with your husband again. . . *No.* Okay. You need more time to find a way. . . Perhaps fourteen year old Brenda, would you please apologise to Dad for feeling so angry and hurt with him? He shouldn't have said that you were boy crazy but I think that he was genuinely worried about you. Really worried. Think you could apologise to him for being so angry with him? *Yes.* You could do that, eh? *Yes.* Good. Dad part, do you accept that apology? *Yes.* Okay. Will you let Brenda relax those muscles and let her husband enter her? Can you do that? Will you do that? *Yes.* And will you let fourteen year old Brenda grow up to be nineteen? *Yes.* Fourteen year old Brenda, will you now grow up? *Yes.* Fourteen year old Brenda, do you now feel just as good as anybody else? *Yes.* Can you give me a smile that says 'yes, I feel great?' *Smiles.*

There appears to be some difficulty in reaching mutually acceptable terms on which Parent and Child can declare an armistice prior to becoming friends. So, the therapist's Adult suggests that perhaps an apology is all that is necessary to obtain Parental forgiveness. This proves to be the case.

The Parent will relinquish its former restrictions.

Ego strengthening is acceptable and the battle is over or is it?

At this point the therapist decided to induce a deeper level of hypnosis and used an eye closure induction technique with imagery. The birth experience was reviewed and found to be satisfactory and Brenda was then asked to come up to any other experience responsible for her symptoms.

DR   How old are you there?

PT   Fifteen.

DR   And what happened there?

This is clearly a very significant experience for the fifteen year old Brenda. Abortions, especially therapeutic abortions, are frequently the source of strong guilt feelings which tend to be very per-

PT   I got pregnant very soon.

DR   You got pregnant very soon. What happened?

PT   I had to have an abortion.

DR   Anybody know about that?

PT   Yes, Mum and Daddy.

DR   Mum and Daddy knew about it, eh? Did you feel bad about that?

PT   Yes.

DR   What was the bad feeling?

PT   Mum and Dad didn't like it and Dad called me names.

DR   What names does he call you?

PT   He said I was a slut.

DR   A slut. What else does he call you?

PT   He said I was a tramp.

DR   Fifteen year old Brenda, are you feeling really, really bad? *Nods.* Did you feel bad about being pregnant? *Nods.* And what about having the abortion, how do you feel about that?

PT   Real bad, but I don't have any choice.

sistent. In this case the guilt feelings are particularly strong and the recriminations and parental accusations of sexual promiscuity remain to create strong unconscious feelings of worthlessness.

Brenda obviously feels very bad about having become pregnant and even worse about having had an abortion.

DR You feel really bad about that abortion. Okay. Is there anything else to tell us, fifteen year old Brenda? *No.*

She has cause to punish herself. However, she appears to be able to accept suggestions for self forgiveness.

At this point the usual procedure is employed to invoke the full help of the Adult to resolve these guilty, sad feelings that fifteen year old Brenda still presumably retained and this is successfully accomplished. However, fifteen year old Brenda does not accept any responsibility for the vaginismus.

Is there any Brenda, between fifteen and nineteen, not smiling? *Nods.* How old is she?. . . You can tell me. .

We are still not through with the analysis. There is still more guilt to be dealt with (evident in the signs of feelings of rejection).

Patient commences to cry. She's feeling real bad is she?. . . There's a Brenda not feeling good at all. How old is she?. . . Is she sixteen? *Nods.* Sixteen year old Brenda, something is happening there that makes you feel really bad. Is that the worst feeling that you have ever had? *Nods.* What's happening there to make you feel so bad, can you tell me? *Nods.* Okay, what's happening there?

PT Tom (her husband) and I are going out together, but there's all these other girls.

Tom is the source of much of her hurt since he also treats her unjustly.

DR Other girls? What about these other girls?. . . Does he like them?

She feels rejected by him and inferior to the other girls in his life (they have not had abortions).

PT Uhum.

DR Does he like them better than you?

PT I think so.

DR   You think so. What makes you think so? You've made them seem better than you. They are really not better than you. Why do you feel that the other girls are better than you?

PT   They're prettier.

DR   Anything else?

PT   He brags about them and it makes me feel that he likes them better than me.

DR   Likes them better? Well why didn't he marry them?

PT   They won't go out with him.

DR   He's not a bad guy is he?... Do you feel that you have picked a bad guy, sixteen year old Brenda? What is the feeling that you have got?

PT   He likes playing around with the girls and the girls play along with him.

DR   Uhum. All right. It sounds as if you are really very sad. Is there anything else to tell us?

PT   I am the only one that's attached.

We now locate a deep feeling of resentment at being tied to Tom.

DR   Uhum.

PT   I want to have more fun.

DR I see, you need to have more fun.

She is also angry with him for monopolising her and she resents his claims upon her.

PT I feel trapped. I want to be with my friends.

DR Sixteen year old Brenda, are you feeling too close with Tom? Feel like you want to be free more?

PT Yes.

DR Are you angry about being tied up with him?

PT Yeah.

DR Okay. And you don't have any way of getting out of it now that you are married and have a baby?

She is trapped and her only way out of the trap is to deny the marriage through the vaginismus which she discovered at fourteen.

PT No.

DR Is there anything else we need to know in order to understand? *No.*

At this point the usual analytical procedure is set in motion and sixteen year old Brenda indicates that she need not keep these feelings of hurt and anger about being married any longer.

Can you find a way for her to let go of all that hurt and anger that she has been carrying around. . . *Long delay*. Found a way for her to do that? *Head shakes*. Is she still going to keep that hurt and anger still? *Head shakes*. Can you let go of those uncomfortable feelings? *No.* Are you still hurting too bad. *Nods.* Okay, feel all of that hurt, feel every

Efforts to persuade Brenda to relinquish her symptoms meet some opposition.

She is unable to find a satisfactory alternative and she still feels that she must still keep her tension.

bit of it and, when you have felt it all, let me know. . . *Nods.* Okay that's a lot of hurt, can you let it go now. *Nods.* Okay let it go now. *Shakes head.* Still hanging on to a bit of it are you? Do you feel guilty in some way. *Nods.* What are you feeling guilty about, can you tell me?

PT   Johnny.

DR   Who's Johnny?

PT   He's my son.

DR   So why should you feel guilty about Johnny, your son, eh?

PT   I don't want to hurt him.

DR   Why, what would you do that might hurt him.

PT   Breaking up.

DR   Breaking up the marriage, eh? Is that it? Do you want to break up the marriage?

PT   Sometimes.

DR   Uhum. Now I see. You really don't want to stay married, is that it?

PT   Yes, sometimes I don't.

She also locates some previously unmentioned guilt feelings and is unable to properly express her anger because of the effects it would have on her marriage and upon her son (and here her guilt is probably compounded by residual guilt about her abortion).

At any rate she cannot yet make a decision about giving up her symptoms.

Toward the end of this session the therapist reviewed Brenda's problem for her: she could keep her symptoms and thus steer her marriage towards its inevitable breakdown bringing with it freedom to do what she wanted but also with the feeling that she would rob her son of the stable family. Alternatively, she could relinquish her symptoms and adjust to the pattern of domestic life that she had immaturely chosen.

This patient cancelled her follow up appointment. When contacted by telephone, she reported that there had been no change in her symptoms and that she and her husband had not been able to have intercourse. Moreover, she stated that she did not want to return for further therapy since she felt that it would not be of value. She said that she was feeling *okay* about things and was relating well to her husband. It was not made clear in what way she felt okay about things but the therapist believed that she was aware that her dyspareunia was a deliberate, if unconscious choice and that she was not yet ready to change it.

The analytical hypnotherapist must be prepared to meet many patients who, when they have discovered a solution to the problems creating their symptoms, choose not to accept it. Giving up the symptoms may mean a loss of secondary gains which remain important; or it may mean that the patient will lose face in his or her own eyes or those of friends and relatives to allow the too ready implementation of a now obvious solution. In these cases the solution is deferred to be implemented at a more opportune time when therapy does not appear to be related to its adoption. So it is, as in this case, that the patient opts out of therapy claiming it to have been of no value and later attributing any success that occurred to some other fortuitous circumstance. The fact that this young patient had seen many therapists about her problem and seemed emotionally unperturbed by this fact, gave the therapist, in retrospect, cause to believe that she was not yet ready to part with her symptoms and would do so in her own good time.

Phobias

Phobias, as has already been pointed out, are in fact only a special group of anxiety reactions and therefore have the same psychodynamics as all anxiety responses. The phobia always results from an experience in which the entire range of emotions associated with it are forbidden full expression at the time of the original experience. Consequently, when the individual is faced with circumstances which remind him of this original experience, all of the emotions are unconsciously recalled but only the fear element is permitted expression. Analytical hypnotherapy seeks to locate all of the hidden emotions, the associated guilt inevitably repressing them, and then to deal with them so that these hidden feelings (which give the phobia its intensity) can be relinquished.

Certainly, behavioural approaches which assume that the fear response can be exhausted by repeated exposure to the fear producing situation in a graduated manner, (Wolpe, 1958) or be reduced by associating the fear producing situation with relaxing thoughts (Kroger and Fezler 1976), have proved effective. However, the analytical understanding of this improvement with purely behavioural approaches assumes that at an unconscious level the individual has gradually been persuaded to accept previously unacceptable feelings. If this is not accomplished, then the phobia will not be eliminated by behavioural methods. Not only is the analytical approach more likely to succeed, but it is also frequently able to accomplish this very rapidly (as we saw in Chapter Twelve, where the guilt of a negative birth experience prevented Pamela from dealing with intense feelings that she could not allow herself to express).

To the analytical hypnotherapist, the classification of the phobias into various groups according to the circumstances which are associated with them is irrelevant. The intense anxiety is always being maintained by one or more ego states whose critical experiences are the source of persistent Child/Parent conflicts. While the critical experiences vary from one individual to another, the retention of the fear response is always due to this unconscious conflict. The Parent will not permit the Child to express unacceptable feeling but will permit or even encourage the fear associated with the experience. Only when this taboo on normal feelings is removed by Adult intervention can the Child be persuaded to relinquish its fear; the phobia then disappears for good.

It must be freely admitted that not all cases of phobia will respond to the analytical approach, since in spite of every effort that the therapist might make, it is not always possible to persuade the Parent to modify its lifetime repressive function. However, when successful, the analytical method is often dramatically so.

The following case provides an excellent example of a good response of a lifetime phobia to analytical hypnotherapy. Mary, at thirty-eight, was separated from her husband but was coping well with the responsibility of bringing up three young children on her own. She sought help through hypnotherapy to deal with her lifelong fear of heights, which was particularly evidenced whenever she was required to climb stairs. She could accomplish this only with the help and support of several people, which was a source of constant embarrassment to her and was the reason she refused to visit certain places where she had to climb stairs. Unfortunately, one of her joys was her involvement in the Naval reserve where climbing spiral staircases was occasionally necessary. She accomplished this at great emotional cost, and only with the aid of sympathetic fellow officers.

When she arrived at the therapist's office for her first appointment she discovered that it had to be reached by two flights of stairs, the steps of which were open and not enclosed by risers. She dreaded open stairs most, and one of the secretaries discovered her standing absolutely paralysed, unable to move either up or down, a short way up the stairs. She had managed to get that far on her own and was convinced that she could go no farther. However, with the help of two secretaries, she eventually made it to the therapist's waiting room.

After Mary had discussed her problem with the therapist, ideomotor responses for 'yes' and 'no' were established and she was asked to allow the part with the fear to raise the yes finger. When this was done, questions were directed to discover the age of this part and it was given as three years of age. The following excerpt commences at this point.

DR   Three years of age? *Patient is looking very distressed.* If you will give a picture of what is happening there, the 'yes' finger will lift. Something scary at three years of age. . . At least I think it is scary. If it is scary you will get a 'yes' feeling. If it is not scary you will get a 'no' feeling. Yes. It's scary, eh? Is it something that makes you feel sad or hurt?. . . If it is something that makes you feel sad or hurt you will get a 'yes' feeling. If it isn't you will get a 'no' feeling. . . just wait. . .

The experience has been reviewed at an unconscious level after having been located by means of the ideomotor response using the associated fear as the affect bridge.

The precise emotional content of the experience is sought and it is expected that some feelings apart from the fear have been concealed.

PT   It's not sad.

DR   It's not sad, eh?

PT   It's my mother screaming at me all the time. *Laughs wryly.*

The hurt response to the mother's screaming remains hidden. The patient attempts to laugh it off.

DR   Your mother's screaming at

you all the time. Yeah, you can hear her, eh?

Dr What are you doing when she is screaming at you? What comes to your mind there? Something happens there. I imagine that it does make you feel sad though nevertheless, doesn't it?

The sad feeling is now admitted to awareness.

PT Yeah.

DR And are you feeling angry with her?

Her anger can not yet be acknowledged. However, resentment, a less aggressive level of anger, is admitted.

PT Not really angry.

DR Makes you feel resentful?

PT Yeah.

DR And do you feel guilty or ashamed or embarrassed? Feel that you are in the wrong?

The constant element of guilt in the Child/Parent conflict is being sought.

PT Yeah, guilty that she would yell at me.

DR Yeah. Okay, let's ask the deep part of your mind: Is there something happening there which is particularly making you scared — something really scary there? If there is, you will get a 'yes' feeling... *Yes*. Yes, what's happening there?

She feels that if her mother yells at her, she must be bad. The source of the intense fear is now being sought by means of the ideomotor signal.

PT I'm going to fall through those stairs.

This is said as if there is no doubt that it will eventually happen. The message is heard at an unconscious level only.

DR She says that? *Yes*. Yeah. That's what she says, eh? *Nods*. Can you hear her saying that to you?

PT   No.

DR   But she does say that to you. Do you fall through the stairs? Look and see if you do.

PT   Yeah.

DR   You do fall through the stairs?

PT   Uhum.

This is a very strong message, so strong that Mary at first feels that she has actually fallen.

DR   And as you fall through them. .

PT   No.

DR   You don't really fall through them.

PT   No, but I feel as if I am going to.

The feeling is as strong as the message causing it.

DR   But you don't fall.

PT   Nobody else does.

DR   But she says that you will. Is that right?

There is a note of petulance in Mary's voice as if she feels that she has been unjustly singled out to be the one to fall through the stairs.

PT   That's what I think in my mind.

DR   Yes, she says that you are going to fall through those stairs. And as she says that to you do you feel scared as if you will fall through them?

PT   Uhum.

DR Yeah, and there is a real frightening feeling, isn't there? *Yes.* Okay. But do you ever fall through them at all? Look and see if you do. If you ever did fall through them, you will get a 'yes' feeling.

The therapist focuses upon the fear and attempts to bring it into proper perspective because the feared event never really happened.

PT I feel like, as I am going on those open stairs, that I am falling through them.

But that feeling persists very strongly, and the Parent, true to form, is keeping it going.

DR Yeah. . . let's ask the deep part of your mind, that falling feeling, does that seem to link up with something that happened before three years of age? If it does, you'll get a 'yes' feeling.

The therapist feels that perhaps there is an earlier concealed experience which will explain the reason for this.

PT *Yes.* Uhum.

DR Could we know what that something is? If we can, you will get another 'yes' feeling. *Yes.* Okay, I'm going to ask the deep part of your mind to go right back to where that something is no matter how far back that something is. When you're there, the 'yes' finger will lift. . . *Yes.* Okay, how old are you there?

The memory of this is probably deeply unconscious, so once again the ideomotor response is enlisted in a careful search.

PT A little before two and a half.

The critical experience is eventually located.

DR Before two and half — what's happening there?

PT My mother lived in an apartment then and there were long stairs and I remember her saying *don't open that door or you're going to fall through.*

This seems to be the link: open door = fall.

DR   Uhum.

PT   *Don't ever open it! (Firmly.)*   The Parent speaks with her
                                              mother's loud voice just as she
DR   Uhum.   would have done.

PT   And ever since then, I've been
afraid because she said I would fall
through.

DR   Uhum.

PT   Now when I am going up stairs   Open stairs (open door) = fall.
that are open I think I am always
going to fall through.

DR   That's right, okay. Let's ask   The therapist believes that this
the deep part of your mind, is there   may not be the entire story and
any experience before two and a   once again returns to the
half that we need to know about, if   ideomotor response in search of
there is the 'yes' finger will lift; if   further information.
there isn't the 'no' finger will lift.

PT   I can't remember.   The patient's conscious effort in-
                                             terferes with the unconscious un-
DR   No, you can't remember. The   covering process.
deep part of your mind remembers
everything. Let's ask the deep part
of your mind: Is there anything before two and a half that we need to
know about in order to understand?
If there is, the 'yes' finger will lift; if
there isn't the 'no' finger will lift. It
will come to you if there is something else. . . *Long pause.*

PT   Can't remember.

DR   We need a 'yes' or 'no' not a   There is still some conscious inter-
'can't remember.' Is there some-   ference in the ideomotor response,
thing before that time when mum   which is a long time emerging.

says 'don't go through that door?'
... *long pause. No.* Okay. Now do
we now know all we need to know
in order to understand? If we now
know all we need to know in order
to understand why it is you have got
that fear, the 'yes' finger will lift.
Yes. Okay. Now, I'm going to ask
you – you have got thirty-eight
years of wisdom and understanding.
There is a two and a half year old
little girl whom you can see and feel
– I don't know whether she ever did
open that door when she shouldn't
have done or maybe she got into real
big trouble for going up the stairs. I
don't know but whatever it was,
you and I know that she doesn't
need to go on feeling scared. I want
you to give her all the wisdom and
understanding that you have, knowing that mum was really trying to
protect her from falling. Mum had a
big fear of stairs in some way or
other and we don't know why she
had that fear but she passed that on
to you because she was very afraid
that you would fall; but she didn't
need to be that afraid because you
never did fall. I am going to ask you
now to give all of that wisdom and
understanding both to that two and
a half year old Mary and to that
three year old Mary and when you
have done that the 'yes' finger will
lift. . . *Yes.* Okay, with that understanding and that wisdom that you
now have, do you still need to keep
that fear? You have been keeping
that fear for the past thirty-four
years – do you still need to keep

Nothing is discovered before the
experience of the two and a half
year old; neither is there anything
else that needs to be known.

We now have all the necessary information to deal with the problem, which the therapist restates
for the benefit of the patient's
Adult.

The therapist's Adult gives some
reasoned input for the further benefit of the patient's Adult. Even
mothers can be afraid and their
fears can now be seen to have been
unnecessary.

Having availed herself of all her
present Adult resources, which
she had not previously been able
to use, there is still some Parental
opposition to the complete relinquishing of the fear.

that uncomfortable feeling? *Yes.*
Are you keeping those uncomfortable feelings to protect yourself with?
No. Are you keeping them to punish
yourself with?

PT   No, they are punishing me!

The patient has some difficulty in
accepting that she is punishing
herself.

DR   That's what I mean. Are you
punishing yourself with those fears?

PT   I seem to be.

DR   Okay. I am going to ask the
deep part of your mind — there must
be some reason why you are still
punishing yourself with that — Is
there some guilty feeling that you
have? If so, the 'yes' finger will lift.
Yes. Something you did wrong.

There is a guilt feeling but there is
also a strong sense of injustice.

PT   I didn't even do it.

DR   Something that you wanted to
do.

PT   She implied that I was going to.

Her mother gave her the idea
which was then difficult to dispel.

DR   Okay, what was that?

PT   Open that door.

DR   Aha. Did you want to open
that door?

PT   Not really. She could have said
anything else but what she said.

There is some expression of the
concealed anger here. After giving
her the idea, her mother accuses
her of it. Naturally she is guilty.

DR   But you felt like she was accus-
ing you of wanting to open that
door.

PT   Uhum.

DR   Okay. Now do you need to keep that guilty feeling any longer. *Yes.* You still need to keep that guilty feeling. You still need to punish yourself then, is that right? *Yes.* Okay, I am going to ask you to really punish yourself right this very minute. Give yourself all of that scared feeling. Really feel scared, more scared than you have ever felt in your life. Feel yourself really falling through those stairs — more scared than you have ever felt. When you have done that, raise the 'yes' finger.

The Parent appears to be a stubborn unrelenting punitive one that needs to retain this function. The therapist gives it permission to do that and more.

This *prescribing of the symptoms* gives the Parent full permission but this is not accepted at first.

PT   I couldn't be any more scared.

The therapist gives further encouragement to experience the fear to the fullest.

DR   Oh yes you can. You can be really scared. You can actually feel yourself fall right through those stairs. When you've done that raise the 'yes' finger.

PT   But I don't want to feel that way.

DR   Oh, but you can do it.

PT   I know.

DR   You can really punish yourself right now and give yourself all the punishment you need right now.

PT   *Yes.* Oh, all right.

This is eventually accomplished.

DR   You've done it!

PT   *Laughs.*

DR   Now that you have done that
do you still need to punish yourself
any more?

That is apparently all that is required to be done. It is followed by
great feelings of relief.

PT   No. *Laughing.*

DR   Okay, now that you have done
that, I am going to ask the deep part
of your mind whether you need to
punish yourself anymore. You don't
need to keep that fear anymore, do
you? *No.* You and I know that you
have climbed stairs up and down
many times without any need to be
scared and hundreds of other people
have gone up and down those stairs
and they are no better able to climb
stairs than you are and they do quite
well. So, I am going to ask you now
to find a way to let go of that fear
and when you have found a way —
you may not even know what that
way is — but what you will feel is a
stong 'yes' feeling. *Yes.* Good, I am
going to ask you to use that way
right now. Three year old, two and a
half year old Mary, let go of that
fear right now and when it has gone
and you know it has gone and can
feel that it has gone, raise the 'yes'
finger. *Yes.* Well, if you have really
let it go, you can give me a big, big
smile which says, *Thank God, that's
gone — I don't need that anymore.* If
you can give me that big smile, raise
the 'yes' finger. *Yes and smiles
broadly.* Okay, now let's walk up
those stairs. Walk up them and as
you walk up them smile on the way

The therapist now encourages the
patient's Adult to apply all of its
wisdom to freeing the patient
from the symptoms.

A way of becoming permanently
free of symptoms still needs to be
discovered. It is better that the
conscious mind knows nothing of
this so that it will not interfere
with this process.

The unconscious mind can readily
use the way however.

When it does so, the relief af-
forded is immediate and then expressed in a positive *smile test.*

Reinforcement of the comfortable
feelings is necessary and so imagery is employed repeatedly to re-

up. When you have done that raise the 'yes' finger. *Yes.*

PT   I'd sure like to do it.

DR   Okay, let's see you do it again. Up those stairs again.

PT   *Laughs.* Okay.

DR   Okay. Smile again. You are doing very well. You have to practice it. Let's go down them now with a big smile. Okay? Good. We know it's okay now, we've said it's okay. We've said that we're not going to listen to mum anymore. That's finished and done with. Let's walk up and down the stairs like anybody else until it becomes a habit to walk up and down stairs without thinking about mum. When you have done that, raise the 'yes' finger.

PT   I would just like to get up them. Then I would see about getting down them.

DR   Let's go up them then and when you have gone up them, let me know.

PT   *Excitedly.* Yeah, I think that I can go up those stairs now.

DR   Okay, now let's go down them again.

PT   Now I'll try and go down.

DR   Now let's do it again. Go up

view the fear producing events until Mary can walk the stairs without any of her former fears.

She has to be without the old frightening thoughts that the Parent would repeat to her. Her first efforts are tentative but later become more enthusiastic as she accomplishes the tasks with increasing ease.

and down those stairs with that good feeling and with that smile on your face. Go down them, go up them. Go up and down them. Just run up and down them.

PT   Oh, my God. *Doubtfully.*

DR   Yes. Feel yourself doing that — up the stairs and down the stairs, have fun now saying to yourself: *I've done it.* I want you to feel very good about this. Really smiling all the time. Go up and down until you are out of breath. Up and down, up and down.

PT   Hmm. *Mildly protesting.* Oh, my Lord.

DR   Isn't that fun?

PT   It must be.

DR   Up and down, up and down. When you have done it ten times, raise the 'yes' finger.

PT   Ten times? Just up and down once would be great.

DR   You are going to do it ten times right now. . . *Long pause.*

PT   Okay.

DR   You've done it ten times?

PT   Yeah.

DR   What a good feeling that is. I

She has succeeded in going up and down the stairs in imagery but the therapist wants her to achieve a complete freedom.

She is so busy with counting up to ten that she has no time to think of the fear and, in any case, each time she accomplishes the task she finds herself feeling more comfortable.
The greatest possible unconscious attention is required for the ego strengthening and assertiveness training suggestions that follow.

bet you are smiling at yourself. Before you open your eyes I want you to listen very carefully to me and when you are listening very carefully to me with the deepest part of your mind, raise the 'yes' finger. . . *Yes.* Listening so very carefully in a way you have never listened before. Now you are listening to me very strongly. Now I believe that you are just as good and just as important as any other human being. If you agree with that nod your head. *Nods.* I believe that you have a right to all of your feelings even your scared feelings. If you agree with that, nod your head. *Nods.*

PT   Uhum.

DR   You have a right to keep those scared feelings, sad feelings, angry feelings for as long as you need to keep them. You don't need to feel guilty about any of those uncomfortable feelings that you have. If you agree with me, nod your head. *Nods.* Okay. You also have a right to let go of those uncomfortable feelings when you don't need them anymore. If you agree with that, nod your head.

Total Parental acceptance of the child is called for.

PT   *Nodding.* Uhum.

DR   You have a right to feel relaxed and calm, and safe and happy and loving, and all those nice feelings, if you agree with all of that nod your head or raise the 'yes' finger.

PT   Uhum.

DR   Good, I am going to ask you, please, to really take care of Mary and make her feel safe. Give her all those nice safe feelings that you really want her to have. You can do that now. You can really take care of her. Don't let anybody put her down. Don't let mum put her down anymore. Will you do all of this? *Nods.* Good. Stick up for her. You can say, mum, don't put me down anymore. *Nods.* Notice how good that feels. There is a strong self-liking feeling. When you have got that, raise the 'yes' finger. *Yes.*

Entrusting the Parent with the job of Protector of the Child ensures that Mary will remain self protective and self assertive. Under no circumstances will she allow a reversion to the old unnecessarily frightened self.

At this point, suggestions were given that Mary could remember as much of the session as she needed to, or could forget anything that she wished to because her unconscious mind could take care of everything. Later, some further analytical exploration was undertaken to deal with other sources of tension, which she identified as resulting from her divorce. She then traced this tension back to her feeling of alienation from her father, who had not been able to accept her when he returned from the war. She was able to relinquish the persisting feelings of rejection which may have contributed to her feelings of isolation. At the end of the session the therapist accompanied Mary to the stairs and watched her walk with delight up and down the stairs without any trace of anxiety.

A week later, Mary was seen again in therapy and declared that for as long as she could remember she had not felt so good. Feeling relaxed and comfortable, she noted that she had lost some weight because she was eating much less. This pleased her because even though she had not regarded her weight as a problem for therapy she had wished to reduce. Contact with this patient was made about six months after her last appointment, and at that time she was still doing very well and remained symptom free.

In reviewing this case to discover the psychodynamics of the phobia, it would appear that at two and a half years of age Mary had the child's natural curiosity about the door and even though she did not intend to disobey her mother, she was made to feel that the very thought of opening the door was bad. Therefore, her Parent had to repress that thought, which it accomplished by using the fear that was offered by her mother: that she would surely fall. This image of falling and hurting (or killing?) herself was so strong that she could not even be aware of any desire to open the door. At three years of age Mary felt resentful of her mother's constant attack on her, but hid her resentment behind an even greater reinforcement of her fear which was then so strong that she could allow herself to negotiate the stairs only when she had the support of her mother. This pattern then became well established and it is probable that she coped with it by using other people as *mothers* (one of whom may well have been her husband). The breakdown of her marriage removed a significant support, particularly because it reminded her of her father's rejection; her phobia which had always been a problem then became even more difficult to control. In spite of the presentation of strong Adult arguments in favour of the Child, the control of the Parent in therapy remained strong and unrelenting. The manoeuvre of allowing the Parent to inflict its full punishment upon the Child appeared to allow it to carry out completely the task assigned to it. Having done this, the Parent could now show leniency toward the Child by withdrawing the thought that the Child will fall. There is at this point no further need for the fear, which is immediately relinquished. The rest of therapy was directed at establishing new responses to the old stimuli so that instead of fear, Mary would experience pleasure in climbing open stairs. With the Parent's support this was easy. Giving the Parent the new task of defending the Child ensured that the symptoms are unlikely to return.

Children and Analytical
Hypnotherapy

Hitherto much of our discussion of analytical hypnotherapy has focused on the treatment of clinical problems experienced by adults. Until recently, hypnotherapy has been viewed as a therapy of last resort; patients who come to the therapist have usually been exposed to many years of other, more traditional therapies and are most likely to have reached adulthood. As hypnotherapy becomes more highly respected, its employment in the therapy of children has increased. Gardner (1976) pointed out that generally, child health professionals have a positive attitude toward hypnosis but have little working knowledge of its specific advantages or applications. Few are aware that children are hypnotisable, indeed more so than adults (London & Cooper, 1969); such common problems as school phobia (Lawlor 1976) are more successfully treated with hypnosis than other forms of therapy. Collison (1974) indicated that hypnosis is suitable therapy for a broad range of disorders commonly found in children, such as enuresis, encopresis, phobias, insomnia and conversion disorders and Gardner (1977) confirmed that children are able to achieve therapeutic results similar to those gained by adults.

The value of direct suggestion in producing analgesia has perhaps been the most widely accepted application of hypnotherapy with children. There are many dentists who attest to the usefulness of hypnotherapy in making their work less distressing for the child. In some hospital emergency departments, the use of hypnoanalgesia in children has been accepted as commonplace. Direct suggestion is also effective in dealing with such disorders as thumb sucking and nail biting and the psychosomatic problems of asthma, behaviour disorders (Plapp 1976), and psychogenic epilepsy (Gardner 1973) have all been shown to respond to direct suggestion in hypnosis. Even problems of a purely emotional nature such as anxiety will often diminish following suggestions for relaxation given to the child in hypnosis. However, as with adults, there is a significant proportion of children who do not respond favourably to direct suggestion alone. This is particularly true regarding children presenting behaviour problems clearly associated with much emotional disturbance. For these children analytical hypnotherapy provides a valuable alternative.

Although Klein (1935) discussed the application of psychoanalysis to children, there has been little actual interest in the application of hypnosis to analysing causes of children's emotional problems. In this author's experience, it is increasingly likely that the analytical hypnotherapist will be called upon to treat adolescents and children who are not responding to other therapies. Provided that the child is old enough to be attentive and cooperative, the induction of hypnosis rarely presents a problem. The child patient is likely to have a limited vocabulary and the therapist must remain well within these limits. Any excursion beyond the child's vocabulary will threaten the unconscious communication so vital to successful therapy. Children will often be reluctant to inform the therapist of a break in communication arising from incomprehension; the therapist must always be sensitive to a possible breach in communication. Because the child is likely to be in constant communication with his own unconscious mind, this avenue of communication is readily available and generally accounts for the child's greater hypnotisability. Imagery techniques are very acceptable: the use of the imaginary television is an effective method of inducing hypnosis, but any imaginary activity with which the child is familiar may be equally effective.

The principles of analytical hypnotherapy already examined regarding adults are equally valid for children and adolescents, though children tend to move very rapidly through some of the essential stages. When the child is directed to accept and understand the initially repressed emotions arising from the critical experience, he may find it easy to discover means of relinquishing them without further direction from the therapist. Nevertheless if success is to be assured, it is just as necessary with children as with adults that each principle of analytical hypnotherapy be followed and each stage be satisfactorily completed.

The physical, emotional and economic dependence of children presents a fundamental problem in their therapy, since the final stage of therapy, rehabilitation, depends upon the quality of the relationship within the child's home environment. It may be impossible for the child without his symptoms, to discover new ways of coping with his environment, particularly if the secondary gains obtained remain essential for his survival in that environment. In these cases, it may be that ego strengthening is the limit of rehabilitation since proper assertiveness training may be threatening to parents with unresolved difficulties of their own. The symptoms may remain, perhaps in a modified form, until a later date when more appropriate behaviour can be established, which may occur long after formal therapy has been terminated. Therefore, the child's environment and dependence must be taken into account in the evaluation of his overall response to therapy. This is also true, but to a more limited extent, of adults with few economic resources.

A variable amount of parental involvement in therapy is essential and sometimes crucial to the final and satisfactory outcome of therapy; on occasion, it may include the establishment of a therapeutic relationship with one or both parents who need to deal with their own emotional problems which are wholly or partially responsible for the child's presenting symptomatology. Where this is advisable but not feasible, more limited objectives than total disappearance of symptoms must be sought and accepted. In any case the child's recognition of the reasons for his symptoms will enable him to relinquish them at a more appropriate time.

Children, because of their greater hypnotisability, tend to regress more readily than adults, and thus ideomotor techniques assume less importance in their analytical hypnotherapy. Although ideomotor signalling is often valuable and can be used in precisely the same manner as with adults, visualisation techniques are often adequate to uncover the critical experiences which need to be dealt with; the child can be encouraged to move freely through his memories to discover those areas which contain the sources of his problems. He is then ready to receive encouragement from his developing Adult to deal with these problems.

The indications for analytical hypnotherapy are the same for children and adolescents as for adults. Such psychosomatic disorders as migraine and asthma appear to respond well to this approach, and all emotional disorders, including anxiety, phobias, obsessions and depressions respond well as with adults. Behaviour problems and learning difficulties, including such handicaps as dyslexia, sometimes respond well after locating and dealing with an unsuspected emotional cause.

It must always be understood when treating children and adolescents that they are part of a family and that any changes effected in the patient inevitably affect other members of that family. Since any change necessitates adjustments and is always accompanied by feelings of uncertainty such changes will be resisted by the family. This resistance may range from minimal to great but seldom is it consciously recognised as resistance. In any case the effectiveness of therapy depends largely upon the patient's ability to deal with this pressure upon him not to change. No matter what the parents or other members of the family at a conscious level assert, at an unconscious level, they will feel threatened by any changes they observe in the patient. This may present a real problem in the therapy of children since the parents' objectives may not coincide with those of the child or therapist. The analytical hypnotherapist's prime goal is the resolution of internal conflicts: the disappearance of symptoms is external evidence of this. The individual must be able to obtain essential secondary gains without relying upon his symptoms. This will often necessitate marked changes in behaviour to which other members of the family may not be prepared to adjust; if the parents cannot adjust to these changes, or if the child cannot be removed from the family environment, it is probable that symptoms will remain. Fortunately the parents can usually be encouraged to deal with the changes that inevitably arise from successful therapy simply by being allowed to understand the objectives sought by the patient and the therapist.

The first illustrative case to be described is that of an eight year old girl who, when her parents' marriage broke down, lived with her father and older brother. She was unable to relate to her new stepmother who had made genuine attempts to befriend her; she had become disobedient, deceitful, sullen and uncooperative, and was a constant source of tension within the family. Betty Jane is bright, attractive, intelligent and in spite of her behaviour disorder, articulate and cooperative with the therapist. Accompanied by her father and stepmother she openly admitted in therapy that she was often very angry and resentful of her stepmother, even though she understood that she was genuinely trying to help her.

In the initial interview Betty Jane was seen first with her parents and then on her own. She confirmed all of what had previously been said about her behaviour and could explain it only by saying that she just felt mad. She agreed that she would like things to be better at home and wanted the therapist to do whatever was possible to improve things. At this point, hypnosis was induced using the rapid induction technique as described in Chapter Three. A few moments after closing her eyes, Betty Jane was viewing her favourite television programme: the analytic phase was begun by establishing an unconscious image of herself (at her present age) on television.

DR   Just turn the channel now to channel eight, will you, and when you turn to channel eight there is an extraordinary thing that you are going to see. You're going to see Betty Jane on television. . . See her?

Eight is Betty Jane's actual age, and is a good place to start. Seeing herself on television enables the patient to communicate with the unconscious body image.

PT   Yep.

DR   What's she doing? Dancing? Smiling? What's she doing?

Betty Jane's imagination immediately puts her unconscious image in a realistic situation.

PT   Dancing.

DR   Is she?

PT   Skating.

DR   Skating, eh? She looks good. We are going to watch her for a bit and when she is finished she'll come up to the front of the television. . . Is she finished?

PT   Yep.

DR   Ask her if she's happy, will you?

The therapist now attempts to discover Betty Jane's unconscious tensions but is impeded by her adherence to realism in her unconscious fantasy. He tries again and meets with no greater success.

PT   She isn't happy because she fell down.

DR   Uhum. Ask her if there is anything that bothers her at all. Ask her if there is anything that worries her and makes her feel bad.

PT   Well, she's embarassed a lot

because she fell down.

DR   Oh yes, sure.

PT   She's worried because she is nervous and she might not make her jumps or something like that.

DR   Is that right, eh? Ask her if she is happy at home.

The therapist makes a third attempt to uncover unconscious feelings and gets a promising response. He pursues this approach and is rewarded by an honest appraisal of Betty Jane's feelings and behaviour.

PT   Sorta.

DR   Ask her if there is anything that goes wrong at home. Ask her that.

PT   Yeah.

DR   What does she say?

PT   She fights and throws things.

DR   Does she?

PT   And she doesn't get along with the other kids.

DR   Is that what she says? Ask her why it is she fights. Ask her if she knows why she fights.

The therapist attempts to maintain a therapeutic dissociation by referring to the unconscious Betty Jane in the third person. Betty Jane, however, moves easily into the unconscious image.

PT   I don't like it when June gets mad at me.

DR   Is that the reason why she fights?

PT   Yep.

DR   Ask her if there's anything inside her that really, really bothers her. Anything deep inside that really makes her feel bad.

PT   I didn't want Dad and June to break up.

Betty Jane confuses June, (her stepmother), with her mother, but soon corrects this error.

DR   Dad and who?

PT   Dad and my Mum.

DR   Is that what's bothering her?

PT   Uhum. I don't like that. I want to live with my Dad and I want to live with my real Mum.

Betty Jane clearly identifies her problem at this early stage.

DR   I bet. Ask her if she's feeling angry about that.

PT   Yep.

DR   Ask her if she gets so angry that she does things. . . to upset people.

The therapist now seeks to identify the emotions which have persisted unconsciously and finds that the main source of tension is one which creates anger and cannot be repressed. It is expressed in a behaviour disorder.

PT   Sometimes.

DR   Does she? Why don't you tell us what she sometimes does when she upsets people. She can whisper it to you if she likes – you don't have to tell me.

PT   Well. . .

DR   Oh, you're going to tell me are you? That's okay.

PT   She acts dumb and stuff.

DR   Does she do anything else. . . because she's so angry?

It is interesting to note that Betty Jane recognises that her acting dumb and stuff has been due to anger.

PT   Well, she takes things out on people.

DR   Does she?

PT   When somebody wants to play a game with her she doesn't usually want to. That makes people upset and sad.

She is also clear about the other ways she has discovered in which she can express her anger. She makes other people sad because, deep down she too is very sad.

DR   Yes, I see. Ask her if she is feeling sad, if she is crying inside.

PT   Uhum. She says yes.

DR   She's crying inside, is she?

PT   Yeah.

Betty Jane is able to get in touch with the pain really responsible for her anger.

DR   That's awful, isn't it?

PT   Yeah.

DR   Ask her if she's scared at all or frightened. Does she ever tell anybody that she's frightened inside?

PT   No, but she is real scared.

The therapist now looks for evidence of any unconscious fear and Betty Jane readily admits to the great fear that she will be separated from her mother permanently.

DR   What is she scared about?

PT   Well, I'm afraid I might not be able to see my mother again.

DR   That is an awful fear, isn't it?

PT   That can happen.

DR   That would be terrible, wouldn't it?

PT   Yep.

DR   Okay. Can you help her at all with that because she is real scared . . . she's more scared than any little girl has ever been isn't she?

The therapist now feels that it is time to call upon Betty Jane's developing Adult to resolve some of the tension, using his own Adult to assist her.

PT   Well, I don't know how to help her.

DR   Well tell her that she needn't be scared that she isn't going to see mum again because you are going to see her.

PT   I know that.

DR   But perhaps she doesn't know that. She keeps getting scared. Tell her that. . . Nods. Have you told her?

PT   Yep.

DR   Does she smile when you tell her?

PT   Yeah.

DR   Is she still crying?

PT   Inside.

There appears to be some good Adult/Child communication being established internally but it is insufficient to relieve her pain. The therapist asks Betty Jane to comfort herself, but the realism of the television construct is allowed to intrude.

DR   Oh, put your arm around her then, can you do that?

PT   No. She's in the TV.

DR   Well pretend that you are in the TV too because we have got to make her feel better somehow.

Although she finds it difficult initially, later she is able to accept the suggestion to give herself love and

PT   Yeah.

DR   Did you put your arm around her?

PT   Yeah.

DR   Isn't that nice? Is she feeling better now?

PT   Yep.

DR   Okay.

PT   Now she's gone. She wanted to change.

DR   Okay, we'll talk to her again. Now let's turn to channel 7. Channel 7. Have you got it?

PT   Yep.

DR   There's Betty Jane. She is only seven. What is she doing?

PT   Skipping.

DR   Is she having a nice time?

PT   Yep.

DR   Okay, when she has finished skipping I want you to ask her to come over to the front of the television so that we can ask her some questions.

PT   She just came up.

comfort. This appears to have a good effect.

By turning the television channels backwards regression to earlier ages can readily be accomplished, as seen here with Betty Jane.

Seven year old Betty Jane appears to be completely carefree.

DR Okay, ask her if she's happy inside.

PT . . . No.

DR What's wrong with her?

PT Same thing. . . mother and father broke up. *Tearfully.*

Underlying the carefree external demeanour is the same deep sadness which Betty Jane attempts to conceal.

DR Is she very sad?

PT Yeah.

DR Crying?

PT Inside, she is. But she is not sure so she is trying to be happy.

DR She's pretending to be happy, is she? Is that why she is skipping?

PT Yeah.

DR Does she get angry at all?

PT She says that she gets angry a lot.

Intense anger is also present in seven year old Betty Jane.

DR If she was happy inside would she be just as angry?

PT No. She wouldn't be as angry as much.

Betty Jane recognises that her anger is, in large measure, due to her sadness. The therapist hopes that, with encouragement, she can find means to relinquish this old sadness.

DR She wouldn't be so angry. Do you think you could help her like we helped eight year old Betty Jane? Will you tell her not to be unhappy? Could you do that?

PT Well, I don't know what to do.

DR Can you put your arm around her like you did before – through the television set?

PT Yep.

DR Does she smile when you do that?

PT Yep.

DR Does she feel better?

PT Yeah.

DR Oh, that's good. Tell her that we'll come back later to speak to her again and tell her to have a nice game. Is she happy inside now?

PT Yes. She has to go in now for supper.

DR But is she happy inside now?

PT Yep.

There appears to be some success.

Seven year old Betty Jane is now okay. It is now time to regress to an earlier age and explore it.

DR Okay. Let's change the channel to channel six. I want you to see six year old Betty Jane. Six year old Betty Jane, you know she is little, isn't she?

PT Yep.

DR What is she doing?

PT She's watching TV.

DR   Okay, let's talk to her. Six year old Betty Jane, do you mind leaving the TV for a minute, we want to talk to you.

PT   Hi.

DR   Six year old Betty Jane, are you happy?

PT   No.

DR   You're not happy, eh? Why aren't you happy?

PT   Well, same thing — my mother and father broke up.

Again, at six, the intense sadness of the separation from mother is found to be a prime source of tension.

DR   Your mother and father, have they just broken up?

PT   No, they broke up a long time ago.

DR   Oh, that must make you feel pretty sad, eh?

PT   Uhum.

DR   Are you very angry about that?

PT   Yeah, I don't like it.

Anger is once again strongly associated with the pain.

DR   Are you unhappy too, eh?

PT   Yeah, I just saw them do it. I just saw when they broke up.

There is a clear memory of the marriage breakdown which is responsible for her sadness.

DR   You saw them break up did you?

PT   Yep.

DR   So even though you are little you saw them break up and that makes you unhappy?

PT   Yep.

DR   Eight year old Betty Jane, you will have to help that six year old Betty Jane. She sounds really miserable. You have got to tell her that things aren't that bad and that she is going to be able to see her mum every so often, will you tell her that?

The therapist calls upon the more Adult Betty Jane to help.

PT   Uhum. She'll only see her mum every three weeks.

The pain of the separation is well understood.

DR   Well tell her that anyway. She is going to have to do that because her dad and her mum couldn't get along.

DR   Will you tell her that? Can you explain it to her and tell her not to be sad?

PT   Uhum.

DR   How is she taking it?

PT   She's still feeling angry.

Her anger is too much to deal with.

DR   Is she? Six year old Betty Jane, you're still feeling angry, eh?

PT   Yep.

DR   Why are you keeping that

angry feeling? You don't need that any more do you?

PT   Because she won't let anything cheer her up, that's why.

DR   Nothing will cheer her up?

Because there is a strong determination to remain loyal to mother, the sadness and anger must remain.

PT   Nope.

DR   She has definitely decided that she is going to go on being miserable has she?

PT   Yep.

There is nothing to be done about it.

DR   Does she want to go on being miserable like that?

PT   No.

DR   Well tell her that she doesn't have to be miserable anymore.

Really, she does not want to remain miserable, but she feels that she must.

PT   She won't listen to me.

DR   Won't she? Talk to her again. You tell her not to be miserable and that you really want to take care of her. Did she listen to you?

The therapist attempts to obtain more help from her Adult but this, it appears, is not effective.

PT   Yep.

DR   What did she say?

PT   She said, *I still feel miserable inside.*

DR   Ask her what she wants you to do to stop her feeling miserable be-

The therapist seeks some beneficial compromise and Betty Jane

cause it's no good going on being miserable like that.

emerges with one: she must see more of her mother.

PT She wants to see her mum more often.

DR Does she?

PT Yes, every two weeks.

DR I see. Does her mum want to see her more often too?

PT Uhum.

DR So she is pretty mad because she can't see her mum more often is that right?

PT Yep.

DR Okay. Tell her that you understand and now that you really understand can you tell her to stop being so mad?

The anger will persist until the objective of more frequent contact with mother is achieved.

PT She won't listen to me.

DR Hey, come on now, six year old Betty Jane, stop being mad. It is not going to help being so mad. . . You have got a right to be angry haven't you?

PT Yeah.

DR Don't you think that you have had enough of being angry now?

PT Yeah.

DR   Would it be nice to let it all go now?

PT   Yep.

DR   Okay, put your arm around her and say, 'come on, it's okay now. We're going to have fun instead of being angry'.

The therapist may have succeeded in persuading her to give up her anger.

PT   Yeah.

DR   Have you got her smiling?

PT   Yep.

DR   Good. Okay, let's turn the channel to channel five and see five year old Betty Jane. Can you see five year old Betty Jane?

PT   I can't remember anything then.

DR   No you can't, can you? You will have to look at the television because you can't remember this so you'll just have to watch this now. Five year old Betty Jane — there she is. You couldn't remember this now could you?

The therapist emphasizes the dissociation between Betty Jane's conscious mind that cannot remember and the unconscious mind that contains all of the memories.

PT   No.

DR   What's she doing? You can see.

PT   She's eating.

DR   Would you ask five year old Betty Jane to speak to us? Just stop

eating for a minute. Has she stopped?

PT   Yep.

DR   Ask her if she really, really is
feeling good inside. See what she
says.

PT   She's feeling good.

DR   Feeling good, eh? Ask her if she
is smiling inside.

PT   She's smiling.

DR   Oh, good. She is feeling really
happy, is she?

PT   Yep.

DR   Okay, now let's turn to channel four. Have you got it?

PT   Yep.

DR   Four year old Betty Jane,
you're just little. We don't even remember you at all. What are you
doing?

PT   I'm in bed.

DR   Are you? Are you asleep?

PT   Yep.

DR   Are you dreaming nice
dreams?

For some ill defined reason five
year old Betty Jane appears to be
okay. Presumably, this was before
June's definitive entry rendered
the prospect of her father's recon-
ciliation with mother very remote.

However the four year old Betty
Jane is very close to the actual
marriage breakdown, and consequently feels it acutely.

PT   No. She's dreaming of when her mum and dad broke up.

DR   Is that what she is dreaming about?

PT   And she had to go and live with June and she didn't like that.

DR   And she is only four?

PT   Uhum.

DR   Is she angry about having to live with June?

Her first close association with June makes her very angry.

PT   Yeah.

DR   Okay, why don't you talk to her in her sleep. . .

PT   She's awake now.

DR   Oh, dear. I thought she was still asleep. We must have woken her up, eh?

PT   Yep.

DR   Ask her if she can stop being angry now because she has been angry for such a long time. She's been angry for four years now.

It seems that she can be persuaded to find means of relinquishing this old anger.

PT   Uhum. She's not angry very much now.

DR   You've told her not to be angry any more?

PT   Yeah. She doesn't think about it too much now.

DR   Is she smiling now?

PT   Yep.

DR   Is she really okay?

PT   Yep.

DR   Okay. She can go back to sleep again now, can't she.

At this point Betty Jane is regressed to three years of age, then to two years and then one year, and finally to birth. At each stage she indicates that she is feeling very happy, which would indicate that there was no problem prior to the age of four years when the parents separated.

DR   Okay let's go back along all the channels again now. Channel one, how's that? Is little Betty Jane still feeling good?

PT   Happy.

DR   Channel two?

PT   Happy.

DR   Channel three?

PT   Happy.

DR   Channel four?

PT   Happy.

DR   Are you sure? She wasn't happy when we spoke to her before.

In the rapid review of various ages and associated experiences, it seems that Betty Jane has really dealt with all of her unconscious discomfort until age five, an age which was previously believed was without discomfort.

Is she really happy now? You must have worked hard on her. Is she really happy?

PT   Yep.

DR   Channel five?

PT   She's a little sad.

Five year old Betty Jane is hurt and resentful still.

DR   Oh, come on, you will have to help her now won't you?

PT   Uhum.

DR   You don't want her to be sad do you?

PT   No, she's still mad.

DR   Okay will you talk to her and help her? Tell her that it's not going to help much if she stays mad.

PT   She wants to be happy.

DR   Good. Dad doesn't want her to be mad, does he?

PT   No.

DR   Okay, channel six?

PT   She's happy now.

DR   Good. Channel seven.

PT   Happy now.

DR   Channel eight?

It would now appear that all of the old tensions have been relinquished although with a struggle, and that there exists now some internal peace.

PT She's happy.

DR All happy?

PT Yep.

DR Big smiles all around?

PT Yep.

DR Oh, isn't that nice. Okay we'll go back to the other station now. What's on there now?

PT The Flintstones.

The remainder of this first interview was taken up with strong ego strengthening suggestions and suggestions for greater calm and well being.

Betty Jane was seen on three more occasions. At each meeting she declared that she was remaining happy although still wanted to be with her mother and continued to show some resentment towards her stepmother. The separation from her natural mother, with their infrequent meetings, was the source of intolerable pain for the child. This was made clear in some writings that she produced, in which she wrote of her need to be with her mother. Despite the desire to maintain custody of his daughter (for which he had fought long and hard) her father agreed to allow Betty Jane to return to the custody of her mother and to visit him and his new family on a regular basis. This proved to be satisfactory for a short while only. Betty Jane, her mother and her mother's partner rapidly became embroiled in a bitter triangular conflict which worsened to the point where it was clear to everyone, including Betty Jane, that she would be much better off back with her father and that the solution she had so long sought to her separation anxiety produced more distress for her than being parted from her mother. There was therefore unanimous approval to her return to her father following which there was a dramatic change in her behaviour. Betty Jane became cooperative and congenial and all the family agreed that she had become a joy to be with. Although therapy did not resolve Betty Jane's problems, a clear understanding of them was rapidly gained. Also, therapy enabled her to relinquish much of the anger and hostility that she initially displayed. Evidently some part of the personality had stubbornly remained untouched by therapy and adhered determinedly to the goal of returning to her mother. This return had probably been a secondary goal; prior to therapy, Betty Jane, had perhaps unconsciously determined that she must reunite her parents. In any event, having gained this secondary goal, Betty Jane was able to relinquish her former delinquent behaviour entirely.

Although headaches are common in children, it is unusual for them to suffer from migraine. Larry was an eleven year old boy experiencing migraine headaches which occur every four to six weeks. Characteristically, they begin over the left eye rapidly becoming sufficiently severe for him to go to bed. Usually, he would vomit and then fall asleep, awakening without symptoms. They mostly occurred in the evenings and his mother felt that they were associated with tension. He had been subjected to all of the customary investigations for headaches but no cause for them was detected. Immediately prior to attending for therapy, he experienced attacks of migraine almost every week. Recently, he had used a medication apparently effective in controlling the headaches, but producing the undesirable side effect of depression. At the time of the first interview, Larry was not taking any medication. Larry's mother reported that many foods had been suspected as possible precipitating factors but the search for a food allergy had eventually been abandoned. She described headaches that Larry experienced when no more than five years of age; seven years later, he is still experiencing these headaches. Larry proved to be a cooperative patient and the following transcript begins as hypnosis is induced.

DR Okay, are you comfortable there? *Nods.* Great. I want you to take a nice deep breath and then close your eyes. Let your breath go right out. Now I want you just to pretend. I want you to pretend that you just cannot open those eyes and when you are pretending I want you to test them and see that they just won't work. *Pt. tries to open his eyes unsuccessfully.* Test them hard. Now spread that very comfortable feeling all the way through. It feels

With an eleven year old, as with an adult, the relaxation from deep breathing may be helpful. The eleven year old has a fertile imagination, and he is able to pretend successfully. The fact that the eyes will not open is proof of an unconscious response to suggestion. Hypnotic response and the transition to the imagery of home and television are relatively easy.

really good. Now I want you to picture yourself at home. Do you have a television set at home?

PT   Yes.

DR   Would you switch it on please? *Pt. lifts his arm.* What programme is that?

PT   Bugs- Bugs Bunny.

DR   Bugs Bunny, what is he doing?

PT   Climbing up a tree.

DR   Is he? Okay. You watch him and enjoy that. Let me know when you get to the commercials, will you?. . .

PT   There now.

DR   You've got to the commercials?

PT   Yep.

DR   I want you to look at the dial on this television set. It's different to what you've noticed before. Different altogether. And as you look at the dial you'll see that there are other channels that you've never seen on your television set before so will you just switch to the one that says 'Larry'.

PT   Yeah.

Some time is spent on the unconscious activity of recalling television programming prior to commencing therapy.

The imaginary television is a ready device for the promotion of regression.

DR   You've got it eh? Do you see Larry on television? You see him?

The unconscious body image is immediately accessible as is the associated unconscious mind.

PT   Yeah.

DR   What's he doing?

PT   Smiling.

DR   Smiling is he? Right. How old is he there?

PT   He's little.

Already Larry has regressed with specific direction. Presumably this is due to his pre-therapy expectation of dealing with the time of the onset of his migraine.

DR   He's little? How little is he?

PT   About five.

DR   He's about five and he's smiling. Is there anything bothering him at all?

PT   No.

DR   Good. Now keep watching because this is really interesting. You're going to see him at the very first time he has a migraine attack. I don't know how small he is there at the very first time — he might even be younger than five. I want you to watch and tell me what happens. Is he five or is he smaller?

The therapist now directs him to the first attack of headache, and Larry moves even further back in time.

Prior to defining its emotional attributes, it seems wise to ascertain whether this is indeed the first experience associated with migraine.

PT   He's a bit smaller.

DR   About four?

PT   Yeah.

DR   Or three?

PT   About four.

DR   Does he seem scared?

PT   A little bit.

DR   Does he look sad?

PT   Yeah.

DR   Is he crying?

PT   Yeah.

DR   Is he a bit angry at all?

PT   Yeah, a little.

DR   Does he feel guilty or ashamed
or embarrassed?

PT   No.

DR   What's happening to make   Here the therapist hoped to locate
him feel like that?   the emotional problem more
                                       clearly. Questioning is directed at
PT   Well he's got a pain in his eye. determining the circumstances as-
                                       sociated with the headache which
DR   Got a pain in his eye? Where is   might be the source of emotional
he?   discomfort.

PT   He's at the Chinese restaurant.

DR   I see. Look around the restaurant and tell me, is there anybody else
there with him?

PT   Yeah, the whole family is there.

DR   And he's got a pain over his eye
has he?

PT   Yeah.

DR   Does anybody know? Has he told anyone?

PT   No.

The only important fact emerging here is that Larry does not let anyone know about the distress he is experiencing.

DR   He doesn't tell anyone at all that he has a pain over his eye. He keeps it to himself does he?

PT   Yep.

DR   Oh, what happens next?

PT   They get in the car and he lays down in the back seat.

DR   Is he feeling bad?

PT   Yeah.

DR   And what happens next?

PT   Then they drive home and he gets sick to his stomach.

DR   He throws up does he?... Now that you've seen all of that I want you to roll those pictures right back to before he gets the pain in his eye and you are going to see everything that's happening before he gets the pain in the eye. What's happening there?

The therapist does not feel that he has learned anything that would indicate the cause of the pain so he must persuade Larry to search his memories prior to the pain. Larry accomplishes this with ease.

PT   He's eating chicken balls.

DR   He's eating chicken balls is he?

PT   And rice.

DR   And rice. Is he feeling good?

PT   Yeah.

DR   He loves that food?

PT   Yeah.

DR   What else is he eating?

PT   He tasted some of the hot curry.

This is the only problem that can be located: hot curry! It makes Larry very thirsty.

DR   Does he like that?

PT   No.

DR   What happens when he tastes the hot curry?

PT   He drinks a glass of orange pop.

DR   And what happens as he drinks the orange pop? Does he feel okay?

PT   Yeah.

DR   Okay. What else happens?

PT   He asks for more chicken balls.

DR   He eats more chicken balls.

PT   Yeah.

DR   Is he still okay?

PT   Yeah.

DR   What happens next?

PT He's finishing his meal. He starts to feel sick.

Larry has indulged himself on an unusual food.

DR Does he tell anybody?

PT No.

DR You can help him. With this particular television set you can tell him that he's going to be okay. Will you do that?

The therapist exhorts the patient's Adult to intervene.

PT Yeah.

DR Is he alright now?

This is apparently successful.

PT Yeah.

DR You've got him feeling better?

PT Yeah.

DR That was good wasn't it?

PT Yeah.

DR You really got him over that. Is that the first time he's ever had that?

Nevertheless the therapist is still not certain that he has located the all-important critical experience.

PT I don't know.

DR Ask him. Ask him if he's ever had one before. He'll tell you. This is a special television set. You can talk two ways on this set.

PT I think that he's had one before.

His hunch is confirmed: there is an earlier critical experience to be dealt with. It is readily located.

DR He's had one before has he? Okay would you please switch the channel to where it says: 'Small

Larry — first headache'. Have you got it?

PT   Yeah.

DR   How old is he there? Is he four, is he three or two, how old is he?

PT   I think he is three.

DR   He's three. My goodness, he is small. What is he doing?

PT   He's playing out in the back.

DR   Uhum. What's happening?

PT   He's playing soccer.

DR   He's a pretty clever guy playing soccer at three. Is he having a good time?

PT   Yes. Then he wants to go inside. He's feeling sick.

A common feature of these early attacks is this nausea.

DR   Then what happened?

PT   He goes to his room and starts to cry because he has a pain over his eye.

DR   He's got a pain over his eye. Ask him which eye?

PT   He says 'his left eye'.

Even at this early age the left eye is involved.

DR   His left eye, he says. Who's with him?

PT   His mum. She's telling him to

go and lie down and he goes and lies down.

DR What happens?

PT He starts to cry real hard because he is really upset.

DR Can you tell him that he's going to be alright? Could you take the headache away for him? Tell him you'll take it away for him. Have you done it?

It is time to call upon Adult intervention to gain control of the headache.

PT Yeah.

DR That's marvelous isn't it? He really feels good.

There is an immediate resolution of tension.

PT Yes.

DR Okay. So three year old Larry's feeling really great. Just check that television and look and see if there are any other Larry's younger than three with headaches. You'll have to switch the channels and see. Do they have any headaches?

However here is a need to make certain that the problem did not commence even earlier than age three.

PT No.

DR Are they all happy?

PT Yes.

DR Okay, let's come back to three year old Larry again. Have you got him smiling and okay now?

Since the cause of the headaches has not been eliminated, this is still another check to see that no old tension is present at three years. Another check at four years of age is indicated.

PT Yeah.

DR Okay. Let us turn back to channel four and look at four year old Larry. How is he now? Is he still feeling good?

PT Yeah.

DR Really good?

PT Yeah.

DR Okay. So three year old Larry's feeling good, four year old Larry's feeling good. Now just have a look at this television and see if there are any other Larry's that you can find that have important headaches. Headaches that are important to our understanding of them.

The search continues for more clues to the reasons for the headaches.

PT Yeah.

DR How old is he there?

PT Eleven.

At this point the patient describes his most recent headache; it occurred in the morning just before school started so that he had to return home to bed for the rest of the day. Although it lasted all day he was sufficiently recovered to take part in a baseball game during the evening.

DR Okay. We've learned a lot about him haven't we? We've learned a great deal about him. Now I am going to tie this finger *touching the right index finger* to the very deep part of the mind, Larry, and it will float up like that *lifting it gently* whenever the deep part of your mind wants to say 'yes'. I'm going to

The therapist is not yet satisfied that an understanding of the causes of the headaches has yet been reached and so he resorts to establishing ideomotor signalling in a very direct manner by assigning *yes* and *no* signals to specific fingers.

ask the deep part of your mind to look at all of those headaches – there's a whole lot of them to look at – to see if there's anything that really makes Larry feel upset before the headaches come on. If there is something that makes him feel upset that 'yes' finger is going to float up. Now if there is nothing before those headaches that makes him upset then this 'no' finger *touching the middle finger of the right hand* will float up to say 'no'. I am just asking the deep part of your mind to look through all of those headaches to see if there is something that upsets Larry. *Yes finger begins to float up.* There is something there. Okay. I am now going to ask that deep part of your mind, could we know what it is that upsets Larry and causes those headaches? Can we know what it is?

This approach proves to be immediately successful and the deeply concealed reason for the headaches is readily located. Permission is then sought to bring that information to a higher level of consciousness.

PT   Yes.

DR   Oh, you've got it, have you?

PT   Yeah.

DR   What causes those headaches?

PT   He didn't get what he wanted.

At last the answer: the headaches are a means of securing attention and of providing an excuse for failure.

DR   Didn't get what he wanted, oh, I see.

PT   Or didn't do something.

DR   Something didn't work for him, eh?

PT   Yes.

DR   I see, so whenever that happened he got a headache, is that
right?

PT   Sometimes.   It is not always necessary to resort
                                       to a headache.

DR   A lot of the time?

PT   Most of the time.

DR   I wonder if we can help him to   The therapist now attempts to re-
find a way to get what he wants   frame the intent behind the
without having a headache. I'm   headache so that Larry can
going to ask that deep part of your   achieve his goals without employ-
mind to see if you can find a way   ing this symptom.
that Larry can get what he needs
without having to have a headache
or whether he can put up with not
getting what he wants. If he can find
a way to do this then the 'yes' finger
will float up. If he cannot, then the
'no' finger will float up. . . *Yes.* Oh,
that's good. You've found a way.   Fortunately this proves to be suc-
Okay. I'm going to ask you to see   cessful and the new *frame* is put to
yourself on the television using that the test and found to be satisfac-
way or putting up with not getting   tory.
what you want or finding other
ways of getting what you want
without having a headache. When
you can see Larry doing that raise
the 'yes' finger. . . *Yes.* Good. Let me
ask him, Larry, do you have to have
any more headaches? If you do,
raise the 'yes' finger, if not raise the
'no' finger. . . *No.* Oh good, good.   Larry claims that he no longer
Now I want you to go to a time   needs his headaches. This does not
when Larry doesn't have any   necessarily mean that he will have
headaches at all and when you are   none.

there the 'yes' finger will lift. . . *Yes.*
How old are you there?

PT   I'm two.

DR   Mm?

PT   I'm two.

DR   Okay you're two — just a little guy. Let me ask two year old Larry — you don't have any headaches, how is that?

PT   He didn't want — he doesn't want toys or anything.

DR   I see. Two year old Larry, there's eleven year old Larry here who would like to get rid of his headaches. How could he get rid of them?

Pt   Just try to understand that he can't have everything he wants.

DR   Okay. He is to try to understand that he can't have everything. Is there anything else that you can tell us, two year old Larry?

PT   He shouldn't ask for everything he wants.

DR   I see. Eleven year old Larry, did you hear all of that? Can you do that?

PT   Yes.

DR   You think you could? Okay,

When asked to go to a time when he had no headaches, Larry surprisingly reverted to two years old. The therapist had expected him to move forward in time. Because two year old Larry has limited expectations, he can advise eleven year old Larry similarly to limit his demands.

This advice is accepted by eleven year old Larry and the therapist now wants to test it by progression to twelve years of age.

416   Analytical Hypnotherapy

let's go forward in time to twelve year old Larry. Twelve year old Larry, do you have headaches any more?

PT   Yes.

DR   You heard that bit of advice, didn't you?

Twelve year old Larry appears still to need the headaches because he is unable to limit his needs sufficiently.

PT   Yes.

DR   Why do you still have headaches then?

PT   Because he still wants things.

DR   You still want things. Okay. ·Do you have the headaches as often as you used to?

However twelve year old Larry does agree that he can reduce the *frequency* of the headaches.

PT   No.

DR   You don't have them as often as you used to, twelve year old Larry and it seems like you know why you have them, is that right?

PT   Yeah.

DR   Okay. I'm going to do something now, Larry, that you're going to find very interesting. I'm going to count. I'm going to count to ten. When I get to ten you'll have a really bad headache. Probably the worst headache you have ever had. Let me know as I count. . . One. Feel it coming?

Because Larry needs to keep the headaches, the therapist decides to teach Larry certain manoeuvres which will enable him to gain control of them.

Linking the severity of the headaches to numbers gives him a direct control of their intensity.

PT   Yes.

DR   Two. . . stronger still? It's getting real strong. Three. . . Four. . . how bad is it now?

PT   It's pretty bad.

DR   Five. . . how bad is it now?

PT   Worse.

DR   Worse still? Six. . . shall I go any further?

PT   No.

DR   Six. . . is that too much?

PT   Yeah.

DR   I'd better not go any further, eh?

PT   No.

DR   Okay. Five. . . four. . . three. . . two. . . one. . . nothing. It's gone, right?

PT   Yeah.

DR   Gone completely. Completely gone. Okay, Larry, now I want you to do this. I want you to count. You count yourself and when the headache gets as bad as you can stand let me know. . . What are you up to — I can't hear.

PT   Five. . . six. . . seven. . . bad. . . six.

Larry is able to produce his own headache by counting, thereby demonstrating to his own satisfac-

DR   Six?

PT   Five. . . four. . . three. . . two. . . one. . . nothing.

DR   Nothing there now, is there?

PT   No.

DR   Okay. We're going to do something else interesting. I'm going to ask you to imagine that there are a lot of switches in your head. There's a whole row of switches. Can you see them?

PT   Yes.

DR   Now above each of them there is a coloured light. I don't know how many there are there. There may be a hundred or so but you only need to see a few of them and all of the lights are lit up, right?

PT   Yeah.

DR   Now each of those switches is attached to a wire and one of those switches is attached to a wire that goes right down to this hand here *touching the back of the right hand.* Right?

PT   Yeah.

DR   What colour light is that one?

PT   Red.

tion, that he can exercise control over them, since he can diminish them down to nothing as he counts down to nothing.

In case this manoeuvre does not prove adequate to control his headaches, the therapist decides to teach Larry a method of producing hypnoanaesthesia which he can use to relieve any headache that might occur.

Most children are able to produce a localised anaesthesia by the use of this *switch* technique and Larry is no exception.

DR There's another wire that goes to this hand here *touching the left hand*. What colour light is that one?

PT Blue.

DR Blue. So you've got the red on this side and the blue on that side, eh?

PT Yeah.

DR And you've got the red light switched on?

PT Yeah.

DR And the blue one is switched on? Now something interesting is going to happen. If you turn off the red switch the light goes out and you'll have no feeling in this arm at all. It will be completely gone. Will you do that – switch it off?

PT Yeah.

DR Is it switched off?

PT Yes.

DR This arm does not feel anything at all. *Testing by pinching the back of the hand*. Is that right?

Larry successfully develops and demonstrates a glove anaesthesia.

PT Yes.

DR So it is really switched off. Okay, now switch it back on again.

PT Yeah.

DR Now you'll see that now it's switched back on again it can feel again. *Pinches again and Larry pulls his hand away.* That hurt?

PT Yeah.

DR Yes right, that really hurt. Okay what is the switch for the head?

Good subjects like Larry have no difficulty in assigning a colour to different parts of the body.

PT Orange.

DR Which bit is for the left eye?

PT Yellow.

DR You've got a yellow one for the left eye. Okay. Switch off the left eye switch, will you?

PT Yeah.

DR Got it switched off?

PT Yeah.

DR Now I'm going to test you over the eye and you won't feel anything at all. *Taps him fairly hard over the left eye and there is no evidence of discomfort.* It's gone off completely isn't it?

Larry effectively demonstrates good control of feeling over the site of his usual headaches.

PT Yes.

DR You can now switch off any switch you need. If you ever get a headache switch off the yellow switch. Okay?

PT   Yes.

DR   Okay now switch it back on again. Are all switches on now?

PT   Yeah.

DR   Everything working?

PT   Yes.

DR   No pains anywhere?

PT   No. I don't feel anything.

At this point the therapist gave Larry a posthypnotic cue to re-enter hypnosis, awakened him and then gave him the cue to which he immediately responded.

DR   Listen to me very carefully. Nod you head when you are listening to me very carefully. *Nods.* Larry, do you think that you could let those headaches go now? Are you ready to do that yet?

Reinduction of hypnosis on a cue usually results in a deep level of hypnosis, characterized by marked conscious/unconscious dissociation; this was the objective here.

PT   Yeah.

DR   Do you think that you'll need to have those headaches anymore?

Larry no longer *needs* his headaches but this does not mean that he might not use them as before and give them to himself.

PT   No.

DR   Have you made your mind up about that?

PT   Yes.

DR   Well, if you do ever get them again you can always switch off that yellow light. Is that right?

PT   Yeah.

DR   What is the other thing you can do?

PT   Count down from ten to nothing.

DR   Good. You know that sometimes we give ourselves headaches but when we've had enough of them we want to get rid of them. If you want you can always do that.

The therapist takes this opportunity to indicate to Larry that even if he does give himself more headaches, he can always control them.

PT   Yes.

DR   Larry, I want you to give yourself a bad headache, would you please?

A demonstration of this control seems to be advisable and Larry is able to give himself a headache which he readily controls.

PT   *Counting quietly.* Yes it's aching.

DR   What number did you get up to?

PT   Five.

DR   Five. Okay. Is that a usual headache, give?

PT   Uhum.

DR   Okay. Count yourself out of that.

PT   Four. . .three. . .two. . .one. . . nothing. . . It's gone.

DR   It's gone.

PT   Yeah.

DR   This time I want you to give yourself a really bad one, as bad as you can give yourself right now.

It seems wise to have Larry deal with a really severe headache, one that almost makes him vomit.

PT   *After a pause.* Eight.

DR   Got an eight? That's a beast, isn't it?

PT   Uhum.

DR   Do you think that you're going to throw up?

This is a really bad headache but Larry has no difficulty in controlling it.

PT   Yeah.

DR   Okay where is that yellow switch? Switch it off.

PT   Yeah.

DR   Now what's happened to your headache?

PT   It's gone.

DR   It's gone. Don't forget that. You've got a yellow switch and when you are sure that the headache is not going to come back turn the yellow switch back on again, right?

He is successful. Switching off the yellow light emphasizes his further control and he makes sure that he switches the light back on again so that he does not retain his hypnoanaesthesia.

PT   Yep.

DR   Now I am relying upon you, Larry to take care of those headaches, will you?

PT   Yes.

DR   Is that a promise?

PT   Promise.

DR   You can have a few headaches
if you really need them.

PT   Okay.

DR   Right... No more than a few, a
very few, because I'd like to hear
that twelve year old Larry doesn't
have any headaches at all. That
would be great, wouldn't it?

PT   Yes.

DR   It is up to you, Larry to prac-   This suggestion had an interesting
tice everything that you learned   posthypnotic effect.
today.

PT   Yes.

At this point some general ego strengthening suggestions were given
prior to the termination of this first session. Since he was a good
subject some suggestions that he would be able to use his abilities to
concentrate upon his school work were also given.

For one reason or another Larry did not return for a follow up visit
until some six weeks had elapsed. He reported that he experienced a
migraine attack the day after therapy but that with some effort he
managed to control it by the use of the yellow switch. In fact, he had
attacks of migraine for the next four days – perhaps due to the
suggestion made in therapy to practice everything learned – but in
each case he was able to abort them by the simple expedient of
switching off the yellow light, and within minutes was totally free of
discomfort.

Larry then remained free of all symptoms for about one month
when he had an atypical headache occurring in the occipital region of
the head just above the nape of the neck. He was perplexed by this
since he had never previously experienced a headache in this site. He
discussed this with his mother who encouraged him to try to re-

member everything that he had been taught in therapy. He went to his room, but a few minutes later, his mother was surprised to find him watching television, apparently free of discomfort. He told her that while lying down, he recalled how to count down from ten and when he had reached zero, his headache had gone.

At a subsequent session, hypnosis was readily induced by means of the cue established at the first meeting. Larry was instructed to review his progress and he indicated that there were no unconscious reasons remaining that would cause a return of his headaches. In any case, he now had total control over them. He accepted ego strengthening and assertiveness training suggestions very well and there was clearly no need for further therapy. He was instructed to return if his symptoms ever recurred and/or appeared to be out of his control.

At the time of writing one year later Larry, now twelve, has had no further significant migraine.

Children are as varied as adults in their response to therapy, but as a general rule, they enter hypnosis more quickly and deeply, tend to require fewer sessions and are usually less complex as far as the origin of their symptoms is concerned. One must always be prepared to accept the need for the child patient to keep his symptoms for reasons that are known only unconsciously and may not be divulged to the therapist. With children, the likelihood that significant changes will occur making it possible to relinquish symptoms eventually, is always great. Thus, symptoms retained at the end of therapy stand a good chance of disappearing in due course.

Hypnotisability and Therapy, Optimum Dissociation and ACE

PART TWO   Chapter 18

Increased hypnotisability is clearly synonymous with increased response to suggestion and there is little doubt that the highly hypnotisable subject will exhibit those hypnotic phenomena of therapeutic benefit. Certainly the reduction of pain using hypnoanaesthesia has been demonstrated by Hilgard and Hilgard (1975) to be more successful in persons of high hypnotic ability.

Although there have been few studies to support the relationship between hypnotisability and favourable therapeutic outcome, several authors stress the importance of hypnotic depth in the successful therapy of various psychosomatic disorders. Collison (1975) in an excellent study of the response of asthmatic patients to hypnotherapy, found that 19 (76%) of the 26 who were pronounced cured by hypnotherapy were deep hypnotic subjects and only 7 (12.5%) of the 56 who showed no improvement were deep hypnotic subjects. None of those who were cured was unhypnotisable whereas more than 50% of those showing no improvement gave no response whatsoever to hypnotic suggestion. Asher (1956) demonstrated a similar relationship between hypnotisability and the response of warts to suggestion. Of the 15 that were completely cured, 11 (73%) were deep hypnotic subjects, but of those who showed no improvement to hypnotic suggestion only 2 (14%) of the total of 14 were deep hypnotic subjects. The closely parallel results of these two studies is too obvious to be overlooked, and yet many clinicians still believe, as did Gill and Brenman (1959) that there is no correlation between the depth of hypnosis obtainable and the patients' therapeutic result.

Black (1963), in his study of the inhibition of a hypersensitivity response to suggestion, also supported the premise of the greater clinical response of the more highly susceptible subject. In 8 subjects who showed an inhibitory response to suggestion, 6 (75%) were deep trance subjects whereas of the remaining unresponsive 4, only 1 (25%) was a deep trance subject. Butler (1955) likewise indicated in his study that, of the 12 cases of terminal cancer treated with hypnosis, only the 5 somnambulistic patients were thought to have unequivocally benefitted from therapy.

This author previously shared the view with many of his colleagues in clinical therapy, that so long as there was some response to hypnosis the degree of hypnosis was immaterial in therapy. It was not until he received an independent appraisal of his work, (summarised in the appendix to this book), which clearly demonstrated a direct relationship between the outcome of therapy and the capacity for hypnosis, that he was forced to change this view. Of a total of 359 patients evaluated by the therapist, only 5 (15%) of the 32 complete failures were among the highly hypnotisable (ACE grade 3, 4, 5,); whereas 40 (40%) of the 99 complete successes were rated as good subjects.

If greater hypnotisability is indeed associated with greater clinical responsiveness to therapeutic suggestions, then it behooves the clinician to endeavour to obtain the maximum hypnotisability from each of his patients to assure the maximum benefit from hypnosis. Yet there are many experimenters in hypnosis who assert as do Äs, Hilgard and Weitzenhoffer (1963), that hypnotisability is a relatively stable trait. Hilgard and Hilgard (1979) challenged the widespread belief that unresponsive individuals might be trained to become hypnotically responsive because it rests upon no documented scientific evidence; such an erroneous impression, they claimed, has been gained from the occasional elimination of an initial resistance to hypnosis. Of course it may be true that resistance to hypnosis is the real reason for reduced hypnotisability, and that in the *experimental* setting this resistance tends to remain constant. In the *clinical* setting, on the other hand, the motivation to benefit from therapy becomes an important factor in the reduction of this resistance. Schafer and Hernandez (1978) have suggested that it is the situational elements in therapy that are more important than susceptibility and which render patients more highly motivated to accept therapeutic suggestions. Recently, there has been some experimental evidence to indicate that hypnotisability can be modified and Diamond (1977) has demonstrated how this occurs when hypnotisability is treated as a skill that can be learned. De Voge and Sachs (1973) maintained that significant and consistent increases in hypnotic susceptibility can be induced by an approach which emphasises imitative behaviour.

In summary then, it is likely that motivation will increase hypnotic responsiveness, particularly when initial resistance has been over-come. This responsiveness may be significantly greater than that indi-cated by initial hypnotic susceptibility tests, and is presumably respon-sible for the beneficial outcome to hypnotherapy.

What, then, can be done to ensure that the maximum hypnotic responsiveness of which the patient may be capable is available for use in therapy? If hypnosis is indeed the process of communication with the unconscious mind, it follows that any procedure that improves this communication will increase hypnosis. We have already noted some support for the hypothesis that hypnosis involves greater activation of the right hemisphere for most subjects. The left hemisphere is con-cerned with language, logic, numbers and other sequential or time-ordered functions, whereas the right hemisphere has a major role in visuospatial and nonverbal auditory perception (Kimura, 1973) and is involved in emotional expression (Schwartz et al, 1975). Bakan (1969) and Gur and Gur (1974) have demonstrated a significant negative correlation between hypnotic susceptibility and eye movements to the right in-right-handed males which supports the belief that hypnosis is a right hemisphere function for those males who are strongly right-handed. This evidence has received further support from Graham (1977) who noted greater perceived autokinetic movement to the left in hypnosis than in the waking condition. Again this effect was more apparent in males.

These results suggest that hypnosis involves nondominant hemis-phere functioning and that the induction of hypnosis increases non-dominant brain activity or at any rate decreases dominant brain activity. But whatever modifications of brain activity are initiated by the process of hypnosis, these changes are not measurable by any presently available measuring devices (Evans 1979). Nevertheless the concept of a conscious mind more in communication with the individual's outer world and an unconscious mind in contact with his inner world appear to gain strength from these observations. It would seem that therapy is more effective when direct .communication is made with the unconscious mind (as in hypnosis) and that this greater contact is facilitated by diminished activity of the dominant conscious hemisphere. To this end, the greater the dissociation that can be accomplished between the conscious and unconscious minds, the greater the response to suggestion whether of the kind indicated in susceptibility tests or of the kind associated with therapeutic gains.

It would seem logical to suppose that any process which increases nondominant hemisphere (unconscious, right brain) activity and diminishes dominant hemisphere (conscious, left brain) activity would increase hypnotisability and this supposition is confirmed in practice. In this context, it has been repeatedly observed, as by Spiegel and Spiegel (1978), that the highly hypnotisable are trusting, uncritical and imaginative all of these being right hemisphere attributes. Conversely, the poorly hypnotisable are highly logical, critical and generally unemotional individuals, all of which are left hemisphere characteristics.

A greater understanding of the principles underlying effective hypnotic induction procedures can be gained if the hypnotist is aware that he is using suggestion to increase unconscious attention while at the same time decreasing conscious involvement. This is why many such procedures involve manoeuvres which ensure that decreased attention is paid to the external environment.

Non verbal induction is particularly effective in inducing hypnosis, because it completely bypasses the language codings of the left hemisphere and communicates directly with the spatial and patterning associations of the right hemisphere, thereby increasing unconscious involvement in communication with the hypnotist. The verbal techniques direct the individual to reduce his left brain activity and increase the right brain functioning; the promotion of relaxation is effective in attaining this end since the left brain is very much concerned with voluntary muscular activity.

Presumably, it is in this manner that the conscious/unconscious (left/right brain) dissociation characteristic of hypnosis is induced. The Amnesia Capacity Estimation Method (ACE) attempts to measure this dissociation when limited pressure is applied to obtain it. The author has given considerable thought to the lessons learned from the many years of using ACE and believes that there are some simple measures that can be applied in the induction of hypnosis which can ensure that maximum dissociation has been obtained.

In the first stage of the induction of hypnosis as measured by ACE some evidence of unconscious response is all that is needed. In most cases evidence of a general muscular relaxation or a surrender of control of specific muscles will suffice. Already there is evidence of an inhibition of conscious activity associated with the left hemisphere since muscular control is clearly dominant in origin. In the second stage, conscious awareness of a series is inhibited and presumably indicates that inhibition has spread to another function of the left brain with greater conscious dissociation. In the third stage the selective inhibition of a member of the series suggests that in some way the right brain has taken control of the series and will not permit left brain access to them all, thus demonstrating an even greater level of dissociation. In the fourth stage the unimpeded response to a cue instruction indicates that complex instruction was now in the province of the right brain, and the dissociation of the conscious mind can be regarded as great. In the fifth stage, where all unconscious instructions can be kept from the conscious mind, dissociation is complete. Thus it is that the gradual and increasing conscious/unconscious dissociation is monitored and measured by ACE.

It has been frequently noted, in the administration of ACE that early profound relaxation was often associated with the later attainment of the higher grades of four and five. Also it has been noted that some subjects who are initially unable to demonstrate any selective amnesia are later able to do so with surprising ease, when apparently more relaxed. Although relaxation cannot be regarded as synonymous with hypnosis, it becomes increasingly evident that relaxation facilitates hypnotic communication and the responses of hypnotic phenomena. The work of Leva (1974), who demonstrated that training in deep muscle relaxation will increase hypnotisability, supports the notion that inhibition of muscular activity could be an important factor in the production of deep hypnosis.

Relaxation has in fact been the central focus of hypnotic induction procedures since the time of de Puysegur; even Bernheim who rejected the idea of hypnosis being a state of *sleep*, continued to use the suggestion of sleep as the focus of his induction procedures. There has been a tendency to avoid the word *sleep* in modern induction procedures and instead to stress the idea of *relaxation*. This may be because the word sleep has lost some of the connotations that it once had and still has, since the advent of modern anaesthesia and the practice of putting animals to *sleep*, and has gained new connotations that the hypnotist prefers to avoid. Although the stage hypnotist still uses this word in his exhibitions one assumes that in this context when the word is used the other connotations are unlikely to be associated as they might be in the clinical setting. Elman (1964) in his teachings on the production of deep hypnosis used two manoeuvres which appeared to be very successful. The first of these was the suggestion of deep relaxation associated with the imagery of descending three floors and the second was the posthypnotic suggestion of sleep which he maintained produced the deepest levels of hypnosis provided the slow respiration of sleep is obtained.

Edmonston (1979) supported Pavlov's view (1927) that the induction of hypnosis is accompanied by progressive cortical inhibition with reduction of voluntary motor activity. To state that hypnosis involves the irradiation of cortical inhibition is, in the words of Edmonston, probably an oversimplification. It is likely that other areas are inhibited in hypnosis, some of which are probably subcortical; it is also probable that this inhibition is not confined to one hemisphere. However, for practical purposes, the induction of deep hypnosis can be considered to involve the inhibition of those functions normally associated with conscious activity.

After considering these valuable studies, the author, in his search for means of achieving maximum dissociation, devised the following technique which seems to produce a larger proportion of the higher grades of hypnotic susceptibility when tested with ACE.

I would like you to make yourself very comfortable. Are you comfortable? Good. Now I would like you to take a nice long deep breath. . . and as you let it out, close your eyes. Good. Now I want you to relax those eye muscles until they are so relaxed that they just do not want to work, and when you have relaxed them to the point where you are sure that they do not want to work, when you are sure that they will not work, then test them. Test them to see that they just will not work. Test them hard.

Of course, it goes without saying that general comfort must be established if any degree of relaxation is to be achieved.

The eye muscles appear to be the easiest to relax and to demonstrate a dissociation of voluntary control. A permissive attitude is maintained throughout and voluntary control of the eye muscles is relinquished.

Now let that nice, relaxed feeling that you've got spread all the way down to your toes. You are so relaxed that not a single muscle really wants to move. So relaxed that when I lift this hand up and drop it, it will be so heavy, so limp, so loose, so relaxed that it will just drop back with a plop as if it were as heavy as lead. Just let it drop with that plop. .

Once established, the relaxed dissociation can readily be spread to involve all voluntary musculature and already there is much inhibition of consciousness readily demonstrated if the hand drops heavily. In this case the therapist can proceed directly to the *deepening by levels* phase of the technique.

Now you have a beautiful relaxation there. It's really lovely. Now I would like you to be relaxed even more than that; so in a moment I am going to have you open your eyes and close them again and when I do so that relaxation will be twice as great as it is right now... All right now, open your eyes please. That's good. Now close your eyes. Now feel that relaxation twice as great, all the way through. That's right. And you can relax even more than that. In a moment, when we do that again, that relaxation will be ten times as great — ten times as great. All right. Open your eyes. Good. Now close your eyes... Feel that relaxation ten times as great. That's good. Now, when I lift your hand up, it will be even more relaxed. It will drop with a heavy plop... That's fine. You've relaxed beautifully. But I know that you can relax even more deeply that that. You know that when you go to sleep at night your body falls asleep before your mind falls asleep. I would like you to keep your mind wide awake to listen to me but let your body relax as deeply as when you are in bed asleep at night. Now in order to get down to that beautiful relaxed level there are three levels that you can go through to reach that nice deep level of relaxation where your body is sound asleep. And to get to that level I would like you to imagine yourself going down through those three levels, level A, level B, and level C. To get down to level A, I

In this verbalisation it is assumed that the relaxation so far obtained is less than optimal and needs to be increased. This method of repeated induction (as advocated by Elman 1964) usually proves to be very effective in producing even greater relaxation.

Ten times as great can be interpreted in any manner that the individual wishes but is clearly requesting a much greater level of relaxation than has so far been achieved.

Even greater relaxation is to be achieved and the goal is now defined. The total relaxation that occurs during sleep is the aim of the technique and it is now made clear to the patient that it is not ordinary sleep that is being requested, since the mind must remain awake. In this manner the total dissociation of deep hypnosis is to be established with that part of the mind responsible for voluntary activity becoming inactive as in sleep yet leaving the remainer of the mind (?unconscious mind) alert and in communication with the therapist.

would like you to imagine yourself taking an elevator or an escalator or, if you prefer, a staircase all the way down to that first level. At level A you will be twice as relaxed as you are right now. So relaxed. You will know that you are at level A because not a single muscle in your body will want to move. Your arms won't want to move, your legs won't want to move, your head will not want to move. Not a single muscle in your body will want to move. You will just want to stay exactly where you are. When you are at level A, not wanting to move a muscle, you can let me know that you are there just by saying A or by letting this finger lift. Okay. Start down now, all the way down to level A. Twice as relaxed. . . When you are at level A you will know that you are there because your whole body will be totally and completely relaxed, so relaxed that not a single muscle wants to move. The legs do not want to move, the arms do not want to move, the head does not want to move. *Pt. A.* Good.

That's a lovely relaxation, but you know that you can relax even more deeply that that, and I would like you to go down to the next level, level B. And you can take your elevator or escalator or the stairs all the way down to the next level, level B. When I tell you to you can start all the way down. And when you are there you will know that you are there at level B because you will

A double bind in which the choice given is limited to the means of descending to deeper levels of hypnosis. In this popular deepening technique some modifications have been incorporated to make it more meaningful to the patient. The first level is equated with total relinquishing of the desire to move which is a common subjective experience in hypnosis.

He is counselled to associate this increasing desire not to move, with its implication of greater conscious inhibition, with an idea of descent to greater levels of relaxation. He retains control (?unconscious) of this descent and it is he that informs the therapist when he has reached the appropriate level.

At this stage good relaxation is usually evident and the patient is once again given the choice as to how he will make further descent.

The catalepsy of the deeper levels

notice that not a single muscle in your body can move. Your arms will not be able to move. Your legs will not be able to move. Your head will not be able to move. Not a single part of your body will be able to move and you will find it so relaxed. Twice as relaxed as you are now. If for any reason you do not wish to stay at that level you can easily come back up by elevator, escalator or stairs any time you wish. Now when you get to level B you will be so relaxed that you will not be able to speak so I am going to ask this finger here *touching a convenient finger* to float up to let me know when you are all the way down at level B and so relaxed that not a single muscle can work. Start down now. All the way. All the way down to level B. When you are there that finger will float to let me know. *Finger lifts*. Good. So comfortable. So pleasant. Not a single muscle can move.

But you know, you can relax even more deeply that that. Keeping your mind awake you can let your whole body go sound asleep, just as sound asleep as when you are in bed at night. So, in a moment, I am going to ask you to go down to the deepest level where every muscle in your body will be sound asleep. And when you are at that level you will know you are there because your breathing will be deep and slow and regular just as deep and slow and regular as when your body is sound asleep when you go to bed at night.

of relaxation can be profound and perhaps threatening to the patient; he is reassured that the decision to remain in this state will always be his and that he can return to lighter levels of relaxation should he begin to feel uncomfortable. This reassurance enables him to become even more cooperative. Even the power of speech can be relinquished and is further evidence that all voluntary motor activity has ceased. Involuntary (unconscious) ideomotor activity is now utilised to monitor progress and can later be incorporated in the establishment of ideomotor signalling for analytical purposes.

There is something else that characterises complete conscious/unconscious dissociation and this is probably contained in the concept of sleep. The suggestion that the body but not the mind will be asleep invokes this concept and the associated dissociation. The evidence of deep, slow and regular respiration is useful since it further emphasises absence of voluntary control.

But keep your mind awake to listen to me, to hear me and to pay attention to me. This finger can lift again to let me know when you are there. Okay, start down now. All the way down to level C. Letting your body go deeply soundly asleep. . . *Finger lifts.* Good. Stay deeply asleep. Now you can listen to me with the very deepest part of your mind and allow your conscious mind to sleep and when you are listening to me with that very deep part of your mind only that finger will lift to let me know. . . *Finger lifts.* Good. Now any time I use the words, *close your eyes* those are the words I shall use. Any time you hear me use those words: *close your eyes,* that is the signal for you to close your eyes and immediately go deeply, soundly asleep as you are right now. Just as deeply asleep as when you are in bed at night. Any time I ask you to close your eyes, you will immediately relax as deeply as you are right now and listen to me as carefully as you are doing right now with the deepest part of your mind only. And when I have you open your eyes, you can forget that I have given you that suggestion. In fact you can forget that we have had this conversation but you will respond to it and any time I ask you to *close your eyes* you will immediately close your eyes and go deeply, soundly asleep as you are right now.

All right, open your eyes please. That's good. How do you feel?. . .

Once again the unconsciously initiated ideomotor signal is employed to indicate when the appropriate level has been reached.

An even greater degree of conscious/unconscious dissociation is requested, and the ideomotor signal indicates when conscious attention has ceased. This is a good time to establish a simple, readily acceptable cue for the reinduction of hypnosis. The response to this cue can give the therapist an indication of the degree of dissociation, a rapid response suggesting marked dissociation.

This suggestion for posthypnotic amnesia discourages conscious interference with the reinduction response.

Alternatively, the indirect suggestion for amnesia can be made that *it will seem as if you have only closed your eyes for a moment.*

Rapid awakening appears to facilitate later dissociation.

Are your comfortable?. . . All right. Close your eyes. . . when you are deeply soundly asleep, listening to me with your deep inner mind only, this finger will lift to let me know. . . *Lifts.* Good. Continue to sleep very deeply. I would like you now to have a pleasant dream seeing yourself in a place where you like to be, doing something that you like to do and I shall be talking to you again in a few moments.

A smile or an expression of surprise indicates that the dissociation has been considerable.

The imagery established here adds pleasant and attractive features to the hypnotic experience which encourgages future cooperation.

At this point the patient is ready for therapy but testing to ascertain the degree of conscious/unconscious dissociation can also be done. Good responses during the induction period indicate that a deep level of hypnosis has been reached and this can be confirmed quite readily. The simplest means of accomplishing this is by applying the test for grade four, the cue response test of ACE in which a cue for the reentry into hypnosis, established while in hypnosis, is given when the subject is clearly no longer in hypnosis (see chapter four). An immediate response to the administration of a cue indicates that a very deep level of hypnosis has been attained (grade four). Some patients may have reached the deeper level of grade five as evidenced by total amnesia for all of the events of hypnosis if this has been requested by the therapist. An example of a confirmatory test for this deeper level of hypnosis is to suggest (in hypnosis) that an arm is totally without sensation; when the patient indicates that this is so a test is made by pinching that limb. If the response is satisfactory, the further suggestion is made that on awakening this part will remain asleep and without feeling – *as if it isn't there.* When alerted from hypnosis this posthypnotic anaesthesia is usually profound and can be readily transferred to other parts of the body by waking suggestion. Indeed, it can sometimes be so profound that the patient remains unaware of its existence.

For those patients who do not give a good cue response (grade four) it can usually be attributed to their inability to relax as requested down to the deepest levels (level C). However, in time, a high proportion of these patients will, if they are motivated, improve their ability to relax. If desired, the level of hypnotisability can be further ascertained by applying the test for series amnesia (grade two) and the test for selective amnesia (grade three).

The above described technique is very effective in producing marked conscious/unconscious dissociation, characteristic of deep hypnosis, in a high proportion of cases. When considering the reasons for its effectiveness, it seems to this author that the frequent use of the word *sleep* (popularized by the older hypnotists) is of great importance. The concept of the body going to sleep with the mind remaining awake, while a rather novel one, appears to be almost universally acceptable; this *sleep* does not hold the fear of unconsciousness normally associated with going to sleep and as such, is important in producing good conscious/unconscious dissociation.

It is important to achieve early dissociation of the eye muscles. If the eyes should open when tested, the therapist must remind the patient not to test them until he (the patient) is certain that they will not open; for if he is truly certain that they will not open, then they will certainly remain closed on testing. The repeated induction with eyes opening and closing is necessary only if general physical relaxation is not obtained following the instruction to *spread the relaxation all the way down to the toes*. General physical relaxation – demonstrated by the hand dropping heavily and limply into the lap – implies that much conscious/unconscious dissociation has already taken place.

In this deepening procedure, each of the three levels is given a specific goal to which the patient's efforts are directed. The objective of level A is the inhibition of voluntary motor activity to the point where all desire to move has been relinquished. The objective of level B is the inhibition of conscious control of motor activity to the point where voluntary movement can no longer be initiated. This relative powerlessness is rarely threatening if the patient understands his role in achieving this objective. At level B, there is marked conscious/unconscious dissociation. Level C, with its strong association with sleep, is somewhat difficult to define even though at some unconscious level it is perfectly understood. Presumably, at this level, all conscious communication with the body has been suspended as indicated by the involuntary nature of the breathing. It is probable that a deeper level of hypnosis is secured by asking for communication with *the deeper part of the mind only*; this requests total conscious/unconscious dissociation in which the conscious mind is no longer in communication with the environment (including the therapist). Sometimes quite complex movements are seen even after level B has been reached and signalled. Since these are unconsciously motivated, they can be ignored because only voluntary immobility is being requested.

At no time during the procedure is any direct testing of hypnotic depth undertaken because it might produce a destructive performance anxiety (which perhaps accounts for the stability of hypnotisability tests). The task of proceeding to greater depths is presented as dependent only upon the discovery of a suitable vehicle for accomplishing descent; the elevator, escalator and stairs usually provide sufficient choices. Those patients who will not allow themselves to descend to those levels of relaxation have unconscious fears which must be overcome. They must be reassured that at some level of consciousness (unconsciousness?) they retain adequate control, as indicated by the ideomotor signals. Success in obtaining satisfactory depth is entirely due to the totally permissive nature of the deepening procedure, throughout which the patient moves at his own rate. In practice, these deep levels of hypnosis may initially take up to ten minutes to attain, but this is time well rewarded by a decrease in the time necessary for therapy, since unconscious responses are far less likely to be delayed by conscious interference.

It is probable that every highly motivated person can be led into the marked conscious/unconscious dissociation of deep hypnosis using this or some similar technique. If so, it would appear that all hypnotisability scales are dependent upon induction techniques which define and, thereby perhaps, limit hypnotic performance. The success of this technique depends upon the presentation of clearly stated and easily attainable goals.

Although it has been emphasised that excellent hypnotherapy can be conducted in lighter levels of hypnosis — where little or no evidence of conscious/unconscious dissociation is present — it is to be hoped that the more frequent use of these deeper levels of hypnosis will result in a greater proportion of successful outcomes from analytical hypnotherapy.

Analytical Hypnotherapy and Healing

A wealth of evidence is accumulating to support the already widely held belief that the mind can influence diseases of the body both adversely and favourably. Nowhere has this been more clearly documented than in the treatment by suggestion of cutaneous warts. Many apparently effective old wives' remedies have been derived from the characteristic of warts to disappear following the employment of different incantations or manoeuvres. Many investigators have demonstrated control of healing warts by suggestion given in hypnosis. Sinclair-Gieben and Chalmers (1959) demonstrated conclusively the role of suggestion when they were able to restrict the healing of warts to one side of the body only. Asher (1959) noted that good healing was related to suggestibility in the hypnotic treatment; this would tend to confirm the unconscious nature of the resource of healing. The mechanism by which the unconscious mind effects healing is seen by Sulzberger & Wolf (1934) and later by Ullman (1959) to be via the autonomic nervous system. Barber (1978) in summarizing experimental studies concluded that suggestion can have a direct effect upon the skin through the unconscious control of cutaneous blood flow. Clawson and Swade (1975) felt that this autonomic control is used in the unconscious healing of warts to restrict the blood flow to them; they further suggested that other tumours might perhaps be similarly controlled. In his discussion of the treatment of venereal warts by suggestion in hypnosis, Ewin (1974) noted that the failure to heal might be due to emotional factors. He cited a case in which the resolution of such factors led to the acceptance of the direct suggestion for healing.

Since the time of Mesmer, this unconscious resource of healing has been repeatedly demonstrated to be accessible to suggestion in hypnosis; every hypnotherapist will have experienced many examples of the effectiveness of direct suggestion in hypnosis in producing healing effects. Mason (1952) described a dramatic example of the healing of congenital ichthyosiform erythroderma of Brocq (fish skin disease); Jabush (1969) described a case of chronic recurring multiple boils treated successfully with hypnotherapy. Although skin diseases in particular provide dramatic and irrefutable pictorial evidence of response to suggestion, all kinds of illnesses have at times been shown to respond well to hypnotherapy. Franklin (1964) reported his experience with chronically ill patients in which symptom removal was achieved through hypnotherapy. As early as 1893, Hudson expressed his belief that chronically ill patients become more suggestible; further to this, Cheek (1969) declared that critically ill or unconscious patients can be regarded as though in hypnosis and can readily accept suggestions. Collison (1975) noted that poorly hypnotisable asthmatic subjects do not respond symptomatically to suggestion, whereas a high proportion of those who are hypnotisable make a good to excellent response to suggestions given in hypnosis.

This and other evidence supports the belief that in certain circumstances the mind can promote healing of the body; indeed the whole of the philosophy of psychosomatic medicine is predicated on the tenet that the mind can also cause illness of the body. Cannon (1957) has documented the reality of so called *voodoo death*, and reported instances where expectancy of death brought it about among primitive peoples whose cultures are conducive to strong beliefs in the power of the curse. Hutschnecker (1951) elaborated this point when he declared that unconsciously, many people lose their will to live and consequently kill themselves through illness. They will recover only when their will to live is restored.

In a study of several disease states Thomas and Duszynski (1974) found that those patients suffering with cancer had a history of greater emotional distance from their parents and family than did those patients with other diseases. LeShan (1977) likewise found that cancer patients often share certain negative emotional characteristics. For example, he discovered that prior to the onset of cancer, there was a loss of a sense of purpose in life. These patients had depended upon a single relationship with a person or a group which had catastrophically been terminated. No other relationship had been established to take its place, and nothing else gave life a purpose. Another frequent finding was an inability on the part of the individual to express anger or resentment; thus they experienced strong hostile feelings which could not be verbalized.

Simonton et al (1978) have pursued this examination of the role of emotion in malignant disease and have come to regard the development of overt cancer as due to a breakdown of the body's immune system. The defective cells which initiate the development of a malignant tumour are presumed to be normally destroyed by the active surveillance of the immune system probably based upon the lymphocytes of the blood. Emotional stress is believed to be a potent factor in modifying the activity of the immune system and experimental work (Solomon, Amkraut, and Kosper, 1974) in animals has shown that damage to the hypothalamus, a part of the brain concerned with emotional responses, interferes with the animal's ability to make an appropriate antibody response. Selye (1956) has shown how chronic stress suppresses the immune system and Bathrop (1977) found further support for this discovery in the depression of lymphocyte function in those who had recently been bereaved.

Simonton's work in the therapy of malignant disease utilising visual imagery, in which the patient is encouraged to imagine his cancer being actively destroyed, has produced results which confirm the belief that suggestion can stimulate the unconscious mind to utilise its resources for healing. Significantly, he has found that a change in attitude of mind is important in achieving improvement. As a result, an important part of therapy has been to discover the patient's negative thoughts about himself or his disease and to work toward removing them and replacing them with positive attitudes. In Simonton's approach the promotion of self acceptance is as important as the technique of visual imagery and much time is spent encouraging this acceptance by dealing with feelings of guilt and the suppression of normal emotions.

Of increasing interest to the analytical hypnotherapist is the accumulating evidence which suggests that a favourable outcome in the treatment of such diseases is related to the patient's positive outlook. Stavraky et al (1968) in a study on a group of cancer patients found some evidence of psychological abnormality in all. Those who showed the best prognosis were well integrated but with considerable underlying aggressiveness. This is the antithesis of the *hopelessness* described by Engel (1965) and Shmale and Iker (1966) as being a strong factor in the etiology of cancer. Greer et al (1979) arrived at similar conclusions when they found that recurrence free survival in breast cancer patients was significantly greater in those who reacted with a fighting spirit than in those who responded with feelings of helplessness and hopelessness. These observations are clearly of great importance to the analytical hypnotherapist called upon to aid in the treatment of intractable disease. Often he will find that direct suggestion proves to be of only temporary benefit in the relief from symptoms. In such cases it may well be that the unconscious motivation for recovery is poor or absent resulting in reduced mobilisation of available unconscious resources following suggestion. In fact, there may persist an unconscious wish for self destruction inevitably increasing the likelihood of continued or increasing disability.

When faced with such a problem the analytical hypnotherapist should proceed to use the analytical techniques already described in order to uncover and modify any of the persistent, negative, self rejecting attitudes which so frequently exist. These attitudes will certainly remain below the level of conscious awareness; consciously the patient will be aware only of his increasing discomfort and disability which cause him much distress. This conscious distress may serve only to satisfy unconscious self-punitive needs.

Should the analytical hypnotherapist succeed in isolating and identifying these negative feelings, there is an excellent possibility that he will, with the intervention of current Adult understanding, resolve the underlying Parent/Child conflict upon which this self rejection is always founded. If so, suggestions for comfort and healing may be accepted by an unconscious mind ready to mobilise all of the unconscious healing resources available to it. This is the manner in which analytical hypnotherapy can most benefit organic disease. Certainly the other unconscous resources of relaxation, analgesia and the control of certain body functions are likely to be of immense benefit in providing comfort during therapy. However, we still need to learn more about the resource of healing that can be discovered and utilised by hypnotherapy. Until then we must assume that the evocation of this resource requires no more than strong encouragement once all negative factors preventing its normal use have been removed.

During the course of the author's work in analytical hypnotherapy, there have been many examples of the resolution of unconscious conflicts followed by amelioration of organic disease. This tends to support the assumption that the conflict has impeded the efforts of the individual's normal healing abilities. One such case is that of a woman of thirty-two who initially consulted the author for treatment of severe nailbiting. Although nailbiting will frequently respond to direct suggestions of an aversive kind given in hypnosis, years of clinical experience indicate that it is likely to be a symptom of strong self rejection. Apart from some occasional pains in the shoulder when tired (which she attributed to the tensions resulting from her occupation as a teacher), the patient had no other overt signs of emotional problems. In hypnosis, which was no more than ACE grade one at the first meeting, there were strong indications of a reluctance to allow any uncovering of the unconscious reasons for nailbiting; so therapy was therefore limited to suggestions that the tensions responsible for the nailbtiting could be resolved, that there would be no further need to bite her nails, and that any temptation to do so would be resisted. Ego strengthening suggestions were given but, there was little response to indicate the degree of their acceptance.

At the second meeting a month later, the nailbiting had almost ceased and was confined to one thumb. Although there was still some resistance to hypnosis, responses were improved. It was determined that there was a source of guilt creating unconscious tension. Her mother had had a succession of stillborn male children and had been very distraught by this. The patient had felt very guilty that she had not been a boy to satisfy her mother's needs. Attempts to persuade the patient to deal with this guilt were only partially successful, but she indicated that the nailbiting would eventually cease.

The patient was not seen again for nearly two years, at which time she returned with a great need to talk about a catastrophe that had occurred in her life. After several years of a career and marriage, she gave birth to a baby boy. During the lactation period, she developed a cancer of the breast which had already metastasised to other parts of the body prior to its diagnosis. She indicated in hypnosis that there was an experience causing strong feelings of sexual guilt which could have been a factor in her illness. At following meetings, we repeatedly returned to this area of guilt and only with much difficulty was she able to reduce it significantly. At these meetings, therapy was directed to instructing her in self hypnosis and in the use of imagery to mobilise her healing resources so that they might aid the chemotherapy she was receiving; she began to believe that she would recover from her disease. She was given a tape recording of suggestions for maintaining her ego strength and for enhancing her imagery. These she used on an almost daily basis. She managed to remain at work almost continuously, even though there were times when the combined stresses of the baby, the job and the treatments for the illness were extremely great. Three years after the disease was first diagnosed – and a guarded prognosis of six months had been given – her health deteriorated rapidly. The terminal phase lasted no more than two weeks.

It is tempting to speculate that the illness was directly due to the sexual guilt precipitated by the birth of her boy and that the relatively good health that she was able to enjoy was due not only to the imagery that she had employed, but also to the reduction of guilt that she had felt.

Another example of the amelioration of organic disease is that of a forty-two year old male who presented for help to quit smoking. He found that smoking appeared to retard his response to therapy for Hodgkin's disease of the chest, which had been diagnosed some six months previously. His shortness of breath was primarily due to a collection of fluid in the pleural cavity which was not responding to therapy. He was aware that he smoked to relieve tension which he believed was related to the anxieties and bitterness of his divorce proceedings, which were going on at that time. He was able to identify in hypnosis an experience which occurred some three years previously, which was associated with strong unconscious feelings of sexual guilt. He was encouraged to deal with this guilt and also with another experience apparently associated with much anger and hurt. He indicated that this experience was directly associated with the onset of his disease and aggravated his need to smoke. He was given direct suggestions that he could remain calm without smoking and would no longer need cigarettes.

His immediate response to therapy was to stop smoking and he then noted an all-round improvement in his health. At subsequent sessions, suggestions for imaging his defences actively attacking and destroying his disease were given, and he was taught self hypnosis during which he would repeat these suggestions. A review of unconscious tensions showed their eventual complete relinquishment, and this paralleled a great improvement in his response to treatment for Hodgkin's Disease. His breathing improved so that he was able to return to an active programme of calisthenics and eventually resumed his career as a singer and a teacher of singing. He found that hypnotherapy had altered his response to chemotherapy in that it greatly diminished the severity and duration of nausea following treatment. He occasionally returned to smoking for short periods, during which his evident discomfort renewed his determination to quit this habit.

The most striking response was his optimism, which peaked after about a month of therapy and has remained high since. He was certain that he would become cured of his disease and planned, and eventually completed, some song recitals and a teaching tour in Europe. He also began a literary project that he had previously set aside. At the time of writing, some three years after hypnotherapy began, he remains well and believes that he has his disease under his control. There can be no doubt that his mental attitude has been the direct result of hypnotherapy. It cannot be certain, however, that his disease was directly affected by the imagery suggestions or by his change in attitude toward himself. Although it is widely accepted that Hodgkin's disease is now curable by modern techniques of chemo- and radiotherapy, the fact remains that this patient did not make a good response to that therapy until analytical hypnotherapy techniques had been employed.

The Analytical Hypnotherapist
and the Interview

The therapist-patient relationship, with its myriad of multidimensional interpersonal experiences, is an important dynamic in every therapeutic encounter. This relationship is of utmost importance in psychotherapy, for as Kolbe (1968) stated: 'Through this relationship the patient comes to know that he can share his feelings, attitudes and experiences with the therapist and that the latter, with his warmth, understanding, empathy and support, will not depreciate, censure or judge him no matter what he may reveal but will respect his dignity and worth'. Kolbe's observation is never more relevant than when the analytical hypnotherapist first meets the patient.

The belief that the establishment of good rapport facilitates therapy is supported by the work of Hartman (1967) who in his study of the variables affecting hypnotisability found that the experimenter who exhibits a friendly attitude elicits higher levels of suggestibility in his subjects than one who exhibits a neutral or harsh attitude. As Barber and Calverley (1964) noted, even the therapist's tone of voice is important in establishing this rapport. There are many events that will occur even prior to the first interview which can have a marked effect upon the degree of rapport that can be established. Chief among these are the misconceptions about hypnosis mentioned earlier: ideas fostered by stage presentations of hypnosis, the distorted views of friends and family concerning hypnotherapy or psychotherapy, or even the kind of referral that has resulted in the person's presenting for therapy. Such a referral may hold the implicit suggestion that hypnotherapy is a kind of punishment for unwanted behaviour, especially for the child brought unwillingly to the therapist as a last resort.

Cronin, Spanos and Barber (1971) found that the presentation of favourable information about hypnosis was a very important factor in producing maximum hypnotic response; consequently, in the first interview, every effort should be made to discover what misconceptions are held by the patient. Such misconceptions are always sources of fear and produce great natural anxiety which are bound to prove inimical to the establishment of the good rapport essential for effective therapy. For example, the belief that some religious groups hold, (despite their own extensive, if unwitting, use of the modality) that hypnosis is Satanic in origin, will, if held by the patient, mitigate against any satisfactory cooperation. The therapist in such instances might be successful if his techniques closely match those of the religious group (e.g. praying). Strong motivation for cooperation is more likely in a patient who has had previous personal experience of hypnotherapy which has proved beneficial or who has had a friend or relative whose experience of hypnotherapy has been good.

During the preinduction talk in which these misconceptions are dealt with, it is good practice to indicate the wide variety of responses to suggestion that are possible. Barber and Calverley (1969) have found that subjects' reports on whether they experienced hypnosis depend upon their previous conception of what hypnosis is and whether their experiences dovetail with these preconceptions.

Hodge (1976) stated that the skillful hypnotherapist will clarify his expectations of therapy. Such expectations should be clear but minimal and well within the patient's capability (e.g. to be comfortable; to let things happen; to stay awake etc.). Other goal-directed prehypnotic suggestions (Schneck 1975) can be formulated which outline the contract implicitly established between therapist and patient. Field and Kline (1974) noted that a high proportion of those patients who suffer from problems usually associated with analytical psychotherapy (e.g. anxiety and depression) have had psychotherapy prior to analytical hypnotherapy. It is important that these patients be directed towards realistic goals which may differ considerably from those that they had anticipated.

Since most of the problems that bring a patient to the analytical hypnotherapist originate in experiences of rejection, every effort should be made by the therapist and his staff to counteract the long term effects that these experiences will have had by the expression of an accepting and inviting attitude toward the prospective patient. Thus the patient's reception by the therapist's secretary when handling preappointment arrangements is vitally important. A comforting and pleasing manner does much to allay the patient's natural anxiety. There should be a frank discussion of the financial arrangements under which therapy will be conducted, at which time any monetary restrictions can be discussed with tact and understanding. The furnishings of the therapist's office should be conducive to relaxation. Although the presence of pleasant background music in the waiting area is a matter of individual preference, there is some support for the belief that light classical music is conducive to relaxation and general comfort.

The motivations which bring the patient to the therapist are many and varied. Berne (1961) sees the Child motivated patient as coming for a treat whereas the Adult motivated patient comes for treatment. It is hoped that every patient can be persuaded to become Adult motivated. Berne might have added that many are Parent motivated and view therapy as a means of self-discipline during which their recalcitrant Child originated symptoms will be *properly* repressed. Shevrin (1979) believed that while patients consciously wish to cooperate, they unconsciously wish to be cared for and may be angry and disappointed following therapy if these expectations are not met. Erickson (1954) on the other hand has pointed out that there are some patients who seek therapy and yet are openly hostile, antagonistic and resistant and seem unwilling or unable to accept the therapy that they have sought. Sanders (1977) elaborated this view in stating that the resistant patient is one who has lost hope and is imposing that loss upon the therapist. Wolberg (1964) even declared that some resistant patients are only seeking satisfaction of dependency needs and regard hypnotherapy as a kind of magic which will do things for them without any effort required on their part.

It is clear that the analytical hypnotherapist must maintain a philosophy which enables him to handle, with relative equanimity, different problems presented to him. This can be very difficult since he needs to avoid the temptation expressed by Hill (1955), and to which every therapist is subject, to conceal a need to dominate behind the professed motivation of helping other human beings. It is very tempting for the psychotherapist to set himself up as superior to and condescending toward his patients, thus expressing unconscious needs to dominate, control and force patients into preconceived patterns of behaviour. Hill believes that every psychotherapist should learn as much as possible about himself, not only to avoid this particular temptation but also to be able to understand more of what his patients reveal.

Wolberg also warns of this danger and goes further to say that the use of hypnosis may release powerful strivings of a sadistic nature in the therapist which, by destroying the therapist's perception, objectivity, sensitivity and empathy, irreparably damage the proper therapeutic relationship. It would therefore seem that the therapist should be free of any serious emotional problems himself and have already reached the goals of self acceptance and self esteem that he seeks for his patients. He will then be immune from the temptation to indulge in feelings of omnipotence when successful, and conversely be spared emotional devastation when unsuccessful – as he frequently will be.

The analytical hypnotherapist rarely needs to take a detailed history of the patient's illness prior to hypnosis. It is necessary to know only, but in some detail, the changes that the patient wishes to make, the reasons why he wishes to make them and why he has not been able to accomplish this prior to therapy. The most relevant history is likely to be obtained only through the medium of hypnosis. The analytical hypnotherapist is also well advised to follow the advice given by Harris (1967) to resist the temptation to reach an accurate psychiatric diagnosis. He believed, as does this author, that therapy can actually be hindered by a psychiatric diagnostic label. Harris maintained that the patient unconsciously knows where his problems, (due to a Parent-dominated blocked-out Child) really are, and can be emancipated from his past without the dubious assistance of a label. He also held that a preoccupation with the symptom complex is really unnecessary in therapy. Rather the therapist's goal should be the reduction of the inner conflict responsible for the symptoms since it is their persistence which indicates the continuation of the conflict. Throughout therapy the process is facilitated by keeping the patient's Adult in charge.

The attitude of the therapist should always be one of total acceptance of the patient, no matter what the symptoms may be, since any rejection of the patient is very likely to produce resistance to therapy. No prejudice against any symptoms or behaviour should be expressed by the therapist although, conversely, neither should he express approval of symptoms which are clearly distressing. While the therapist should always protect himself from any hostile attacks by the patient he should also avoid allowing himself to be provoked into returning the patient's assaults. It is however entirely appropriate to inform the patient of any defensive feelings aroused in him by the patient's hostile behaviour. If the therapist has been able to reach the goal of complete self acceptance, he is also able to remain independent of the patient's approval and deal with any disapproval without losing sight of the goals of therapy. Sometimes these goals are not achievable during therapy but they may be attained by the patient after therapy has been terminated.

The duration of each session of hypnotherapy is a matter for individual decision but most therapists have discovered that, if some useful uncovering is to be attempted during the first meeting, no less than one hour should be set aside. As therapy progresses subsequent sessions may be scheduled for shorter periods. In practice, it has been found that a second session one week after the first is the most practical since this interval appears to give both patient and therapist enough time to assess the initial response to therapy. There are some exceptions where either a much shorter or a much longer interval is advisable. Usually, after the first few weekly sessions have proved satisfactory, longer intervals between meetings should be scheduled, since the work done in a session of analytical hypnotherapy is often of a very intense nature and these longer intervals give time for changes to occur.

In those cases where the original symptoms have gone and the patient, having become adequately self accepting and self protective, feels good about himself, it will have become evident that further therapy is no longer necessary. Although no further appointments need be scheduled, it is good practice to make it understood that therapy can be reinstituted at any time should the need arise.

On those occasions where no progress whatever is being made in therapy, continuation imposes unnecessary stresses both upon the patient and the therapist. The wise therapist should call a halt to therapy by explaining to the patient that a rest from therapy might be beneficial to them both and that it can always be recommenced should any change occur. The failure of therapy to make progress is usually due to the direct opposition of a strong unconscious ego state that cannot always be clearly defined, but which appears to be determined to sabotage all of the therapist's attempts to deal with the problem. It would seem that such an ego state maintains an overwhelming interest in the persistence of the symptoms that have remained inaccessible to therapy. Other signs of this opposition are the failure to keep an appointment or tardiness. Unless this ego state can be identified and confronted, persistence of symptoms is likely. This is the most common cause of failure in analytical hypnotherapy.

During therapy positive and important personality changes will often be noted. Greater self-confidence, increased self-esteem and self-acceptance, allied with a more positive outlook, are all excellent prognostic signs and may in fact occur before the presenting symptoms diminish or disappear. A high degree of patience and a determination to locate and deal with the origin of symptoms, combined with confidence in the ultimate success of therapy, are indispensible attributes which the therapist must cultivate. So long as the patient is attending of his own free will, it must be assumed that there is a part of the personality that is allied with the therapist in the task of dealing with the problem.

A posture of *helper* rather than *rescuer* should be maintained throughout therapy, which implies that the patient himself has the resources for cure and does not need to seek them from others. Thus the role of the therapist is emphasized as a guide to these resources. This attitude will enable the therapist to avoid the temptation of perceiving himself as a saviour when a series of successes might give him the illusion of possessing some special power. It also enables him to reject the responsibility for therapeutic failure in the face of the patient's determined opposition to change.

Failures of Therapy

Although a highly optimistic note has been maintained throughout this book and successful approaches to therapy have been detailed for illustrative purposes, it cannot be denied that the proportion of failures in this author's practice is significant. Even when only those 359 patients who have been subjected to the therapist's evaluation are considered, only 99 (27%) are claimed as complete successes. Once again, of the 234 who gave their own evaluation a similar percentage – 60 (26%) – claim complete success. In this group, 73 (31%) regarded therapy as having failed completely, while the reamining 101 (43%) claimed partial success. (See Appendix)

While it is hoped that, with greater experience in dealing with the difficult problems that present for therapy, these figures will improve, it would be unrealistic to assume that the proportion of failures will become insignificant in the forseeable future. There are many reasons for these failures of therapy and the understanding of the principles of analytical hypnotherapy has been immeasurably advanced by a close study of these reasons. In cases where these reasons have been identifiable, there has consistently been a clear violation of these important principles.

A small proportion of failures is directly attributable to the fact that there has been no hypnosis, that is to say no unconscious communication has been made and so hypnotherapy has never been invoked. Until more is understood about hypnosis one can only speculate why some people appear to be unable to make this kind of communication. A more important reason for failure lies in a violation of the first principle of analytical hypnotherapy, namely the location and identification of the critical experiences. In some cases the critical experience has been located but not all of its characteristics have been identified; they remain beyond the reach of therapeutic intervention and continue to be responsible for unconscious conflict. In other cases some critical experiences have been adequately dealt with but the one responsible for a peristent unconscious ego state in conflict remains unresolved and continues to be the source of symptoms. If for some reason the other principles of analytical hypnotherapy have not been adhered to, the old Child/Parent conflict remains intact to perpetuate symptomatic behaviour.

The complexity of the human personality is being increasingly revealed. Small wonder is it that not all of the wounds received during the unarmed psychological combat of infancy and childhood can be healed by the crude instruments of analytical hypnotherapy presently available. However it behooves those of us interested in this discipline to refine it further by application of greater understanding and wisdom until analytical hypnotherapy becomes sufficiently sophisticated to enable all who wish for cure to achieve it. It is to this end that this book has been written.

Results of Therapy Alan R. Bull, Ph.D.

APPENDIX

The Practice

In practising analytical hypnotherapy the author, like most therapists, is generally guided in his present actions by what he has been successful with in the past. While this procedure is adequate in most cases, the desirability of a less memory-dependent method of evaluating patient/therapist interactions led the author to undertake a comprehensive statistical analysis of patient records. Before examining the results of this analysis, however, a brief description of the context in which the data have been collected, the hypnotherapy practice itself, is warranted.

The present practice is devoted entirely to clinical hypnotherapy, with particular emphasis on the analytical use of hypnosis to resolve both primary and secondary presenting symptoms. Prior to restricting his interest to hypnotherapy, the author practiced family medicine in the area for a number of years. The practice is located in a small city (population 60,000) which contains a major Canadian university, numerous penal and rehabilitation centres (medical and psychological), and a military base. A number of small communities within a 50-mile radius brings the total population accessing the only local hypnotherapy practice to over 100,000 people.

Patients are accepted on a referral basis only. Although on a few occasions referrals have been accepted from non-medical personnel such as psychologists or social workers, generally they originate from a physician or dentist. While the majority of referrals are made at the request of the patient, an increasing proportion of physician-initiated cases has been noted as the benefits of hypnotherapeutic intervention become more widely recognized in the medical profession. At the same time, increased public sensitivity to drug-based therapies, coupled with a wider awareness of treatment alternatives has resulted in greater acceptance of hypnotic therapies in general. At the local level, this trend has been encouraged by reports from individuals who have experienced first-hand the positive benefits of clinical hypnotherapy.

The Survey

Any ongoing therapy programme requires the constant monitoring of patient/therapist interactions on both an individual and a collective basis. This task has been considerably facilitated in the present practice by the introduction of computer-based record-keeping techniques. The advantages of such a system are immediate. The author has found that the systematic exploration of demographic, personal and therapy-related details has enhanced his ability to focus rapidly and effectively on his patients' needs.

Initiated in 1978 on hypnotherapy records collected since 1975, the following survey related information concerning factors such as age, gender, marital status or level of education to information based on presenting symptoms (primary, secondary or tertiary), technique of hypnotic induction or clinically estimated indices of hypnosis. Other variables include the patient's feelings concerning his or her birth experience as revealed through hypnotic age regression, the success of therapy as estimated by both the therapist and the patient, the number of sessions attended prior to termination of therapy, and the mode of therapy termination, whether consultative or unilateral.

Demographic Information

Of the 1247 patients whose personal hypnotherapy records have been analysed to date, approximately 78% (971/1247) are female. This preponderance of females to males is not uncommon in practices dealing with problems of an emotional origin. While such an imbalance may arise from the reluctance of many males to seek assistance for problems that are not explicitly organic, it may also be a reflection of the greater degree of psychological stress that our society imposes on women. The demographic variables of Age, Marital Status and Educational Level are presented in Table 1 as a function of Patient Gender.

TABLE I

Classification of patients by (A) Age, (B) Marital Status and (C) Educational Level as a function of Patient Gender. Figures in columns 2 and 4 indicate the percentage each cell total represents of the respective column (n) total.

| | Patient Gender | | | |
| | Female | | Male | |
	n	%	n	%
A. Age (N=1247)				
under 15	13	1.3	14	5.1
16-30	365	37.6	92	33.3
31-45	367	37.8	99	35.9
46-60	193	19.9	59	21.4
61-75	32	3.3	10	3.6
over 75	1	0.1	2	0.7
total	971	100.0	276	100.0
B. Marital Status (N=1247)				
single	170	17.5	64	23.2
married	664	68.4	174	63.0
separated	41	4.2	18	6.5
divorced	67	6.9	18	6.5
widowed	29	3.0	2	0.7
total	971	100.0	276	100.0
C. Educational Level (N=870)				
grades 1-6	25	3.7	10	5.4
7-9	68	9.9	31	16.7
10-13	393	57.5	91	48.9
university 1-2	106	15.5	22	11.8
3-4	75	11.0	20	10.8
postgrad 5+	17	2.5	12	6.5
total	684	100.0	186	100.0

From this table it can be seen that the majority of patients seeking hypnotherapy are between the ages of twenty and forty, married and have a senior secondary or junior-level post-secondary education. The relatively high educational level may be attributable in part to the local presence of a major university in a relatively small community. This factor may also suggest to some extent the intellectual maturity of those willing to undertake a less conventional form of personal therapy.

Unlike orthodox psychoanalytic techniques, clinical hypnotherapy typically involves a relatively small number of treatment sessions: for example, patients in the present survey spent an average of only four sessions in therapy before discontinuing treatment. However, as shown in Figure 1, the distribution of attendance across sessions is different from that suggested by the mean. Approximately 44% of all

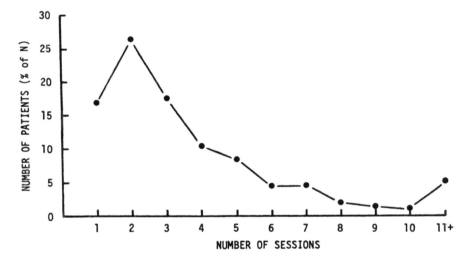

FIGURE 1

Number of sessions spent in therapy for 1247 patients (expressed as a percentage of N).

patients (534/1247) undertook therapy for one or two sessions only. A closer look at this large group is instructive. Patients could leave therapy in one of three ways: after consultation with the therapist (by 'mutual agreement'), by their own decision alone ('patient-cancelled') or, rarely, when therapy was unilaterally ended by the therapist ('therapist-terminated'). Of the 543 patients who elected to leave after just one or two sessions, 69 discussed their decision with the therapist beforehand. They indicated that despite the brevity of treatment, hypnotherapy had either been immediately successful, or that they felt confident about resolving any remaining problems on their own but would not hesitate to return to therapy should the need arise. Of those in the 'patient-cancelled' group who left therapy without such consultation, subsequent follow-up procedures revealed some whose expectations were met by clinical hypnotherapy as well as some who were dissatisfied by the process. Two reasons appear to predominate amongst the latter patients: inadequate understanding of the hypnotherapeutic process itself ('I wasn't hypnotized at all' or 'I expected it to feel much different'), or dissatisfaction with the therapist's fee structure (the government-subsidized universal health plan does not completely cover all therapy costs). It is evident that despite the distribution of literature before the first appointment describing both these concerns in detail, even greater pains must be taken within the initial session to ensure that the patient understands all aspects of the therapeutic undertaking before the commencement of therapy.

As suggested above, the number of patients leaving therapy after only one or two sessions does not necessarily indicate dissatisfaction with the hypnotherapeutic process. A major factor that bears on the number of sessions spent in therapy relates to the perceived effectiveness of the therapy itself, both from the therapist's and the patient's perspective. This relationship will be discussed in the next section.

Outcome of Therapy

The assessment of treatment success in a purely medical practice is usually straightforward; either the symptoms respond to treatment in short order or they do not and a new treatment is prescribed. In a practice which treats psychological rather than organic problems, however, the evaluation process is often somewhat more subjective. Data pertaining to two types of evaluations have been gathered in the present situation. In the first, the therapist assesses the patient's apparent well-being at the end of each session, basing his estimate on both verbal and non-verbal indicators observed during the course of therapy. While this method is not without its shortcomings (in particular, the possibility of bias), a subsequent evaluative procedure offers at least a partial reliability check of the therapist's evaluation. In this second method, a follow-up questionnaire is sent to every patient approximately six months after the last session, regardless of the way in which therapy was ended.

During the period of the survey, just over half the sample of 1247 patients was formally evaluated by the therapist (637/1247). Clinical hypnotherapy was judged as either partially or completely successful for approximately 79% (502/637) of these patients. On the other hand, of the 446 respondents to the follow-up questionnaire, only 61% (273/446) reported any degree of success as a result of hypnotherapy. Some of this apparent discrepancy, of course, might arise because the evaluations were made by two different observers, the therapist and the patient himself. An even more significant factor in accounting for the evaluation differences lies in the fact that the two samples do not include exactly the same patients. When the therapist-evaluated and patient-evaluated data are combined so that the same cases are considered by both (Table 2), it becomes apparent that despite differences in timing and evaluator, a relatively high degree of inter-rater reliability does exist. An examination of the cell entries located along the negative diagonal of Table 2 shows that the therapist and the patient were in complete agreement on a specific evaluation category almost 67% of the time (173/260). Although this figure is both important and interesting, a more comprehensive appraisal of the utility of clinical hypnotherapy may be obtained by collapsing Table 2 to combine 'partial' and 'complete' estimates of success for both evaluators. By this means, therapy is judged to be either of some success (positive but unspecified as to evaluator or degree) or not successful at all (as judged by both evaluators). For the tabled data, then, therapist and patient are seen to be in whole or partial evaluative agreement approximately 82% of the time (214/260).

One outcome category in particular, however, seems to point to a significant divergence of opinion. As shown by the marginal entries of Table 2, the patient is far more likely than the therapist to characterize therapy as 'unsuccessful'. Although this difference at first appears to suggest the possibility of therapist bias, it may be more reasonable to attribute it to changes in the patient's post-therapeutic state during the six-month period between evaluations. As suggested previously, any decline over time of therapeutic effectiveness would be expected to show up most clearly as a shift from the therapist's assessment of the treatment being 'partially successful' to the subsequent 'no success' estimation of the patient. For example, such a shift may be seen when the combined therapist-patient evaluations are examined as a function of the patient's marital status. This analysis reveals that the two evaluations are less consistent if the patient is divorced or separated than if married or single. In the therapist's experience, these results reflect his observation that the unsettling consequences of a marital breakdown in a separated or divorced individual continue to exert negative pressure during the six-month post-therapeutic period on what were initially perceived by both to be partial therapeutic benefits.

TABLE 2

Joint evaluations of therapeutic results by Therapist (during therapy) and Patient (six months after therapy). Bracketed figures indicate the percentage each cell total represents of the sample total. (N=260)

		Patient's Evaluation			
		no success	*partial success*	*complete success*	*row total*
Therapist's Evaluation	*no success*	31 (11.9)	7 (2.7)	2 (0.8)	40 (15.4)
	partial success	33 (12.7)	93 (35.8)	18 (6.9)	144 (55.4)
	complete success	4 (1.6)	23 (8.8)	49 (18.8)	76 (29.2)
	column total	68 (26.2)	123 (47.3)	69 (26.5)	260 (100.0)

Further to the possibility of therapist bias; if bias is present at all, it does not appear to be a function of the patient's gender. When the Therapist x Patient evaluations presented in Table 2 are further examined according to whether the individual is male or female, the results do not depart significantly from the tabled analysis.

As observed in the previous section, a relatively large number of those referred for clinical hypnotherapy withdrew (with or without consultation) after only one or two sessions. While some patients reported benefits from even a single session, it is evident from Figure 2 that using the less stringent criterion previously described, the probability of a successful therapeutic intervention (partial or complete) increased and unsuccessful outcomes declined as a direct function of the amount of time spent in therapy.

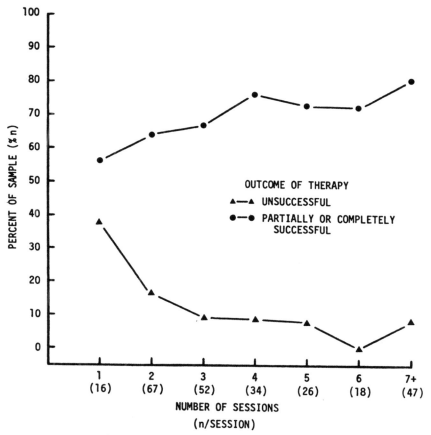

FIGURE 2

Joint evaluations of success of therapy by Therapist (during therapy) and Patient (six months after therapy) as a function of the number of sessions spent in therapy.

Although two methods of estimating hypnotisability are now routinely administered to all incoming patients, use of such scales was less systematic between 1975 and 1978 when the present data were collected. Two hypnotisability indices have been employed: the author's own *Amnesia Capacity Estimation* (ACE) scale and Spiegel's *Hypnotic Induction Profile* (HIP). The positive relationship between outcome of clinical hypnotherapy and hypnotic involvement as measured by ACE is shown in Figure 3 for the 152 patients so tested. When the percentage of therapy success (partial or complete) is plotted as a

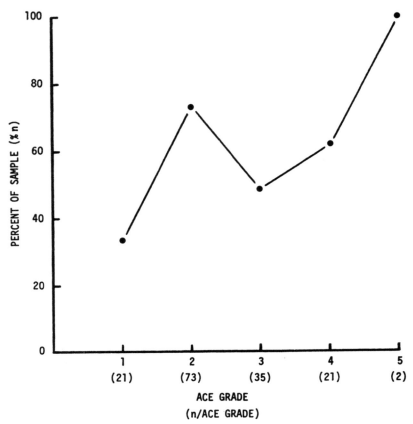

FIGURE 3

Relationship between score obtained on ACE Scale (ACE GRADE) and outcome of clinical hypnotherapy.

function of ACE grade for patients who were both therapist- and self-evaluated, the greater the index of hypnotisability the higher the likelihood of successful symptom alleviation.

Similarly, Spiegel suggests that a positive Control Differential (CD) score, as an indicator of high hypnotisability, will also be associated with positive results in hypnotherapy. Despite the small sample of patients for whom HIP scale and both forms of evaluation data were available, a reasonably strong degree of relationship between Control Differential and outcome of therapy was seen to exist. This relationship was most evident between positive CD and jointly-evaluated successful therapy: 99 of 154 patients (64.3%) obtained positive results from therapy while only 5 patients (3.3%) received no therapeutic benefits. The results for patients obtaining negative CD scores were not as dramatic, however, with only 3 of 12 therapist- and self-evaluated patients remaining unaffected by therapy as predicted while 5 of 12 (41.7%) found therapy to be beneficial.

Age seems to play a minor but interesting role in the likelihood of obtaining positive results when an individual undertakes clinical hypnotherapy. Outcome of therapy as assessed by both therapist and patient is plotted against age (in 15-year blocks) in Figure 4. Hypnotherapy appears to be most beneficial, with either partially or

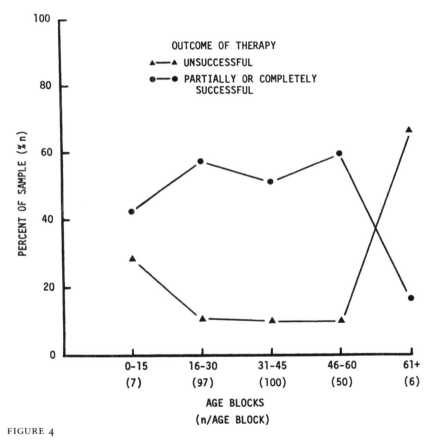

FIGURE 4

Joint evaluation (Therapist and Patient) of outcome of clinical hypnotherapy as a function of Patient Age (in 15-year blocks).

completely successful results, for patients between the ages of 16 and 60, and least successful for those over sixty years of age. Although the sample of children and teenagers is too small to warrant any conclusive statements, therapy for those counselled in this age bracket (0 – 15 years) appears to be either completely successful or quite unsuccessful. While the probability of a partially successful outcome appears to increase with age, however, completely successful results decline. Although conjectural, this effect may result from the growth over time of increasingly complex problems associated with the primary presenting symptom for which treatment is sought.

Birth Experience
As first described in Chapter 13, the present therapist believes that a patient's hypnotically-obtained memories of his own birth experience play a significant role in the direction and possible treatment of his primary presenting symptoms. Birth experience (B.E.) information was obtained from 876 patients, generally those seeking therapy during the latter stages of the period surveyed. Of these, 245 or 28% reported negative feelings attached to the occasion of their own birth. Such reports ranged from the feeling that "I was an 'accident' " to the rejection felt by a patient whose mother had tried unsuccessfully to induce an abortion and had subsequently spurned all contact with the child. A small difference was observed between males and females (44/187 or 23.5% vs. 201/689 or 29.2%) reporting a negative B.E. Although it is tempting to speculate that such a difference might be related to the generally higher social desirability of a male child, substantiation awaits the collection of comparison data from a nonpatient sample.

As shown in Table 3, a constellation of primary presenting symptoms appears to share a common negativity when compared to the 28% level of unsatisfactory birth experiences observed overall.
In many cases personal reports of diminished self-esteem accompanied such symptomatology, suggesting a connection between acceptance or rejection of self and the birth experience factor. A secondary presenting symptom, Depression (B), has been included in Table 3 since depression is often noted as a concomitant symptom of many of the primary disorders presented for therapy. The similarity of Depression (B) and Depression (A) is striking, with roughly 38% of both samples reporting negative feelings concerning the circumstances of their birth. Although the primary presenting symptom of Hair Pulling was not included in Table 3 because of its small sample size, all three patients requesting therapy for this obviously self-rejecting behaviour reported having an unhappy birth experience. Along the same lines, it is in-

TABLE 3

Primary Presenting Symptom associated with a high negative Birth Experience (B.E.) factor relative to the overall negative B.E. level of 28%. (N=1247)

primary presenting symptom	number of cases	%N reporting negative B.E.
Alcoholism	11	45.5
Anxiety	150	34.7
Depression (A)	26	38.5
Depression (B)	51	37.3
Insomnia	15	40.0
Marital Problems	12	41.7
Tension	12	41.7

teresting to note that nail-biters share this high incidence of negative feelings (8/16 or 50%), suggesting that nailbiting too is a manifestation of self-rejecting beliefs.

The unsatisfactory B.E. associated with the presenting symptom of Marital Problems (Table 3) is reflected to a lesser extent in the relationship of birth experience to the demographic variable of Marital Status. Of the 100 patients who were self-reported as separated or divorced, 34% indicated negative feelings compared to 27.3% of those whose marriages were intact at the time of hypnotherapy. These figures suggest that one of the factors that may make a marriage relationship difficult to maintain is the self-rejecting behaviours that may result from a negative birth experience.

To a considerable extent the success of a therapeutic intervention relies on the establishment of an air of mutual trust and confidence between patient and therapist. Placebo therapy, for example, depends entirely on the degree to which previous medical treatment has satisfied both the physical and psychological needs of the patient. In the interactive approach of clinical hypnotherapy, any patient variable that inhibits the development of such trust will be counter-productive unless it is dealt with effectively during the early stages of therapy. As previously suggested, a negative birth experience may be a causal factor in a patient's feelings of low self-esteem. This same factor is also thought to underlie some initial difficulties experienced by some patients in establishing a trusting relationship with the therapist. This suggestion is borne out in examining ACE scale results which have been categorized into hypnotisability 'depth' ratings of 'light' 'medium' and 'deep' (ACE scores of o & 1, 2 & 3, 4 & 5 respectively). As may be seen in Figure 5, birth experience reports vary as a function of ACE depth ratings: the greater the index of hypnotisability, the lower the probability of a patient reporting a negative birth experience.

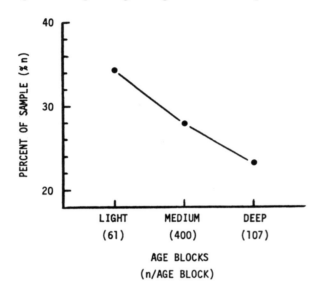

FIGURE 5

Negative Birth Experience as a function of Depth of Trance as measured by the ACE Scale.

The influence of the B.E. factor on hypnotisability as measured by the ACE scale is confirmed by the observations of a similar relationship with elements of Spiegel's HIP scale. Spiegel states that a 'decrement' profile, or a negative Control Differential score alone, is associated with poor hypnotisability. The decrement profile occurs when a patient with a positive eyeroll sign does not show any evidence of post-hypnotic suggestibility in the form of an observable difference between left and right arm movements (negative Control Differential score). In the present survey 41.5% (17/41) of those patients showing a decrement profile reported a negative birth experience, whereas only 26.7% (136/509) reported similar feelings in those HIP profiles positively associated with hypnotisability.

Since it has been previously demonstrated that the extent of hypnotic involvement is related to therapeutic success (Figure 4), it is imperative that any factor which affects hypnotisability, such as birth experience, must be minimized at the onset of therapy. In the present study the therapist consciously worked to undo the detrimental effects on self-esteem of a negative birth by ego-strengthening and related suggestions. That such procedures are effective may be seen in the failure of the B.E. factor to have any bearing on combined therapist/patient evaluations of treatment outcome. Furthermore, clinical experience in a few cases where there has been a poor response to therapy or a relapse has shown that both may be associated with the presence of a false positive birth experience. In such cases further questioning has revealed a negative birth factor which, when dealt with, has been a strong predictor of recovery.

Of the 1247 cases examined in the present survey, thirteen were unilaterally terminated at the therapist's request because severe problems in communication rendered further therapy impossible. Of the eight patients from whom B.E. information was obtained, four expressed negative attitudes when questioned about their feelings concerning their birth. It is possible that such memories play a prominent part in a patient's defences against therapy, further emphasizing the importance of dealing rapidly and effectively with the negative birth experience early in the therapeutic relationship. It is notable that of the many types of therapy currently offered to alleviate psychologically-related distress, clinical hypnotherapy is almost alone in its ability to deal effectively with problems apparently based on the residual feelings attached to one's own birth.

Bibliography

ADLER, A. *The Practice and Theory of Individual Psychology*. New York: Harcourt Press, 1924.

ALLISON, R.B. *Diagnosis and Treatment of Multiple Personality*. Santa Cruz: Allison, 1977.

ALMAN, B. 'Comparing the Effectiveness of Direct and Indirect Suggestion.' Paper presented at the Annual Meeting of The American Society of Clinical Hypnosis, San Francisco, November, 1979.

ANDERSON, J.R. AND BOWER, G.H. 'Recognition and Retrieval Process in Free Recall.' *Psychological Review*, 1972, 79, 97-123.

ANSEL, E.L. 'A Simple Exercise to Enhance Response to Hypnotherapy for Migraine Headache.' *International Journal of Clinical and Experimental Hypnosis*, 1977, 25, 68-71.

AS, A., HILGARD, E.R. AND WEITZENHOFFER, A.M. 'An Attempt at Experimental Modification of Hypnotizability through Repeated Individualized Hypnotic Experience.' *Scandinavian Journal of Psychology*, 1963, 4, 81-89.

ASHER, R. 'Respectable Hypnosis.' *British Medical Journal*, February 11, 1956, 309-313.

BAKAN, P. 'Hypnotizability, Laterality of Eye Movements and Functional Brain Assymmetry.' *Perceptual Motor Skills*, 82, 927-932.

BANDLER, R. AND GRINDER, J. *The Structure of Magic*, Vols 1 and 2. Palo Alto, California: Science and Behaviour Books Inc., 1975.

— — *Frogs into Princes*. Utah: Real People Press, 1979.

BARBER, J. 'Rapid Induction Analgesia: A Clinical Report.' *American Journal of Clinical Hypnosis*, 1977, 19, 3.

BARBER, T.X. *Hypnosis: A Scientific Approach*. New York: Von Nostrand, 1969.

−− 'Hypnosis, Suggestion and Psychosomatic Phenomena: A New Look from the Standpoint of Recent Experimental Studies.' *American Journal of Clinical Hypnosis*, 1978, 21, 1.

−− 'Suggested ('Hypnotic') Behaviour: The Trance Paradigm Versus an Alternative Paradigm,' in *Hypnosis: Developments in Research and New Perspectives*, ed. E. Fromm and R. Shor. New York: Aldine Publishing Co., 1979.

BARBER, T.X. AND CALVERLEY, D.S. *Experimenter's Tone of Voice as a Variable Affecting Hypnotic Like Suggestibility*. Harding, Mass.: Medfield Foundation, 1963.

−− 'Multidimensional Analysis of 'Hypnotic' Behaviour.' *Journal of Abnormal Psychology*, 1969, 74, 209-20.

BARBER, T.X. AND DEMOOR, W. 'A Theory of Hypnotic Induction Procedures.' *American Journal of Clinical Hypnosis*, 1972, 15, 112-35.

BARBER, T.X., SPANOS, N.P. AND CHAVES, J.F. *Hypnotism, Imagination and Human Potentialities*. New York: Pergamon Press, 1974.

BARNETT, E.A. 'Amnesia Capacity Estimation: A Clinical Method of Estimating Hypnotizability.' Paper Presented at the Annual Meeting of the American Society of Clinical Hypnosis, Atlanta, 1977.

−− *Unlock Your Mind and Be Free*. Glendale, CA, 1979.

−− 'Hypnoanalysis and the Negative Birth Experience,' *Medical Hypnoanalysis*, 1980, 68-74.

−− 'The Ideomotor Questioning Finger Technique: Some Problems in its Performance and Interpretation,' *Medical Hypnoanalysis*, 1980, 169-72.

BATHROP, R.W. 'Depressed Lymphocytic Function after Bereavement.' *Lancet*, 1977, 834-836.

BELLACK, L. AND SMALL, L. *Emergency Psychotherapy and Brief Psychotherapy* (2nd ed). New York: Grune and Stratton, 1977.

BERG, S. AND MELINE, E. 'Hypnotic Susceptibility in Old Age,' *International Journal of Clinical and Experimental Hypnosis*, 1975, 23, 184-9.

BERNE, E. *Transactional Analysis in Psychotherapy*. New York: Grove Press, 1961.

−− *What Do You Say After You Say Hello?* New York: Grove Press, 1972.

BERNHEIM, H. *De La Suggestion et de ses Applications a La Therapeutic*. Paris: 1886.

– – *Suggestive Therapeutics.* New York: Putnam's.

BERNSTEIN, M. *The Search for Bridey Murphy.* New York: Doubleday, 1956.

BERTRAND, A.J.F. *Traite du Somnambulisme et des Differentes Modifications qu'il Presente.* (Treatise on Somnambulism and its Various Modifications). Paris: J.G. Dentu, 1823.

BETTELHEIM, B. *The Use of Enchantment.* New York: Alfred Knopf, 1976.

BIBRING, E. 'Therapeutic Results of Psychoanalysis.' *International Journal of Psychoanalysis,* 1937, 18, 178.

BINET, A. *Les Alterations de la Personalité.* Paris: 1892.

BLACK, S. 'Inhibition of Immediate Type Hypersensitivity Response by Direct Suggestion of Hypnosis.' *British Medical Journal,* 1963, 990-2.

BLAKESLEE, T.R. *The Right Brain.* New York: Anchor Press, Doubleday, 1980.

BOWERS, K.S. *Hypnosis for the Seriously Curious.* Monterey, California: Brooks Cole, 1976.

BOWERS, M.K. ET AL. 'Therapy of Multiple Personality.' *International Journal of Clinical and Experimental Hypnosis,* 1971, 19, 57-65.

BRAMWELL, J.M. *Hypnotism: Its History, Practice and Theory.* London: Grant Richards, 1903. Reissued: New York: Julian Press, 1956.

BRANDEN, N. *The Disowned Self.* New York: Nash Publishing Company, 1972.

BRAUN, B.G. AND BRAUN, R.E. *Clinical Aspects of Multiple Personality.* Unpublished paper, 1979.

BRENMAN, M. AND GILL, M.M. *Hypnotherapy: A Survey of the Literature.* New York: International Universities Press, 1947.

BREUER, J. In Freud, S. and Breuer, J. *Studies on Hysteria,* Vol 1 of *The Standard Edition of the Complete Psychological Works of Sigmund Freud.* London: Hogarth Press, 1955.

BROWN, W. *Psychology and Psychotherapy.* London: Arnold, 1921.

BRUHN, J.G., MCCRADY, K.D., AND DU PLEISSIS, A.L. 'Evidence of "Emotional Drain" Preceding Death from Myocardial Infarction.' *Psychiatric Digest,* 1968, 29, 34-40.

BRUCH, G. *Eating Disorders: Obesity, Anorexia Nervosa and the Person Within.* New York: Basic Books, 1973.

BUTLER, B. 'The Use of Hypnosis in the Care of the Cancer Patient,' part 3. *British Journal of Medical Hypnosis,* 1955, 6, 9-17.

CANNON, W.B. 'Voodoo Death.' *Psychosomatic Medicine,* 1957, 19, 182-90.

CAPLAN, G. *Principles of Preventive Psychiatry.* New York: Basic Books, 1964.

CHAMBERLAIN, D.B. *Reliability of Birth Memories: Evidence from Mother and Child Pairs in Hypnosis.* Read at 23rd Annual Scientific Meeting of The American Society of Clinical Hypnosis, Minneapolis, November, 1980.

CHEEK, D.B. 'Unconscious Perception of Meaningful Sound During Surgical Anesthesia as Revealed Under Hypnosis.' *American Journal of Clinical Hypnosis,* 1959, 1, 101-13.

– – 'Communication with the Critically Ill.' *American Journal of Clinical Hypnosis,* 1969, 12, 75-85.

– – 'Sequential Head and Shoulder Movements Appearing with Age Regression in Hypnosis to Birth.' *American Journal of Clinical Hypnosis,* 1974, 16, 261-6.

– – 'Maladjustment Patterns Apparently Related to Imprinting at Birth.' *American Journal of Clinical Hypnosis,* 1975, 18, 75-82.

– – 'Short Term Hypnotherapy for Frigidity Using Exploration of Early Life Attitudes.' *American Journal of Clinical Hypnosis,* 1976, 19, 20-7.

– – 'The Significance of the Depressed Finger in Ideomotor Questioning.' Private Communication, 1981.

CHEEK, D.B. AND LECRON, L.M. *Clinical Hypnotherapy.* New York: Grune and Stratton, 1968.

CHERNENKOFF, W. 'A Case of Frigidity.' *American Journal of Clinical Hypnosis,* 1969, 11, 195-8.

CLAWSON, T.A. AND SWADE, R.H. 'The Hypnotic Control of Blood Flow and Pain. The Cure of Warts and the Neutral Use of Hypnosis in the Treatment of Cancer.' *American Journal of Clinical Hypnosis,* 1975, 17, 160-9.

COLLISON, D.R. 'Hypnotherapy with Children.' *Australian Journal of Clinical Hypnosis,* 1974, 2, 106-11.

– – 'Which Asthmatic Patients Should be Treated by Hypnotherapy?' *Medical Journal of Australia,* 1975, 1, 776-81.

CONN, J. In Foreword to Kroger, W., *Clinical and Experimental Hypnosis.* Philadelphia: Lippincott, 1977.

CRONIN, D.M., SPANOS, N.P. AND BARBER, T.X. 'Augmenting Hypnotic Susceptibility by Providing Favourable Information about Hypnosis.' *American Journal of Clinical Hypnosis*, 1971, 13, 259-64.

DAMASER, E. 'An Experimental Study of Long Term Post Hypnotic Suggestion.' Harvard University, 1964.

DAVIS, S., DAWSON, J.G. AND SEAY, B. 'Prediction of Hypnotic Susceptibility from Imaginative Involvement.' *American Journal of Clinical Hypnosis*, 1978, 20, 195-8.

DE BOEUF, J.R.L. *Le Magnetisme Animal*. Paris: 1889.

DE SHAZER, S. 'Brief Hypnotherapy of Two Sexual Dysfunctions: The Crystal Ball Technique.' *American Journal of Clinical Hypnosis*, 1978, 20, 203-8.

— — 'Investigation of Indirect Symbolic Suggestions.' *American Journal of Clinical Hypnosis*, 1980, 23, 10-15.

DE VOGE, J.T. AND SACHS, L.B. 'The Modification of Hypnotic Susceptibility Through Imitative Behaviour.' *International Journal of Clinical and Experimental Hypnosis*, 1973, 21, 70-7.

DEVOGE, S. 'Use of Hypnosis for Assertive Training and Self Concept Change in Women: A Case Study.' *American Journal of Clinical Hypnosis*, 1977, 19, 226-30.

DITTBORN, J.M. AND ANSTEGUIELA, A. 'Expectations and Spontaneous Posthypnotic Amnesia: An Experimental Note.' *American Journal of Clinical Hypnosis*, 1962, 4, 268-9.

DIAMOND, M.J. 'The Modification of Hypnotizability: A Review.' *Psychological Bulletin*, 1974, 81, 180-98.

— — 'Hypnotizability is Modifiable: An Alternative Approach.' *International Journal of Clinical and Experimental Hypnosis*, 1977, 25, 147-66.

EDMONSTON, W.E. JR. 'Stimulus-Response Theory of Hypnosis.' In *Handbook of Clinical and Experimental Hypnosis*, ed. J.E. Gordon. New York: McMillan, 1967.

— — 'Effects of Hypnosis on Conditioned Responses.' In *Hypnosis: Developments in Research and New Perspectives*, ed. E. Fromm and R.E. Shor. New York: Aldine Publishing Co., 1979.

ELLENBERGER, H.F. 'The Pathogenic Secret and its Therapeutics.' *Journal Hist. Behav. Sciences*, 1966, 2, 29-42.

ELMAN, D. *Hypnotherapy.* Glendale: Westwood Publishing Co.

ENGEL, G.L. 'Studies of Ulcerative Colitis, V. Psychological Aspects and their Implications for Treatment.' *American Journal of Digestive Disorders,* 1968, 3, 315-37.

ERICKSON, M. 'Deep Hypnosis and its Induction.' In *Experimental Hypnosis,* ed. J.M. LeCron. New York: McMillan, 1952, 70-114.

ERICKSON, M.H. 'Special Techniques of Brief Hypnotherapy.' *Journal of Clinical and Experimental Hypnosis,* 1954, 2, 109-29.

— — 'Pseudo-orientation in Time as a Hypnotherapeutic Procedure.' *Journal of Clinical and Experimental Hypnosis,* 1954, 2, 261-83.

— — 'Historical Note on the Hand Levitation and Other Ideomotor Techniques.' *American Journal of Clinical Hypnosis,* 1961, 3, 196-9.

— — 'An Hypnotic Technique for Resistant Patients,' *American Journal of Clinical Hypnosis,* 1964, 7, 18-32.

ERICKSON, M.H. AND KUBIE, L.S. 'The Successful Treatment of a Case of Acute Hysterical Depression by Return Under Hypnosis to a Critical Phase of Childhood.' *Psychoanalytic Quarterly,* 1941, 10, 583-609.

ERICKSON, M.H. AND ROSSI, E. 'Varieties of Hypnotic Amnesia.' *American Journal of Clinical Hypnosis,* 1974, 16, 225-39.

— — 'Varieties of Double Bind.' *American Journal of Clinical Hypnosis,* 1975, 17, 143-57.

— — 'The Indirect Forms of Suggestion.' Presented at the 28th Annual Meeting of the Society for Clinical and Experimental Hypnosis, 1976. Published in *Collected Papers of Milton H. Erickson,* Vol 1, ed. E. Rossi. New York: Irvington Publishers Inc., 1976.

— — *Hypnotherapy: an Exploratory Casebook.* New York: Irvington, 1979.

ERICKSON, M.H., ROSSI, E., AND ROSSI, S. *Hypnotic Realities. New York: Irvington,* 1976.

ESDAILE, J. *Natural and Mesmeric Clairvoyance.* London, 1852, rpt. New York: Arno Press, 1975.

EVANS, F.J. 'Hypnosis and Sleep.' In *Hypnosis: Developments in Research and New Perspectives,* ed. E. Fromm and R.E. Shor. New York: Aldine Publishing Co., 1979.

EWIN, D.M. 'Condyloma Acuminatum: Successful Treatment of Four Cases.' *American Journal of Clinical Hypnosis,* 1974, 17.

FABBRI, R. 'Hypnosis and Behaviour Therapy: A Coordinated Approach to the Treatment of Sexual Disorders.' *American Journal of Clinical Hypnosis,* 1976, 19, 4-8.

FARELLY, F. AND BRANDSMA, J. *Provocative Therapy.* Cupertino, California: Meta Publications Inc., 1974.

FELLOWS, B.J. AND ARMSTRONG, V. 'An Experimental Investigation of the Relationship Between Hypnotic Susceptibility and Reading Involvement.' *American Journal of Clinical Hypnosis,* 1977, 20, 101-5.

FIELD, P.B. AND KLINE, M.V. 'Previous Psychotherapy Among Hypnotherapy Applicants."' *American Journal of Clinical Hypnosis,* 1974, 17, 125-30.

FIORE, E. *You Have Been Here Before.* New York: Coward, McCann & Geoghegan, 1978.

FODOR, N. *The Search for the Beloved.* New York: Hermitage Press, 1949.

FRANK, L.K. *On the Importance of Infancy.* New York: Random House, 1966.

FRANKEL, F.H. *Hypnosis: Trance as a Coping Mechanism.* New York: Plenum Medical Book Company, 1976.

– – 'Scales Measuring Hypnotic Responsivity: A Clinical Perspective.' *American Journal of Clinical Hypnosis,* 1978, 21, 208-18.

FRANKEL, F.H. ET AL. 'The Use of Hypnotizability Scales in the Clinic: A Review After Six Years."' *International Journal of Clinical and Experimental Hypnosis,* 1979, 27, 63-73.

FRANKLIN, E.A. 'A Hypnotic Technique in the Treatment of Chronic Illness.' *American Journal of Clinical Hypnosis,* 1964, 6, 366-71.

FREUD, S. *New Introductory Lectures on Psychoanalysis.* New York: W.W. Norton and Co., 1933.

– – *Origin and Development of Psychoanalysis.* London: L. and V. Woolf; Institute of Psychoanalysis, 1937.

– – *The Interpretation of Dreams,* from *The Basic Writings of Sigmund Freud.* New York: Modern Library, 1938.

– – *On Beginning the Treatment. Standard Edition.* London: Hogarth Press, 1953.

FREYTAG, F. *Hypnosis and the Unconscious Body Image.* New York: Julian Press Inc., 1961.

FRIEDMAN, M. AND ROSEMAN, R. 'Association of Specific Overt Behaviour Pattern with Blood and Cardiovascular Findings.' *Journal of the American Medical Association,* 1959, 169: 1286.

GARDNER, G.G. 'Hypnosis with Infants and Preschool Children.' *American Journal of Clinical Hypnosis,* 1977, 19, 158-63.

–– 'Use of Hypnosis for Psychogenic Epilepsy in a Child.' *American Journal of Clinical Hypnosis,* 1973, 15, 166-9.

–– 'Attitudes of Child Health Professionals Towards Hypnosis.' *International Journal of Clinical and Experimental Hypnosis,* 1975, 24, 62-73.

GAZZANIGA, M.S., BOGAN, J.E. AND SPERRY, R.W. 'Some Functional Effects of Sectioning Cerebral Commissures in Man.' *Proceedings of the National Academy of Science,* 1962, 48, 176.

GIBBONS, D.E. *Applied Hypnosis and Hyperempiria.* New York: Plenum Press, 1979.

GINDES, B. *New Concepts of Hypnosis.* New York: Julian Press Inc., 1951.

GORDON, D. *Therapeutic Metaphor.* Cupertino, California: Meta Publications Inc., 1978.

GRAHAM, G.W. 'Hypnotic Treatment for Migraine Headaches.' *International Journal of Clinical and Experimental Hypnosis,* 1975, 23, 165-71.

GRAHAM, K.R. 'Perceptual Processes and Hypnosis: Support for a Cognitive State Theory Based on Laterality.' In *Conceptual and Investigative Approaches to Hypnosis and Hypnotic Phenomena,* ed. W.E. Edmonston Jr.; in *Annals of the New York Academy of Sciences,* 1977, 296, 274-83.

GREER, S., MORRIS, T., AND PETTINGALE, K.W. 'Psychological Response to Breast Cancer: Effect on Outcome.' *Lancet,* Oct. 13, 1979, 785-7.

GROF, S. *Realms of the Human Unconscious.* New York: E.P. Dutton and Co., 1976.

GUR, R.C. AND GUR, R.E. 'Handedness, Sex and Eyedness as Moderative Variables in the Relation Between Hypnotic Susceptibility and Functional Brain Asymmetry.' *Journal of Abnormal Psychology,* 1974, 83, 635-43.

GWYNNE, P.H., TOSI, D.J. AND HOWARD, L. 'Treatment of Non-assertion through Stage-directed Hypnotherapy (R.S.D.H.) and Behavioural Rehearsal.' *American Journal of Clinical Hypnosis,* 1978, 20, 263-71.

HADFIELD, J.A. *Functional Nerve Disease.* Ed. Crichton-Miller. London: 1920.

HALEY, J. *Uncommon Therapy*. New York: Norton, 1973.

– – 'An Interactional Explanation of Hypnosis.' *American Journal of Clinical Hypnosis*, 1958, 1, 141-57.

HARDING, C.H. 'Hypnosis in the Treatment of Migraine.' In *Hypnosis and Psychosomatic Medicine*, ed. J. Lassner. New York: Springer Verlag, 1967.

HARRIS, T.A. *I'm O.K. You're O.K.* New York: Harper and Row, 1967.

HARTLAND, J. *Medical and Dental Hypnosis*. London: Bailliere, Tindal and Cassell, 1966.

– – 'Further Observations on the Use of Ego Strengthening Techniques.' *American Journal of Clinical Hypnosis*, 1971, 14, 1-8.

HARTMAN, B.J. 'Hypnotizability as Affected by Attitudinal and Motivational Variables.' *International Journal of Clinical and Experimental Hypnosis*, 1967, 15, 86-91.

HILGARD, E.R. *Hypnotic Susceptibility*. New York: Harcourt, Brace and World Inc., 1965.

– – 'Post Hypnotic Amnesia: Experiments and Theory.' *International Journal of Clinical and Experimental Hypnosis*, 1966, 14, 104-11.

– – *Divided Consciousness*. New York: John Wiley & Sons, 1977.

– – 'Divided Consciousness in Hypnosis: The Implications of the Hidden Observer.' In *Hypnosis: Developments in Research and New Perspectives*, ed. E. Fromm and R. E. Shor. New York: Aldine Publishing Co., 1979.

HILGARD, E.R. AND HILGARD, J.R. *Hypnosis in the Relief of Pain*. Los Altos, California: William Kaufman, 1975.

HILGARD, E.R. AND HOMMEL, L.S. 'Selective Amnesia for Events Within Hypnosis Related to Repression.' *Journal of Personality*, 1961, 29, 205-16.

HILGARD, J.R. *Personality and Hypnosis: A Study of Imaginative Involvement*. Chicago: University of Chicago Press, 1970.

HILL, L.B. *Psychotherapeutic Intervention in Schizophrenia*. Chicago: University of Chicago Press, 1955.

HODGE, J.R. 'Contractual Aspects of Hypnosis.' *International Journal of Clinical and Experimental Hypnosis*, 1976, 24, 391-99.

HUDSON, T.J. *The Law of Psychic Phenomena*. Chicago: McClurg, 1893.

HUTSCHNECKER, A.A. *The Will to Live*. New York: Prentice Hall, 1951.

IVESON, J. *More Lives Than One*. London: B.B.C. Vociotape, 1976.

JABUSH, M. 'A Case of Chronic Recurring Multiple Boils Treated with Hypnotherapy.' *Psychiatric Quarterly*, 1969, 43, 448-55.

JAMES, M. AND JONGEWARD, D. *Born to Win*. Massachusetts: Addison-Wesley Publishing Co., Inc., 1971.

JAMES, W. *Principles of Psychology*. New York: Holt, 1980.

JANET, P. *L'Automatisme Psychologique*. Paris: Felix Alcan, 1889.

JUNG, C.G. *Contributions to Analytical Psychology*. Trans. H.G. Baynes and C.F. Baynes. London: 1928.

KAMPMAN, R. 'Hypnotically Induced Multiple Personality.' *International Journal of Clinical and Experimental Hypnosis*, 1976, 24, 215-27.

KAPLAN, H. *New Sexual Therapy*. New York: Quadrangle Press, 1974.

KIMURA, D. 'The Asymmetry of the Human Brain.' *Sci. Am.*, 1973, 278, 70-78.

KINSBOURNE, H. 'Eye Movements and Laterality.' *Science*, 1972, 176, 539-41.

KLEIN, M. *The Psychoanalysis of Children*. New York: Norton, 1935.

KLINE, M.V. (ED.) *A Scientific Report on the Search for Bridey Murphy*, 1956.

KOLB, L.C. *Noyes' Modern Clinical Psychiatry*, 7th edition. Philadelphia: Saunders, 1968.

KROGER, W.S. 'The Conditioned Reflex Treatment of Alcoholism.' *Journal of the American Medical Association*, 1942, 120, 714.

KROGER, W.S. AND FEZLER, W.D. *Hypnosis and Behaviour Modification: Imagery Conditioning*. Philadelphia: J.B. Lippincott, 1976.

KUBIE, L.S. 'The Neurotic Process as the Focus of Physiological and Psychoanalytical Research.' *The Journal of Mental Science*, 1958, 104, 435.

KUBIE, L.S. AND MARGOLIN, S. 'The Process of Hypnotism and the Nature of the Hypnotic State.' *American Journal of Psychiatry*, 1944, 100, 619.

LAWLOR, E.D. 'Hypnotic Intervention with "School Phobic" Children.' *International Journal of Clinical and Experimental Hypnosis*, 1976, 24, 74-86.

LEAVITT, H.C. 'A Case of Hypnotically Produced Secondary and Tertiary Personalities.' *Psychoanal. Rev.*, 1947, 34, 274-95.

LECRON, L.M. 'A Hypnotic Technique for Uncovering Unconscious Material.' *Journal of Clinical and Experimental Hypnosis*, 1954, 1, 76-79.

– – *Clinical Hypnotherapy*. Cheek and LeCron. New York: Grune and Stratton, 1968.

LESHAN, L. *You Can Fight For Your Life*. New York: M. Evans and Co., 1977.

LEVA, R.A. 'Modification of Hypnotic Susceptibility Through Audiotape Relaxation Training.' *Percept. Motor Skills*, 1974, 39, 872-4.

LEVINE, E.S. 'Indirect Suggestions Through Personalised Fairy Tales for Treatment of Childhood Insomnia.' *American Journal of Clinical Hypnosis*, 1980, 23, 57-63.

LINDNER, R.M. *Rebel Without a Cause: The Hypnoanalysis of a Criminal Psychopath*. New York: Grune and Stratton, 1944.

LONDON, P. 'The Induction of Hypnosis.' In *Handbook of Clinical and Experimental Hypnosis,* ed. J.E. Gordon. New York: McMillan, 1967.

LONDON, P. AND COOPER, L.M. 'Norms of Hypnotic Susceptibility in Children.' *Developmental Psychology*, 1969, 1, 113-24.

MASON, A.A. 'A Case of Congenital Ichthyosiform Erhthroderma of Brocq Treated by Hypnosis.' *British Medical Journal*, Aug. 23, 1952, 422-3.

MASTERS, W.H. AND JOHNSON, V.E. *Human Sexual Response*. Boston: Little, Brown, 1966.

MATHESON, G. AND GREHAN, J.F. 'A Rapid Induction Technique.' *American Journal of Clinical Hypnosis*, 1979, 21, 297-9.

MEARES, A. *Hypnography*. Springfield: Charles C. Thomas, 1957.

– – *Shapes of Sanity*. Springfield: Charles C. Thomas, 1960.

– – *A System of Medical Hypnosis*. Philadelphia: W.B. Saunders, 1960.

MELTZOFF, A.N. AND MOORE, M.K. 'Imitation of Facial and Manual Gestures by Human Neonates.' *Science.* 1977, 198, 75-8.

MILLER, M.M. 'Treatment for Chronic Alcoholism by Hypnotic Aversion.' *Journal of the American Medical Association*, 1959, 171, 164.

MORGAN, A. AND HILGARD, E.R. 'Age Differences in Susceptibility to Hypnosis.' *International Journal of Clinical and Experimental Hypnosis,* 1973, 21, 78.

MOTT, T. "The Clinical Importance of Hypnotic Susceptibility.' *American Journal of Clinical Hypnosis,* 1979, 21, 263-9.

MUSAPH, H. *Itching and Scratching. Psychodynamics in Dermatology.* Basel: S. Karger, 1964.

PAVLOV, I.P. *Conditioned Reflexes.* London: Oxford University Press, 1927.

PEDERSON, L.L., SCRIMGEOUR, W.G. AND LEFCOE, N.M. 'Comparison of Hypnosis Plus Counselling, Counselling Alone, and Hypnosis Alone.' *Journal Consult. Clin. Psychol.,* 1975, 43, 920.

— — 'Variables of Hypnosis Which are Related to Success in a Smoking Withdrawal Program.' *International Journal of Clinical and Experimental Hypnosis,* 1979, 27, 14-20.

PENFIELD, W. AND LAMAR, R. *Speech and Brain Mechanisms.* Princeton, N.J.: Princeton University Press, 1959.

PENFIELD, W. 'Memory Mechanisms.' *American Medical Association Archives of Neurology and Psychiatry,* 1952, 67, 178-98.

PERLS, F. *Gestalt Therapy Verbatim.* Lafayette, California: Real People Press, 1969.

PLAPP, J.M. 'Experimental Hypnosis in a Clinical Setting: A Report of the Atypical Use of Hypnosis in the Treatment of a Disturbed Adolescent.' *American Journal of Clinical Hypnosis,* 1976, 18, 145-52.

PORTER, J. 'Suggestions and Success Imagery for Study Problems.' *International Journal of Clinical and Experimental Hypnosis,* 1978, 26, 65-75.

PUYSEGAR, A.M. MARQUIS DE Letter (on the discovery of artificial somnambulism) to a member of the Societe de Harmonie, March 8th, 1784. Reproduced in A. Teste (ed.) *Practical Manual of Animal Magnetism.* Translated from the second French edition by D. Spillan. London: H. Bailliere, 1843.

RADO, S. 'Developments in the Psychoanalysis Conception and Treatment of the Neuroses.' *Psychoanalytic Quarterly,* 1939, 8, 428.

RAIKOR, V.L. 'Age Regression to Infancy by Adult Subjects in Deep Hypnosis.' *American Journal of Clinical Hypnosis,* 1980, 22, 156-63.

RANK, O. *The Myth of the Birth of the Hero: A Psychological Interpretation of Mythology* (Nervous and Mental Diseases Monographs, No. 8), 1914. New York: Random House, 1959.

REIDER, N. 'Symptom Substitution.' *Bulletin of Meninger Clinic,* 1976, 40, 629-40.

SANDERS, S. 'An Exploration of Utilization Techniques in Short Term Hypnotherapy.' *American Journal of Clinical Hypnosis,* 1977, 20, 76-9.

SCHAFER, D. AND HERNANDEZ, A. 'Hypnosis, Pain and the Context of Therapy.' *International Journal of Clinical and Experimental Hypnosis,* 1978, 26, 143-53.

SCHILDER, P. AND KANDERS, O. *Hypnosis.* New York: Nerve and Mental Diseases Publishing Co., 1927.

SCHMALE, A.H. AND IKER, H.P. 'The Effect of Hopelessness and the Development of Cancer.' *Psychosomatic Medicine,* 1966, 28, 714.

SCHNECK, J.M. 'Prehypnotic Suggestion in Psychotherapy.' *American Journal of Clinical Hypnosis,* 1975, 17, 158-9.

SCHWARTZ, G.E., DAVIDSON, R.J. AND MAER, F. 'Right Hemisphere Lateralisation for Emotion in the Human Brain: Interaction With Cognition.' *Science,* 1975, 190, 286-8.

SECTOR, I.I. 'An Investigation of Hypnotizability as a Function of Attitudes Towards Hypnosis.' *American Journal of Clinical Hypnosis,* 1960, 3, 75-89.

SELAVAN, A. 'Hypnosis and Transactional Analysis Theory.' *American Journal of Clinical Hypnosis,* 1975, 17, 260-6.

SELYE, H. *The Stress of Life.* New York: McGraw Hill, 1956.

SHEEHAN, P. AND ORNE, M.T. 'Some Comments on the Nature of Post Hypnotic Behaviour.' *Journal of Nervous and Mental Diseases.* 1968, 146, 209-20.

SHEEHAN, D.V., LAFF, W.D., REGINA, E.G. AND SMITH, G.M. 'Empirical Assessment of Spiegel's Hypnotic Induction Profile and Eye Roll Hypothesis.' *International Journal of Clinical and Experimental Hypnosis,* 1979, 27, 103-10.

SHEVRIN, H. 'The Wish to Cooperate and the Temptation to Submit: The Hypnotized Subject's Dilemma in Hypnosis.' In *Hypnosis: Developments in Research and New Perspectives,* ed. E. Fromm and R.E. Shor. New York: Aldine Publishing Co., 1979.

SIMONTON, O.C., MATTHEWS-SIMONTON, S. AND CREIGHTON, J. *Getting Well Again.* New York: J.P. Tarcher, 1978.

SINCLAIR-GIEBEN, A.H.C. AND CHALMERS, D. 'Evaluation of Treatment of Warts by Hypnosis.' *Lancet,* Oct. 3, 1959, 480-2.

SMITH, D.E. 'Hypnotic Susceptibility and Eye Movements During Rest.' *American Journal of Clinical Hypnosis,* 1980, 22, 147-55.

SMITH MOORHOUSE, P.M. 'Hypnosis in the Treatment of Alcoholism.' *British Journal of Addiction,* 1969, 64, 47.

SOLOMON, G.F., AMKRAUT, A.A., AND KOSPER, P. 'Immunity, Emotions and Stress.' *Annals of Clinical Research,* 1974, 6, 313-22.

SONTAG, L.W. 'Studies in Foetal Behaviour: IV The Measurement of Three Types of Foetal Activity.' *Journal of Comparative Psychology,* 1941, 32, 521-30.

SPANOS, N.P. 'Goal Directed Fantasy and the Performance of Hypnotic Test Suggestions' *Psychiatry,* 1971, 34, 86-96.

SPANOS, N.P. AND BODOVIK, H.L. 'Suggested Amnesia and Disorganised Recall in Hypnotic and Task Motivated Subjects.' *Journal of Abnormal Psychology,* 1977, 86, 295-305.

SPANOS, N.P. AND HAM, M.L. 'Cognitive Activity in Response to Hypnotic Suggestion: Goal Directed Fantasy and Selective Amnesia.' *American Journal of Clinical Hypnosis,* 1973, 15, 191-8.

SPIEGEL, H. 'Grade 5 Syndrome: The Highly Hypnotizable Person.' *International Journal of Clinical and Experimental Hypnosis,* 1974, 22, 303-19.

– – *Manual for Hypnotic Induction Profile: Eye Roll-Levitation Method,* Revised Edition. New York: Soni Medica, 1973.

SPIEGEL, H. AND SPIEGEL, D. *Trance and Treatment.* New York: Basic Books Inc., 1978.

STEINER, C. *Scripts People Live.* New York: Grove Press Inc., 1974.

STEKEL, W. *Techniques of Analytical Psychotherapy.* New York: Norton, 1940.

STEVENSON, I. *Twenty Cases Suggestive of Reincarnation.* New York: American Society for Psychical Research, 1966.

STAVRAKY, K.M. ET AL. 'Psychology Factors in the Outcome of Human Cancer.' *Journal of Psychosomatic Research,* 1968, 12, 251-9.

STEARN, J. *The Search for a Soul: Taylor Caldwell's Psychic Levels.* New York: Doubleday, 1973.

STUNKARD, A.J. AND MENDELSON, S. 'Obesity and the Body Image.' *American Journal of Psychiatry,* 1967, 123.

SULLIVAN, H.S. *The Interpersonal Theory of Psychiatry.* New York: Norton, 1953.

SULZBERGER, M.B. AND WOLF, J. 'The Treatment of Warts by Suggestion.' *Medical Record,* 1934, 140, 552-7.

SWITRAS, J.E. 'A Comparison of the Eye Roll Test for Hypnotizability and the Stanford Hypnotic Susceptibility Scale, Form A.' *American Journal of Clinical Hypnosis,* 1974, 17, 54-5.

SZASZ, T.S. *The Myth of Mental Illness.* New York: Harper, 1961.

TAYLOR, W.S. AND MARTIN, M.F. 'Multiple Personality.' *Journal of Abnormal Social Psychology,* 1944, 39, 281-300.

THOMAS, C.B. AND DUSZYNSKI, K.R. 'Closeness to Parents and the Family Constellation in a Prospective Study of Five Disease States: Suicides, Mental Illness, Malignant Tumour, Hypertension and Coronary Heart Disease,' *Hopkins Medical Journal,* 1974, 134, 251-70.

ULLMAN, M. 'On the Psyche and Warts: Suggestion and Warts − A Review and Comment.' *Psychosomatic Medicine,* 1959, 21, 473-88.

VAN NEUMANN, J. *The Computer and the Brain.* New Haven: Yale University Press, 1958.

VERNEY, T. 'The Psychic Life of the Unborn.' 5th World Congress of Psychosomatic Obstetrics and Gynaecology. Rome, November 1977.

WATKINS, J.G. *Hypnotherapy of War Neuroses.* New York: Ronald Press, 1949.

− − 'The Affect Bridge.' *International Journal of Clinical and Experimental Hypnosis,* 1971, 19, 28.

WATKINS, H.H. 'Hypnosis and Smoking: A Five Session Approach.' *International Journal of Clinical and Experimental Hypnosis,* 1976, 24, 381-90.

WIJESINGHE, B. 'A Case of Frigidity Treated by Short Term Hypnotherapy.' *International Journal of Clinical and Experimental Hypnosis,* 1977, 25, 63-7.

WILLIAMS, G.W. 'Difficulties in Dehypnotizing.' *Journal of Clinical and Experimental Hypnosis,* 1953, 1, 3-12.

WILSON, S.C. AND BARBER, T.X. 'The Creative Imagination Scale as a Measure of Hypnotic Responsiveness: Applications to Experimental and Clinical Hypnosis.' *American Journal of Clinical Hypnosis,* 1978, 20, 235-49.

WINGFIELD, H.E. *An Introduction to the Study of Hypnotism.* London: Bailliere, Tindall and Cox, 1920.

WOLBERG, L.R. *Hypnoanalysis.* New York: Grune and Stratton, 1964.

– – *Medical Hypnosis,* Vol 1. New York: Grune and Stratton, 1948.

WOLF, S., CARDON; P.V., SHEPARD, E.M. AND WOLFF, H.G. *Life Stress and Essential Hypertension.* Baltimore: Williams and Wilkins, 1955.

WOLPE, J. *Psychotherapy by Reciprocal Inhibition.* Stanford: Stanford University Press, 1958.

ZEIG, J. 'Symptom Prescription and Ericksonian Principles of Hypnosis and Psychotherapy.' *American Journal of Clinical Hypnosis,* 1980, 23, 16-22.

ZIMBARDO, P.G. *Shyness.* Reading, Mass.: Addison-Wesley Publishing Company, 1977.

Index of Names

Adler 72
Allison 193
Alman 257
Amkraut 446
Anderson 51
Ansel 324
Anstequiela 51
Armstrong 49
As 431
Asher 428, 442

Bakan 430
Bandler 14, 45, 157
Barber, J. 35, 256
Barber, T.X. 18, 19, 36, 49, 442,
    450, 451
Barnett 21, 22, 52
Bathrop 446
Bellack 262
Benedict, Moritz 138
Berg 50
Berne 76, 77, 80, 83, 86, 173, 452
Bernheim 9, 49, 51, 432
Bernstein 231
Bertrand 18
Bettelheim 257
Bibring 72
Binet 9
Black 428
Blakeslee 20, 61
Bogen 20

Bodorik 56
Bower 57
Bramwell 51
Branden 79, 87, 236
Brandsma 257
Braun, B.G. 193
Braun, R.E. 193
Brenman 250, 428
Breuer 8-9
Brocq 445
Brown 10
Bruch 284
Bruhn 264
Butler 429

Caldwell Taylor 229-230
Calverley 450, 451
Cannon 443
Caplan 172
Chalmers 442
Chamberlain 215
Charcot 8
Cheek 14, 119, 214, 215,
    354, 443
Chernenkoff 354
Clawson 442
Collison 382, 428, 443
Conn 87, 88
Cooper 382
Cronin 450

Damaser 51
Davis 49
De Moor 36
De Shazer 111, 256
De Voge J.T. 429
De Voge, S. 236
Delboeuf 9
Diamond 49, 429
Dittborn 51
Duszynski 443

Edmonston 24, 432
Ellenburger 138
Elman 13, 35, 36, 37, 110, 432
Engel 264, 444
Erickson 13, 35, 41, 61, 111,
 118, 255, 256-257, 452
Esdaile 21, 61, 250
Evans 430
Ewin 444

Fabbri 264
Farrelly 257
Fellows 49
Fezler 365
Field 451
Fiore 230
Fodor 215
Frank 214
Frankel 50, 251
Franklin 443
Friedman 264
Freud 7-11, 19, 72, 77, 114
Freytag 115-116

Gardner 236, 382
Gazzeniga 20
Gibbon 28
Gill 250, 428
Gindes 12, 15
Glotman 306
Gordon 256
Graham, G.W. 48
Graham, K.R. 430

Greer 444
Grehan 41
Grinder 14, 45, 157, 239
Grof 215
Gur 430
Gwynne 236

Haley 37, 256
Ham 55
Harding 306
Harris 214, 215, 453
Hartland 41, 236
Hartman 450
Hatfield 10
Hernandez 431
Hilgard, E.R. 19, 20, 37, 48-50,
 53, 55, 56, 175, 194, 231, 251,
 428, 429
Hilgard, J. 428, 429
Hill 452
Hodge 451
Hommel 55
Howard 236
Hudson 443
Hutschnecker 443

Iker 444
Iveson 231

Jabush 443
Jakubowski 241
James, M. 86
James, W. 118
Janet 9, 120
Johnson 354
Jongeward 86
Jung 72

Kampman 194
Kanders 138
Kaplan 354
Kimura 430
Kinsbourne 20
Klein 383

Kline   231, 453
Kolbe   450
Kosper   444
Kroger   344, 365
Kubie   13, 73, 215

Lamar   66
Lange   241
Lawlor   382
Le Cron   14, 119, 253
Le Shan   443
Leavitt   194
Leva   432
Liebeault   9, 51
Levine   257
Lindner   11
London   19, 35, 382

Margolin   73
Martin   193
Mason   443
Masters   354
Matheson   41
Meares   116
Meline   50
Meltzoff   215
Mendelson   284
Mesmer   8, 21, 442
Miller   344
Moore   215
Morgan   50
Mott   51
Musaph   264

Orne   18, 53

Pavlov   24, 432
Pederson   328
Penfield   66, 108
Perls   80
Plapp   382
Porter   254
Puysegar, Marquis de   51, 432

Rado   72
Raikov   215
Rank   214
Reider   251
Roseman   264
Rossi   35, 255

Sachs   429
Sanders   452
Schafer   429
Schilder   138
Schneck   451
Schwartz   429
Sector   50
Selavan   86
Selye   444
Sheehan   51, 53
Shevrin   454
Schmale   444
Simonton   443, 444
Sinclair-Gieben   442
Solomon   444
Sontag   214
Small   262
Smith-Moorhouse   344
Spanos   49, 55, 56, 450
Speigel, H.   42, 60, 251, 431, 464
Speigel, D.   251, 431
Sperry   20
Stavraky   444
Stearn   231
Steiner   284
Stekel   72
Stevenson   231
Stunkard   284
Sullivan   76
Sulzberger   442
Swade   442
Switras   51
Szasz   82

Taylor   193
Thomas   443
Tosi   236

Ullman 442

Verney 214
Von Neumann 67

Wallace 214
Watkins, H. 328
Watkins, J. 10, 45, 112
Weitzenhoffer 429
Wijesinghe 354

Williams 30
Wilson 49
Wingfield 10
Wolberg 3, 11-12, 73, 111, 114, 344, 452
Wolf 264, 442
Wolpe 365

Zeig 257
Zimbardo 236

Index

Abreaction   9, 10, 11, 13, 14, 72,
   111, 113, 141, 143
Addictions   102, 105, 159, 285,
   326-8
Affect bridge   45, 112-113, 366
Alcoholism   105, 179, 273,
   343-344
Alerting from hypnosis   29-30
Allergy   404
Amnesia   8, 28, 34, 45, 51-58, 60,
   121, 192, 193, 194, 231, 343,
   440
   post-hypnotic   12, 51, 178, 439
   selective   53, 55, 56, 432
   series   588
   visual   53, 54
Amnesia Capacity Estimation   52-
   58, 220, 287, 429, 431, 432,
   433, 438, 446, 465, 466
Amnesic barrier   19
Anaesthesia   14, 24, 28, 45, 60,
   67, 68, 251, 253, 327, 432, 438
   glove   420
   hypno-   342, 420
   localised   419
   post-hypnotic   438
Analgesia   67, 68, 343, 445
   hypno-   382
   rapid induction   35
Anchors   15
Anorectics   105

Antagonism   64, 177
Anxiety   12, 73, 80, 104, 150,
   151, 157, 159, 195, 220, 223,
   230, 260-265, 282, 308, 365,
   447, 451
Assertiveness   93, 148, 149, 168,
   169, 224, 236, 241-244, 303,
   320, 324, 353, 384
Association   13, 108
   free   12
   word   13
Asthma   103, 382, 384, 428, 443
Automatic writing   115

Bedwetting   382
Behaviour   147, 157, 158, 159,
   172, 173, 178, 180, 193, 194,
   322, 326, 384, 385, 388, 403
   compulsive   158, 193, 262, 263
   faulty & damaging   8, 327, 382
   hypnotic   18, 19
   inhibitory   158
   maladapted   88, 158, 163, 174,
      385, 450
Bind   255
   double   255
Birth Experience   14, 151, 214,
   215, 216, 217, 218, 224, 225,
   265, 287, 305, 329, 365, 401,
   459, 468-471
   trauma   214
Blackouts   193

Cancer   429, 443, 444, 446
Catalepsy   24, 28, 40, 41, 42, 110
Cathartic Method   8-9
Cerebral Cortex   108, 306
Chevreul's Pendulum   118, 119,
   124, 125
Children   44, 45, 179, 382-420
Conditioned response   24
Confidence, lack of   94
Conscious interference   27
Control differential   466
Control of body function   69
Convulsions, epileptic   66
Convulsive states   25
Counting method   110
Creative Imagination Scale   51
Critical experience   14, 86, 89, 90,
   92, 108, 109, 138, 140, 142,
   144, 148, 149, 151, 156, 157,
   172, 173, 174, 175, 179, 183,
   216, 217, 224, 226, 232, 266,
   275, 279, 287, 290, 305, 323,
   334, 345, 346, 369, 383, 384,
   410
   pre-natal   214, 219-220, 222,
      224, 226, 232, 305
Critical faculty   36, 42, 44, 120
Criticism   240
Crystal ball   111

Deepening by levels   433
Depression   13, 105, 162, 174,
   195, 196, 327, 328, 343, 384,
   404, 451
Dissociation   12, 19, 37, 48, 50,
   52-58, 60, 67, 112, 115, 118,
   120, 150, 287, 431, 432, 433,
   437, 439, 440
Disorders   104-105
   emotional   326, 384
   habit   105-106, 283, 326, 328
   psychosomatic   102-104, 263,
      326, 428

Divided consciousness   19
Dream
   analysis   13
   induction   114
   interpretation   114
Drugs   157, 161, 263, 304, 326,
   327
Dyslexia   384

Ecological Check   160, 161, 165,
   166, 168, 173
Ego State   76, 161, 289, 293, 304,
   305, 309, 337, 349, 356, 454
   Adult   77, 80, 132, 133, 143,
      144, 146, 148, 154, 155, 161,
      164, 179, 181, 189, 191, 192,
      193, 195, 196, 197, 207, 211,
      219, 219, 222, 227, 228, 245,
      268, 270, 273, 281, 289
   Child   77, 78, 133, 141, 146,
      148, 172, 173, 174, 179, 183,
      192, 216, 227, 228, 237, 239,
      243, 245, 269, 270, 273, 307
   complex   142, 144, 145, 149,
      154, 156, 173-175
   Parent/Child conflict   79, 81,
      133, 141, 142, 143, 146, 147,
      149, 172, 173, 174, 175, 191,
      204, 208, 216, 221, 227, 237,
      238, 242, 286, 307, 326, 327,
      328, 351, 367, 456
   hidden   64, 99, 165, 175-180,
      240, 269, 305, 356
   Parent   77, 78, 133, 141, 144,
      145, 146, 148, 172, 175, 192,
      216, 228, 229, 237, 239, 241,
      243, 269, 284, 304, 307, 310,
      321, 333, 348, 354
Ego Strengthening   93, 148, 149,
   168, 169, 223, 224, 284, 285,
   300, 347, 303, 324, 343, 353,
   452

Emotions 74-76, 81, 83, 87, 109, 113, 116, 141, 143, 144, 146, 152, 266, 290, 383, 388, 444, 453
Eye Closure 37, 40, 110
Eye fixation technique 28-29, 36, 66

Frigidity 354

Gambling 161-169
Guilt 79, 90, 91, 104, 141, 149, 155, 157, 174, 196, 215, 216, 217, 222, 223, 224, 230, 261, 262, 264, 282, 284, 310, 318, 319, 323, 333, 347, 348, 363, 367, 446, 447

Hallucinations 34, 49, 60, 66, 231
Hand levitation technique 26-28, 44, 87, 121, 442-448
Healing 69, 87, 121, 442-448
Hemisphere 20, 48, 49
  dominant 48
  left 20, 61, 66, 67, 430, 431
  non-dominant 48, 49, 431
  right 20, 22, 49, 61, 430
Hypertension 103, 265
Hypnodrama 116
Hypnoplasty 116
Hypnosis - definition 22
Hypnosynthesis 13
Hypnotic behaviour 18, 19
Hypnotic coma 21
Hypnotic state 19, 21
Hypnotic Induction Profile 51, 469
Hypnotic Susceptibility 34, 44, 49, 50, 51, 52, 61, 128, 384, 428, 429, 430, 431, 438, 440, 450
Hysteria 8-9

Ideas 26
Ideomotor
  communication 384
  questioning 112-113, 118, 290, 354
  response 14, 26-28, 36, 118, 119, 124, 140, 152, 265, 280, 323, 366
  signals 120-133, 138, 140, 144, 145, 151, 163, 175, 180, 214, 220, 287, 345, 349, 355, 367, 384, 413, 436, 437, 440
Ideosensory
  response 26-28, 36, 119, 159, 160, 163
  questioning 128
  signals 129, 180
Imagery 67, 69, 110, 127, 150, 254, 301, 320, 383, 404, 444, 446
  body 283, 284
  movie picture 13, 111
  television 44, 111, 383, 385, 390, 391, 404, 405
  unconscious body 115-116, 386
Immune system 444
Impotence 264, 354
Incest 196
Induction 18, 34, 261
  hypnotic 10
  levitational 63
  non-verbal 63
  rapid 14, 34-45
  rapid analgesia 35
  rapid for children 44, 45, 385
  sleep 44, 45, 385
  surprise cataleptic 55
Insomnia 382

Knee jerk reflex 24

Laterality theory   48
Levitation   53, 63, 118

Magnetic fields   8
Meditation   23
Memory   27, 51, 60, 65, 66, 67, 68, 72, 73, 89, 108, 110, 140, 148, 194/ 217, 231, 232, 384, 408
Mesmerism   8
Metaphor   256-257
Migraine   103, 253, 306-307, 324, 384, 404, 406
Movie Picture technique   13
Multiple personalities   52, 192-196

Nailbiting   285, 382, 445, 446
Neo-dissociation theory   19, 20, 48
Neurolinguistic programming   14
Neurosis   72, 86, 125
   war   10, 11

Obesity   282-286
Obsessive   104, 105, 384
Overeating   105, 283, 329, 153, 308, 311, 431-433, 435, 436, 478

Panic   75, 150, 180, 262
Phobia   86, 104, 225, 262, 364-366, 378, 382, 384
   school
   snake   89-93
   stairs   378
Pinpointing   110-111
Posthypnotic suggestion   30, 31, 102, 283, 286, 344, 434
Previous life experience   70, 93, 230-233
Progressive relaxation   28
Psychoanalysis   9, 10, 11, 13, 114
Psychogenic epilepsy   382

Psychopath, criminal   11
Psychosomatic disorders   179
Psychosomatic illness   80, 102-104, 263, 305, 384, 428
   cardovascular   264
   gastrointestinal   263
Psychosomatic medicine   443
Psychotic   106

Reframing   15, 45, 157-167, 308, 415
Regression   9, 45, 60, 65, 67, 68, 69, 89, 110, 111, 152, 194, 230, 291, 329, 349, 391, 405, 406, 459
Rehabilitation   93-94, 149, 161, 174, 384
Rejection   195, 237, 241, 292, 327, 354, 378, 379
   self   216, 285, 294, 445
Relaxation   50, 67, 68, 110, 127, 253, 260, 261, 287, 307, 338, 344, 383, 433, 434, 436, 445, 452
Repeated Induction Technique   40
Repressed emotion   9, 292, 327, 354
Repression   9, 12, 55, 76, 78, 79, 87, 111, 172, 261, 334
Resistance   10, 49, 60-65, 129, 130, 133, 139, 161, 175, 177, 233, 303, 305, 385, 429, 430, 452
   active   60, 62
   conscious   62
   passive   60
   unconscious   64

Scripts   86, 88
Secondary gains   93, 99, 148, 149, 283, 364, 383, 388, 404
Selective thinking   36
Self alienation   79, 285, 294

Self esteem, lack of   73, 223, 236, 240
Self hypnosis   23, 306, 324, 446, 447
Sexual abuse   195
Sexual dysfunction   264, 354-355
Sexual feelings   90-92, 283
Skin disorders   102, 104, 264, 443
Sleep   29, 30, 43, 57, 115, 432, 434, 436, 439
Smile test   147, 148, 149, 156, 218, 219, 220, 247, 270, 274, 276, 290, 317, 320, 331, 337, 374, 403
Smoking   328-329, 338-343
Snake phobia   89-93
Stanford Hypnotic Clinic Scale 51
Stage hypnotist   13, 34, 35, 432
Stimulus response mechanism   24
Stress   459
Suggestion
  direct   9, 69, 250, 252, 263, 282, 307, 323, 382, 442
  indirect   13, 252, 437
Suicide   105, 262
Symptom prescription   257-258, 373
Symptom removal   252-258

Tension   144, 145, 146, 147, 148, 149, 154, 155, 161, 173, 174, 208, 211, 219, 220, 282, 307, 308, 386, 388
Therapeutic metaphor   256-7
Trance   19, 27, 35, 51
Tranquilliser   105, 157, 162, 307, 327
Transactional Analysis   76, 88

Ulcerative colitis   102, 263, 264

Unconscious
  resources   31, 48, 67, 82, 112, 114, 158, 174, 230, 251, 253, 254, 261, 274, 286, 301, 311, 445, 446, 455
  response
Unconscious body image   115-116
Uncovering   72, 88, 108-116, 118, 121, 138, 139, 140, 175
  indirect   113-116

Voodoo Death   443

For catalog of HYPNOTISM and MIND POWER Books, Cassettes and Videocassettes write to:

WESTWOOD PUBLISHING CO.
700 S. CENTRAL AVE., DEPT. BA
GLENDALE, CA 91204
OR CALL 818-242-1159